developmental
biology

BROWN

biology readings series

George E. Brosseau: *Evolution*

Reed A. Flickinger: *Developmental Biology*

Lester Goldstein: *Cell Biology*

Edward J. Kormondy: *General Biology, Volume I*

Edward J. Kormondy: *General Biology, Volume II*

Bradley Scheer: *Comparative Physiology*

developmental biology

Reed A. *Flickinger*, Ph.D.

Professor of Biology
State University of New York at Buffalo

WM. C. BROWN COMPANY PUBLISHERS
Dubuque, Iowa

Manufactured by WM. C. BROWN CO. INC., Dubuque, Iowa
Printed in U. S. A.

preface

The task of compiling a group of significant articles from the field of developmental biology is difficult for a number of reasons. Hopefully, the more recent significant papers are better than earlier ones, reflecting an advancing state of our knowledge. On the other hand, more recent papers have not yet undergone the "test of time" and hence their importance may be illusory. The restriction of space excuses the absence of a number of important articles, and the actual selection of the papers reprinted here represents only a sample of a number of papers that I consider significant. The recent book, "Foundations of Experimental Embryology," by B. H. Willier and J. M. Oppenheimer, which reprints eleven articles from the older literature, offers the reader an excellent view of some aspects of thought from the early era of experimental embryology. The purpose of this present book is to reprint the work of a number of investigators that I feel has had, or will have, an influence upon the course of thinking in the field of developmental biology. In several cases the selections are review papers which offer a more complete presentation of the work and ideas. Most of the articles are reports of the results of a particular investigation and contain a description of methods and techniques utilized. These papers have the advantage of actually detailing the experimental means that the authors used to approach the problems.

The use of a wide variety of biological material is represented in these selections: slime molds, algae, flatworms, insect larvae, and the developing eggs and embryos of sea urchins, amphibians, chickens and mice. The basic nature of the problem is indicated by the broad array of organisms employed.

Although all of these papers are concerned with the problem of differentiation, many levels of approach are utilized. The papers of Brown and Gurdon; Gross, Malkin and Moyer; and Denny and Tyler are recent investigations at the molecular level concerned with the synthesis of ribonucleic acid and proteins. Stockdale and Holtzer's paper considers the relationship between the synthesis of desoxyribonucleic acid and a specific muscle protein (myosin), while Beerman relates chromosomal morphology to the production of RNA and gene action in insect larvae. The work of King and Briggs, and Gurdon, concerns the biological potencies of embryo nuclei implanted into enucleated amphibian eggs, while Hämmerling considers the role of the nucleus in the differentiation of a unicellular green alga. The results of investigations of the interaction of tissues and subsequent stimulation of differentiation, i.e., embryonic induction, are reported in the papers of Niu and Twitty; Ten Cate and Van Doorenmaalen; and Grobstein. The problem of the morphogenetic assembly of cells is treated by Bonner in his paper on the role of chemotaxis in aggregation of amoeboid cells of the slime mold, while Moscona's report concerns his work on the reunition of mixtures of chick and mouse embryo cells *in vitro*. The feature of polarity as an organizing influence in morphogenesis is considered by Whitaker, and by Marsh and Beams. Finally, the older results of Humphrey offer an example of cells destined to form gametes of one sex being diverted to differentiate into gametes of the opposite sex. The task of ascertaining the role of the cellular environment in interacting with the genetic elements to account for this change offers an example of the task that confronts the investigator in the field of developmental biology. Although much could be written about the significance of each of these papers, it is my feeling that they speak for themselves adequately enough.

The problems of the specialization of cells to form the tissues and organs of the organism and the control of the growth of these cells are among the most important problems in biology. It is hoped that the reprinting of these original papers will afford an insight into the way these problems have been approached and, hopefully, will lead some individuals to devise further experiments concerning these important questions.

R. A. Flickinger

contents

CHAPTER   PAGE

1. Evidence for the Formation of Cell Aggregates by Chemotaxis in the Development of the Slime Mold Dictyostelium Discoideum .   1

2. Nucleo-cytoplasmic Relationships in the Development of Acetabularia   23

3. The Effect of Hydrogen Ion Concentration Upon the Induction of Polarity in Fucus Eggs III. Gradients of Hydrogen Ion Concentration   48

4. Electrical Control of Morphogenesis in Regenerating Dugesia Tigrina I. Relation of Axial Polarity to Field Strength . . .   60

5. Cytological Aspects of Information Transfer in Cellular Differentiation   78

6. Serial Transplantation of Embryonic Nuclei   92

7. The Developmental Capacity of Nuclei Taken From Intestinal Epithelium Cells of Feeding Tadpoles   127

8. Absence of Ribosomal RNA Synthesis in the Anucleolate Mutant of Xenopus Laevis   148

9. Templates for the First Proteins of Embryonic Development . .   160

10. Activation of Protein Biosynthesis in Non-nucleate Fragments of Sea Urchin Eggs   171

11. DNA Synthesis and Myogenesis   176

12. The Differentiation of Gastrula Ectoderm in Medium Conditioned by Axial Mesoderm   190

13. Analysis of the Development of the Eye-lens in Chicken and Frog Embryos by Means of the Precipitin Reaction   195

14. The Development in Vitro of Chimeric Aggregates of Dissociated Embryonic Chick and Mouse Cells 216

15. Autoradiography of the Interzone Between Tissues in Inductive Interaction 229

16. The Development and Sex Differentiation of the Gonad in the Wood Frog (Rana Sylvatica) Following Extirpation or Orthotopic Implantation of the Intermediate Segment and Adjacent Mesoderm 238

1

evidence for the formation of cell aggregates by chemotaxis in the development of the slime mold dictyostelium discoideum*

JOHN TYLER BONNER
Department of Biology, Princeton University, New Jersey
with an Appendix by L. J. SAVAGE
Institute of Radiobiology and Biophysics, University of Chicago

INTRODUCTION

Dictyostelium discoideum is a member of that curious group of amoeboid slime molds, the Acrasiales, which forms one of numerous bridges between unicellular organisms and multicellular organisms. In its life cycle (see Raper, '35, '40a, '40b, '41, and Bonner, '44 for descriptive details) there is both a unicellular stage which subsequently develops by the aggregation of cells to central collection points into a differentiated multicellular organism.

So far as is known the life cycle is completely asexual. Individual capsule-shaped spore cells germinate by splitting down the side and liberating a single, uninucleate myxamoeba. This myxamoeba feeds on bacteria by phagocytosis and divides by binary fission to form many of its own kind, but each daughter myxamoeba remains a separate, independent individual. At the end of this so-called *vegetative stage*, the myxamoebae cease to feed or multiply, thus having a natural separation in their own life histories between growth processes, and purely formative, morphogenetic processes. The myxamoebae subsequently enter the *aggregation stage* and stream in together to form a mass of cells known as a *pseudoplasmodium* (see Fig. 1, 2). The pseudoplasmodium then crawls as a body for variable distances during the *migration stage*.

Vol. 106, No. 1, October, 1947
The Journal of Experimental Zoology

Finally the pseudoplasmodium rights itself and rises up into the air, forming a delicate tapering stalk set at its large basal end in a small *basal disk,* and holding at its apex the *sorus* which is a spherical mass of encapsulated spores. This rise in height and differentiation of the mature fruiting body or sorocarp comprises the *culmination stage.*

The problem that concerns us at the moment is the mechanism by which aggregation occurs; how can great numbers of independent myxamoebae be drawn together to form one unified organism.

In a number of papers Raper ('40a, '40b, '41) reviews the past work done on aggregation and his discussions of the subject will be briefly summarized. There are 2 aspects that he has considered: the external factors affecting aggregation, and the cause of aggregation.

Many authors believe that the primary external factor involved in the stimulation of the initiation of aggregation is food shortage (Potts, '02; Oehler, '22; von Schuckmann, '24; Arndt, '37; Raper, '40b). Raper ('40b) found that the time of initiation of aggregation was shortened and the resulting patterns were made smaller by the following agents: decreased humidity, increased temperature, and light. Potts ('02) and Harper ('32) also noticed that smaller fruiting bodies were obtained in light.

Concerning the cause of aggregation, Olive ('02) and Potts ('02) independently suggested that there were chemotactic stimuli arising from the central mass of aggregating myxamoebae. Neither investigator offered any evidence for this hypothesis but believed that the general appearance indicated such a mechanism. Olive actually tried to influence aggregating myxamoebae with malic acid and sugar solutions, placed in a sealed-off capillary tube, following the work of Pfeffer on the chemotaxis of spermatozoids of ferns, but with no encouraging results. The only other suggestion was that of von Schuckmann ('25) and Harper ('26) that aggregation is caused by a negative hygrotropic response, but Raper ('41) effectively proved that such a mechanism cannot be seriously considered.

There has been one more recent important contribution: that of Runyon ('42). He showed that, if a semi-permeable membrane of cellophane (regenerated cellulose) was placed over an aggregating pattern, and additional myxamoebae were placed on the upper side of the membrane, the upper myxamoebae would follow the myxamoebae below. The streams of incoming myxamoebae and the central collecting points would coincide above and below the cellophane sheet. Thus Runyon showed that the aggregation stimulus could pass through a semi-permeable membrane. From this he concluded that aggregation is caused by the chemotactic response of myxamoebae to a dialyzable substance.

It was thought, in the beginning of this work, that there was no real evidence that the theory of Olive, Potts and Runyon was correct for they gave no supporting evidence at all, and Runyon's ingenious experiment is hardly conclusive. A variety of physical agents besides a diffusing substance could conceivably be responsible for the orientation of the myxamoebae and could also pass through a semi-permeable membrane. But it is clear from the experimental evidence that will be presented in the following pages that the only mechanism that was supported was that of diffusion of a substance to which the myxamoebae respond chemotactically.

METHODS

A large part of the experimental work described here was made possible by the development of new techniques for the study of Dictyostelium. The principal of such innovations is the discovery that, contrary to Runyon's ('42) statement, aggregation will occur under water. This can be achieved by *D. discoideum, D. giganteum, D. mucoroides, D. purpureum, Polysphondylium violaceum* or *Polysphondylium pallidum* on a water-glass interface in depths of water up to 10 cm. Depths greater than this have not been tested because there seem to be no practical or theoretical reasons for so doing. Figures 1 and 2 illustrate the appearance of this under-water aggregation. Development, however, does not proceed any further, leaving a rounded or irregular shaped mass of cells (see Fig. 1, D). Further development (migration and culmination) can only be attained by bringing the mass into contact with an air-water or mineral oil-water interface.

Before discussing the details of this under-water technique, the standard culture technique will be described, followed by a description of the method of preparing the myxamoebae for under-water aggregation.

Culture technique

A large supply of myxamoebae are required for experiments on aggregation. As Dictyostelium feeds on bacteria, a large supply must be obtained and this is done by using a rich medium such as Raper ('40b) describes: (Raper's medium has been slightly modified by adding a buffer to insure a pH of about 6.0.) Peptone, 10 gm; dextrose, 10 gm; $Na_2HPO_4 \cdot 12H_2O$, 0.96 gm; K_2HPO_4, 1.45 gm; agar, 20 gm; distilled H_2O, 1000 ml.

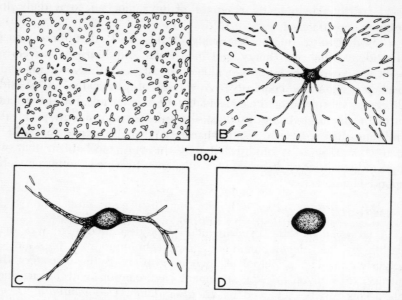

Fig. 1. A semi-diagrammatic representation of 4 stages of the aggregation of Dictyostelium taking place under water on the bottom of a glass dish. A, the beginning of aggregation showing the formation of a small center; B, C, successive stages of aggregation showing the thickening of the streams and the enlargement of the center; D, the final pseudoplasmodium.

The inoculum of Dictyostelium spores and *Escherichia coli* (which is used as a source of food for the myxamoebae) is placed on the nutrient agar in a petri dish (90 mm diameter). The inoculum is spread over the entire surface of the agar by adding a few drops of sterile water and smearing with a sterile glass rod. The culture is incubated at room temperature for 2 days, by which time there is a thick growth of vegetative myxamoebae.

Centrifuge technique

In a culture which has been incubated for 2 days the myxamoebae are found spread out over the whole surface of the agar and surrounded by large numbers of bacteria. For the under-water technique the myxamoebae must be concentrated and freed from bacteria. A simple method is to wash them by centrifugation as was done by Runyon ('42) but since the details of his method have not to my knowledge, been published, the exact procedure used in this study will be described.

No sterile precautions are necessary in the centrifuge method since all nutrients are largely eliminated and there never has been any evidence of deleterious effects of contamination. The 2-day-old petri dish culture is now flooded with distilled water and thoroughly mixed with a glass rod. The suspension of myxamoebae and bacteria is placed in a centrifuge tube and centrifuged gently for 3 minutes. The force of centrifugation is regulated by a few trial experiments so that the myxamoebae will be separated from the bacteria, and thrown down to the bottom of the tube. The liquid containing bacteria is poured off, distilled water added, and the process repeated. A concentrated mass of myxamoebae relatively free of bacteria is finally left in the tube to which a small amount of distilled water is again added.

Under-water technique

The suspension of myxamoebae is placed with a pipette directly into a syracuse or other suitable flat dish containing water. The myxamoebae soon settle to the bottom of the vessel where they subsequently aggregate. At room temperature, with optimum myxamoeba concentrations, aggregation will start in 6 to 8 hours but may be delayed by placing the dish in a cooler environment. In distilled water the myxamoebae lack adhesiveness and the slightest agitation causes them to become detached from the bottom of the dish, but if suitable electrolytes are added the myxamoebae adhere firmly to the glass substratum. This method is based on that of Mast ('29) who showed a similar effect of electrolytes on the adhesiveness of *Amoeba proteus*, and from his data the following standard salt solution (henceforth referred to as "standard solution") was devised and regularly used: NaCl, 0.60 gm; KCl, 0.75 gm; CaCl$_2$, 0.30 gm; distilled H$_2$O, 1000 ml. It is interesting to note that Mast showed that this is not a case of salt antagonism for the effect of the various anions is slightly additive.

Thin film of water technique

In a few of the experiments the myxamoebae were placed on a thin film of water on the underside of a coverslip. The procedure follows: a no. 1, 22 × 22 mm coverslip which has been carefully cleaned in 95% ethyl alcohol and wiped dry, is sealed with a mixture of approximately 2 parts vaseline and 1 part beeswax onto a van Tieghem cell (10 mm deep, 20 mm in diameter). This van Tieghem cell cup with the sealed-on coverslip serving as the bottom is filled about ⅓ full with standard solution and the myxamoebae, prepared in the fashion already described, are added. A microscope slide is then sealed over the open end of the van Tieghem cell. In 20 minutes time all the myxamoebae will have settled to the bottom and adhered to the coverslip. The slide is then gently turned over so that the coverslip is on the upper surface. Since the myxamoebae are in a thin

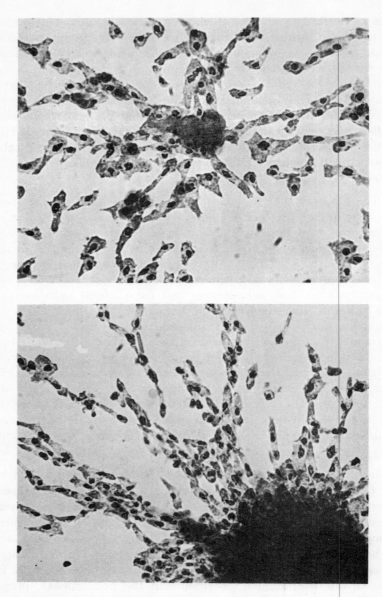

Fig. 2. Photographs of fixed and stained preparations showing 2 stages of the aggregation of Dictyostelium taking place under water on the surface of a coverslip. (Fixed in Shaudin's solution and stained by Bodian's silver impregnation method.) The upper photograph shows the beginning of aggregation with the formation of a small center; the lower photograph shows a middle stage of aggregation with a large center in the lower right hand corner.

film of water in contact with moist air, the organism will go through its complete life cycle producing abundant sorocarps on the underside of the coverslip.

RESULTS

The attraction of myxamoebae at a distance

That contact between myxamoebae is not a controlling factor in aggregation was first emphasized by Raper ('41). It can readily be seen in observing aggregation that isolated individual myxamoebae or groups of myxamoebae will move directly towards one of the radiating streams of incoming myxamoebae (henceforth referred to as "stream") or to the central mass of cells (henceforth referred to as "center").

With the under-water technique it was possible to get a clearer and more quantitative picture of this attraction at a distance. If one removes the center of an aggregation pattern at either of the 2 stages illustrated in Figure 1, C and D, and places it beside the stream, in 3 to 5 minutes time each myxamoeba in the stream will independently turn and start to move toward the center at its new location. They will continue to move toward the center until they reach it and become incorporated into it in the normal fashion. An attempt was made to measure the maximum distance at which the center could influence the myxamoebae, care being taken to have no myxamoebae between the center and the myxamoebae under observation in order to eliminate the possibility that intermediate myxamoebae might affect the attractive power in some way. Some of the results of this type of experiment are given in Table 1.

It is clear that myxamoebae up to 200 μ distant will become, in 3 to 5 minutes, oriented toward the center. If the diameter of a rounded myxamoeba is considered to be about 15 μ, then the distance between the myxamoebae and the center can be represented as over 13 myxamoeba diameters. In a slightly modified type of experiment discussed later even larger gaps are bridged. In fact it was possible to obtain weak but definite orienting effect at a distance of 800 μ or 53 myxamoeba diameters.

The inability of an electric field to affect aggregation

Both vegetative and aggregating myxamoebae were subjected to electrical currents of various densities. The type of chamber and the electrical circuit were essentially similar to those used by Hahnert ('32) on *Amoeba proteus*. Briefly the chamber is a small, rectangular cell (30 $\times$ 10 mm), in which the small ends are completely walled off with 2 platinum ribbon electrodes. To guard the center of the cell

TABLE 1

Table showing the ability of the centers to attract myxamoebae
across various distances.

Distance between Center and Myxamoebae	Attraction
770 μ	none
423 μ	none
358 μ	weak
214 μ	strong
180 μ	strong
128 μ	strong
98 μ	strong

from harmful electrolytic products, a piece of porous material (por-
celain or cellulose sponge) is placed directly in front of and parallel
to each electrode. The experiments on Dictyostelium were done in tap
water and distilled water with the same result in both cases. Parallel
observations were made on *Amoeba proteus* (in tap water). The results
are given in Table 2. As can be seen from the table *A. proteus* shows
the characteristic migration toward the cathode, while the myxamoebae
of Dictyostelium showed no response whatever to the electrical current.

The inability of a magnetic field to affect aggregation

Some very cursory experiments, which are reported here for the
sake of record, were done with an Alnico magnet (1 cm² pole face) at
various angles to aggregation patterns of Dictyostelium. No effect was
observed.

The inability of a conducting metal (tantalum)
to affect aggregation

This experiment is basically similar to the previously described
experiment of Runyon ('42), but instead of separating the center from
the myxamoebae by a semipermeable membrane, they were separated
by a thin sheet of tantalum (about 12 μ thick). A 1 cm² sheet of the
tantalum was placed in a syracuse dish containing standard solution.
Myxamoebae free from bacteria were allowed to settle on one side of
the tantalum, using the standard technique previously described. When
the myxamoebae had just started to aggregate, which they did normally,
the sheet was turned upside down and set on a small stand (a van
Tieghem cell 5 mm deep, 20 mm in diameter) so that it was not
touching the bottom of the dish and yet was completely submerged
in the standard solution. A large active center from another dish was
taken in a micro-pipette and placed on the upper surface of the tantalum.

TABLE 2

Table showing the effect of 3 different current densities on Amoeba
proteus and on the myxamoebae of D. discoideum.

Current Density in μ Amp./MM^2	Effect on A. Proteus	Effect on Myxamoebae of D. Discoideum
5	possible slight orientation	no effect
20	streams towards cathode	no effect
70	immediate death	death

In no case was the effect of the upper center transmitted through
the sheet, and the myxamoebae below, while they aggregated normally,
bore no relation in their pattern to the strong center above.

The impermeability of glass, mica, and quartz to the aggregation stimulus

Using the same technique as described immediately above, coverslip glass (120 μ thick), mica 100-150 μ thick), and quartz glass
50-100 μ thick) were tested. Again, in no case was there any visible
orienting effect transmitted through these materials although aggregation
appeared normal in each instance.

The attraction of myxamoebae around corners

This experiment was designed to see if a center could orient myxamoebae that were not in a direct line with the center, but were
separated by an impermeable substance that could be circumvented.
Some myxamoebae free of bacteria were spread on a no. 1 coverslip
(22 × 22 mm, approximately 160 μ thick) which had been placed in
the bottom of a syracuse dish full of standard solution. When the
myxamoebae had just begun to aggregate the coverslip was turned
upside down and held in such a position so that it formed a shelf,
completely surrounded by standard solution. This is represented diagrammatically in Figure 3, A. An active, strongly attractive center was
placed approximately 60 μ from the edge of the coverslip, on the upper
surface. Very shortly afterwards, the separate myxamoebae on the
underneath surface became oriented towards the point on the edge
nearest the center above and moved up around the edge to join the
center (see Fig. 3, A). In other words the center exerted its influence
around the corner, from the upper surface to the lower surface.

The inability of the orientation of the substratum to affect aggregation

The following experiments involve using the techniques of Weiss
('45) who obtained oriented growth of fibroblasts of chick embryos

by placing them on specific types of substrata. Myxamoebae were placed on a sheet of mica in which shallow grooves had been scratched with a fine steel needle (see Weiss, '45 for the details of the preparation of the mica). Neither the aggregating myxamoebae, nor the wandering vegetative myxamoebae showed any preference for the grooves, but would pass across them as though completely unaffected by their existence. Glass fibers (from glass wool) lying in a heap under water in a syracuse dish were also covered with myxamoebae and again the myxamoebae showed no more tendency to adhere to the fibers than to the glass bottom of the dish.

Attempts to observe structural connections between aggregating myxamoebae

It is not possible in a living preparation, even using an oil immersion (1.8 mm) objective and preparing the material with the thin film of water technique, to see any connections between the aggregating myxamoebae except when the cells are half a cell diameter or less from one another. Then they often are attached by definite filopodia. To examine this point further, aggregation stages were stained with silver using the technique of Bodian. Aggregation was allowed to occur on coverslips under water and at the desired stages they were removed, fixed in Shaudin's solution, and stained. The gold toning was not used. Photographs of such a . preparation are shown in Figure 2. As can be seen from the photographs, and also from careful oil immersion examination of the slides, there is no evidence of any filopodia extending any great distances. Nor is there any evidence of any material, exudate, or ground mat such as Weiss ('45) describes for oriented chick fibroblasts, which he stained in the same fashion.

An attempt to reveal a deposit made by aggregating myxamoebae that might orient other myxamoebae

It was possible to show by experiment that an aggregation pattern leaves behind no structure on the substratum that can orient myxamoebae. The standard solution was poured off a syracuse dish in which the aggregation was complete or nearly so for all the pseudoplasmodia. The dish was then placed in the ice compartment of an electric refrigerator and allowed to freeze. After removal from the refrigerator more standard solution and fresh myxamoebae were added. The old centers that had been killed by freezing could still be seen. Care was taken to observe if the live myxamoebae were affected in any way by any type of structure that the previous aggregation patterns

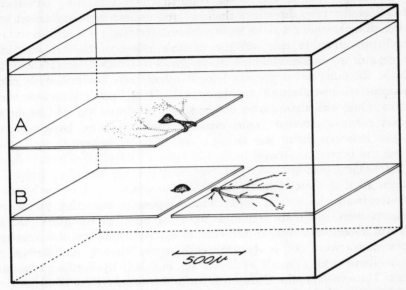

Fig. 3. A semi-diagrammatic representation of 2 experiments done on aggregation in Dictyostelium using coverslip shelves held under water. A, the myxamoebae
previously at random under the coverslip are attracted around the edge to the center
on the upper surface; B, the myxamoebae previously at random on the right hand
coverslip are attracted to the center on the left hand coverslip, across the substratum gap.

might have created. No such effect was demonstrated; the new patterns
bore no relation to the previous ones.

The importance of an interface connecting the center and the myxamoebae

It was found that a center could attract myxamoebae to which
it was not directly connected by an interface. This fact was first
realized in an accidental observation. A hanging drop preparation had
been made with myxamoebae free from bacteria in standard solution
and a clear aggregation pattern formed at the base of the drop, at
the air-water interface. I noticed that above this pattern, on the glass-
water interface, a few myxamoebae were aggregating to a center directly above the center of the aggregation pattern below. Since the
upper center formed at the nearest point to the lower center, one
can reason that this was caused either by the fact that the positions
of both the upper and lower centers were determined by similar tensions

in the drop, or that the lower center, which was the farthest advanced of the two, directly influenced the upper myxamoebae without being directly connected to them by an interface.

In an effort to rule out the possible effect of the tensions in a hanging drop, an experiment was designed in which 2 no. 1 coverslips (22×22 mm) were prepared in standard solution, one with many myxamoebae just starting to aggregate, and the other with one large center. One was then turned over and placed on top of the other, taking care to prevent their surfaces from touching by placing 2 wedges between them, one on each side. The myxamoebae were then facing the center, separated by a thin layer of standard solution. Again an immediate response was obtained and the myxamoebae formed a pattern so that their center was directly opposite, that is the shortest distance from, the strong center on the opposite coverslip. Numerous attempts were made to determine how far apart the plates could be and still obtain an orienting influence of the center on the myxamoebae. If the plates were 500 μ apart the effect was obvious and strong. At 800 μ there was a weak and diffuse, but still discernible orienting effect. Thus without the disturbing surface tension effects of a hanging drop, a center again affected distant myxamoebae to which it was not directly connected by an interface.

This was done in another striking way illustrated in Figure 3, B. Two coverslips were prepared as above and placed side by side in a dish to form 2 shelves, surrounded by standard solution, and separated by a small gap. The center was placed fairly near the edge, and it immediately affected the myxamoebae on the opposite shelf so they all streamed to the nearest point on the edge (see Fig. 3, B). Again the effect of a center was transmitted across a gap which possessed no interface, but merely a layer of water.

A few observations on this experiment should be mentioned. The first myxamoebae that got to the edge appeared to be reaching out into the gap between the coverslips with a sort of hopeless pseudopodial waving. Later when they became more numerous, they formed their own center directly opposite the original center on the other coverslip. However, if the coverslips were closer together so that the gap was very small (about 20-30 μ) then the myxamoebae formed a stream, a bridge right across the gap and joined the center on the opposite side.

The effect of water flowing over aggregation patterns

A flow of water was created over myxamoebae that were about to aggregate or that were in the process of aggregating and a distinct modification of the aggregation pattern was obtained. The flow of water was achieved 2 different ways. In one a glass rod (4 mm in diameter) bent into an "L" shape was attached to a shaft of a 6 RPM electric motor, and held over the center of a syracuse dish (containing bacteria-free myxamoebae) so that the lower bar of the "L" was just submerged in the water, forming a radius to the circular dish. In this way the water was slowly swirled in a circular fashion, creating a fairly linear flow at any spot in the dish other than near the center. The other method of creating a flow involved drawing water through a channel between 2 coverslips (approximately 100 μ apart). A controlled rate of flow was obtained by leading the water from a reservoir to the coverslips through a fine glass capillary tube.

If the myxamoebae were about to aggregate when placed in this current, they continued to do so, but the aggregation patterns, as shown in Figure 4, A, were atypical. Each possessed only one unusually long stream which always approached the center from the downstream side. If the myxamoebae had already started normal aggregation before being subjected to the flow, they would quickly assume a similar form as shown in Figure 4, B. The streams that had existed on the upstream

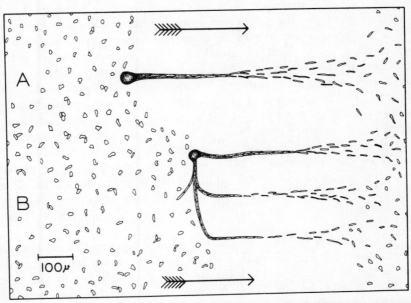

Fig. 4. A semi-diagrammatic drawing showing the effect of a moving stream of water (the arrows indicate the direction of movement) over an aggregation pattern in Dictyostelium. A, an aggregation pattern that formed while the water was in motion; B, an aggregation pattern that formed in still water and was subsequently subjected to a stream of moving water.

side would break up rapidly, and although the downstream and lateral streams remained, they would continue to form only in line with the direction of the flow of water. In both cases the most striking fact was that the myxamoebae, upstream of the center, even those almost touching it, showed no effect of any stimulus from the center and moved in a random fashion. Yet judging from the length of the streams, the stimulus from the center apparently had extended an abnormally long distance downstream. If vegetative myxamoebae were placed under such a current no effect was observed whatsoever, but they continued their random locomotion.

DISCUSSION

If the facts that have been obtained from the experiments described above, and those from the literature are summarized, the following statements can be made of the aggregation process in Dictyostelium: (1) the attraction can operate across a semi-permeable membrane (Runyon, '42); (2) the center will attract myxamoebae at considerable distances; (3) it has been impossible to date to show any effect of an electric field or (4) of a magnetic field on the aggregation pattern; (5) aggregation occurs on the surface of a conducting metal (tantalum), but (6) a center will not attract myxamoebae when separated from the myxamoebae by a sheet of tantalum; (7) nor can a center attract myxamoebae through glass, (8) mica, or (9) quartz; (10) a center can attract myxamoebae around a corner of some impermeable substance; (11) the structure of the substratum does not appear to affect the aggregation pattern; (12) it has been impossible to demonstrate any sort of bridge or connection between a center and distant myxamoebae; (13) there is no evidence of any myxamoeba—orienting substance deposited on the substratum; (14) a center does not have to be directly connected to myxamoebae by an interface in order to attract them; (15) aggregation patterns forming under flowing water are deformed so that only the myxamoebae directly downstream of the center will show any orientation.

In our search for the immediate cause of aggregation in Dictyolstelium, the first fundamental question that arises is, does the center pull in the myxamoebae by force or does it merely orient the myxamoebae by stimulation? There is every indication that the energy of locomotion is contributed by each individual myxamoeba, and that the center orients them by a differential stimulation.

The problem might be approached by examining various reasonable possible mechanisms suggested by investigations on other forms in the light of the facts known about aggregation in Dictyostelium. For instance one might consider the likelihood of aggregation to be: (1) an agglutination process; (2) in some way controlled by an electric or (3) magnetic field; (4) or by some form of radiation; (5) controlled by some type of orienting structure deposited on the substratum; (6) or by the oriented molecules in a molecular surface film; (7) or, finally, controlled by the gradient of a substance to which the myxamoebae respond chemotactically.

Agglutination hypothesis

Some actual immunological work has been done on D. *mucoroides* by von Schuckmann ('25) who showed that when rabbit antiserum to vegetative myxamoebae is added to a culture of similar myxamoebae, they will agglutinate into clumps in an irreversible fashion. Unfortunately von Schuckmann does not describe the details either of the process or of further development, if any, of the clumps; but it is notable that he does not attempt to interpret normal aggregation in terms of agglutination. In some work that will be reported in detail at a future date, I have been able to obtain pseudoplasmodium formation by what is apparently agglutination, and these pseudoplasmodia develop into complete sorocarps. But in such an instance the normal aggregation process has been completely circumvented and the pseudoplasmodium has been achieved by an unnatural means.

There are a number of strong evidences against the "clumping" of myxamoebae found in normal aggregation being an agglutination process. In the first place the fact that a center can attract myxamoebae across great distances is inconsistent with agglutination. A basic property of all agglutination processes is that the cells come together by chance collision; for example as a result of active random motion or brownian motion, followed by a firm adhesion of the collided cells.

Another evidence comes from the fact that the myxamoebae which are in contact can and do normally separate readily from one another. A striking example of this is the case mentioned where a center is removed and placed laterally to its stream. The compacted mass of myxamoebae forming the stream will break up, each myxamoeba becoming unattached and going independently to the new location of the center. Such a phenomenon is never seen in agglutination processes. The nearest they approach it is in the case of reverse agglutination, but then up to the point of reversal the cells are solidly stuck to one another. In Dictyostelium the myxamoebae can be separated at all times.

A final evidence that aggregation is not achieved by agglutination comes from the fact that attraction between the center and the myxamoebae is obtained through a semi-permeable membrane as previously described in the experiment of Runyon ('42). Proteins or complex polysaccharides are the important molecules in immunological reactions, and even the smallest proteins will not (except possibly at an extremely slow rate) pass through the regenerated cellulose dialyzing membranes used. I have repeated Runyon's experiments many times with different types of membranes all presumably impermeable to proteins, and always obtained the same sort of rapid (3 to 5 minute) response of the myxamoebae to the center on the opposite side of the membrane. From these arguments it may be concluded that aggregation in Dictyostelium is not an agglutination process. This does not exclude the possibility that antigen-antibody reactions are factors in development at a later stage. But some other factor must be responsible for initiating the normal "clumping" of the Dictyostelium myxamoebae.

Electrical hypothesis

The evidence weighs against the possibility that aggregation can be explained in terms of an electric field. Consider first the fact that an electric field surrounding aggregation patterns will not affect them. While it is true that such negative evidence is in no way conclusive, it is nevertheless indicative.

Perhaps better evidence comes from the tantalum experiment, where normal aggregation was found to occur on the surface of a conducting metal, but the attraction could not take place through a thin sheet of the metal. If the aggregation mechanism were electrical then the metal would most likely have created a short circuit preventing aggregation, which is not the case. Even granting that aggregation could occur on the surface of the metal, one would further expect the attraction to be conducted through the tantalum sheet.

Magnetic hypothesis

Magnetism is also an unlikely possibility for reasons very similar to those mentioned for electricity. Not only was the aggregation pattern not affected by a magnetic field (which again is only indicative evidence) but also the attraction could not pass through a tantalum sheet, which could be readily achieved by a magnetic force.

Radiation hypothesis

Rays emitted from the center of Dictyostelium could conceivably guide the myxamoebae, but the evidence does not support this view. First, if such a ray exists, it can penetrate water, and cellophane, but is stopped by glass, quartz and mica. This certainly does not eliminate the hypothesis but it narrows the possibilities.

Stronger evidence against a radiation phenomenon comes from the experiment in which a center on the upper surface of a coverslip attracted myxamoebae on the lower surface, around the edge (Fig. 3, A). It is difficult for me to see how a ray mechanism could operate here for if the coverslip were permeable to the ray one would expect the underneath myxamoebae to aggregate to the point nearest the above center, which would be directly below the center on the underside of the glass. If the coverslip were impermeable to the hypothetical ray, then one would expect no effect whatsoever of the upper center on the myxamoebae underneath. But this is not the case; the myxamoebae go around the edge. Rays travel in straight lines and can hardly be expected to pass from one side of an impermeable barrier to the other.

Contact guidance hypothesis

"Contact guidance" designates the idea that the amoeboid processes of cells are oriented by being mechanically guided by either the ultra-structure of the substratum or the direction of flow of an exudate given off by the cell. The concept of contact guidance is that of Weiss ('29, '34, '45) who studied the causes of orientation in cell growth and movement of cells of higher animals in tissue culture.

There is no evidence to indicate that contact guidance plays a part in aggregation for it has been impossible to demonstrate any guiding structure deposited on the substratum, or even that the orientation of the substratum itself has any orienting effect.

Molecular surface film hypothesis

It was thought, since aggregation only occurs at an interface, that a molecular surface film might be involved in orienting the aggregating myxamoebae. But this hypothesis was invalidated by showing that it is quite possible for a center to attract myxamoebae when the center is not connected directly to the myxamoebae by an interface.

CONCLUSION

Diffusion hypothesis

Good evidence that aggregation is achieved by the center producing a substance to which the myxamoebae respond chemotactically[1] comes

---

[1] A note should be made here concerning the use of the word chemotaxis in this paper. As Blum ('35) points out there are 2 separate factors to consider in oriented movements; (1) the orientation of the organism, in this case to the diffusion field of a chemical substance and (2) the movement of the organism which may quite possibly be in no way affected by the chemical substance (since there is movement in the absence of the substance).

from the experiment in which the aggregation patterns are deformed by flowing water. In fact the following deductions can be made from this experiment: (1) No mechanical explanation, such as the direct effect of the current on the myxamoebae, could explain the patterns obtained under flowing water because vegetative cells in the current continued normal random movement. That is, the pattern was not imposed on the myxamoebae by the external moving water, but it arose in the normal fashion as a result of the activities of the myxamoebae themselves. (2) Under the flow of water the center remained the source of production of the stimulating agent for the myxamoebae were attracted to it. (3) The agent was washed downstream—the myxamoebae upstream were not attracted in any way by the center, whereas the myxamoebae downstream were attracted to it from great distances. (4) The only reasonable type of agent that could be carried along in such a fashion by a slow current is a free-diffusing chemical substance. (5) The fact mentioned previously that a substance can only be effective in orienting the myxamoebae when it is in a gradient helps interpret a number of phenomena. For instance: the myxamoebae upstream must have been surrounded by the substance which came from the other centers (and let us assume it is in a high enough concentration to be able to obtain a response) but they showed no orientation because the substance in that region became, by diffusion, more evenly distributed and not in a sufficient concentration gradient to cause orientation. (6) Also the only method in which a gradient could be maintained during aggregation would be by a constant production of the substance of the center. Since diffusion would tend always to obliterate the gradient, and the maintenance of a steady state is necessary, it must be assumed that the substance is produced either continuously or at frequent intervals by the center.

Therefore in summarizing we have deduced from this flowing water experiment that during the aggregation of Dictyostelium there is some type of chemical substance (which is not necessarily homogeneous but might consist of a group of compounds) produced continuously or at frequent intervals by the center, which freely diffuses, and the myxamoebae move in the resulting gradient of this substance towards the point of its highest concentration. The final proof of the existence of the substance (and an important problem for future research) must be its isolation *in vitro*. But considering the present weight of evidence, it seems fitting to propose tentatively a name for the substance. The term *acrasin* is suggested, and it can be defined for the moment as a type of substance consisting either of one or numerous compounds which is responsible for stimulating and directing aggregation in certain members of the Acrasiales. It also may perform other duties in the development of these organisms but such considerations are not within the scope of this paper. Also at a later date I plan to present an examination of the formation of streams during aggregation, a process which may appear puzzling in the light of the present discussion.

One of the most difficult factors to understand in any chemotaxis hypothesis is how it is possible for a single small amorphous amoeboid cell to be sensitive to gradients of diffusing substances. The concentrations of these substances in a great many of these cases must be small, and of course, the molecules in diffusion move at random in all directions. Thus the cell must detect very small concentration differences between one end of the cell and the other.

In an attempt to calculate just what this concentration difference would be between the ends of a myxamoeba in the gradient of a hypothetical substance, Dr. L. J. Savage has been kind enough to derive and evaluate the following approximation (see appendix).

$$\frac{-\Delta c}{c} \simeq \frac{\Delta r}{r}$$

where c is the concentration at any part of the myxamoeba, r is the distance from any part of the myxamoeba to the midpoint of the bottom of the center, Δc is the difference in concentration between the far and near ends of the myxamoeba, and Δr is the length of the myxamoeba. If we choose some reasonable values, letting $\Delta r = 25 \mu$, $r = 500 \mu$ they can be substituted in the above expression:

$$\frac{-\Delta c}{c} \simeq \frac{25}{100}$$

$$-\Delta c \simeq .05c$$

Thus the concentration difference between the 2 ends of a myxamoeba at 500 μ distance from the center would be 5% of the total concentration. Remember that a gap much over 800 μ can no longer be bridged, which would mean that if the concentration difference of the hypothetical substance across a myxamoeba is less than 3%, it no longer would be effective in orienting the myxamoeba. These values appear sufficiently high so that from this point of view the chemotaxis hypothesis is not unreasonable.

SUMMARY

Dictyostelium discoideum is a member of that group of amoeboid slime molds (Acrasiales) characterized by forming the fruiting structure from a compacted mass of uninucleate myxamoebae known as a pseudo-plasmodium. The pseudoplasmodium arises by the aggregation of many myxamoebae which were previously completely independent and separate from one another. In this so-called aggregation stage radial streams of elongate myxamoebae move towards a central point by means of pseudopodial locomotion. Attempts to discover the immediate cause of this centripetal streaming of myxamoebae revealed that it is not an agglutination process; that a spreading molecular surface film phenomenon is not responsible; that an electrical or magnetic force is improbable; that any form of directing ray is not involved; and that no type of predetermined structural matrix exists that could guide the myxamoebae to the center. However, evidence was obtained for a substance diffusing from a central mass of myxamoebae through the liquid medium and the incoming myxamoebae orienting themselves in the diffusion field, moving towards the point of highest concentration. This was shown by inducing a gentle stream of water to flow over an aggregation pattern, causing in the usually· radial pattern of incoming myxamoebae an asymmetry that can only be interpreted as the warping of the diffusion field of a substance to which the myxamoebae are sensitive. This type of substance has been tentatively called *acrasin*.

APPENDIX

The derivation and evaluation of the approximation used to calculate the difference in concentration of acrasin between the 2 ends of an aggregating myxamoeba. By L. J. SAVAGE.

If a hemispherical source resting on the bottom of a large tank produces Q gm/day of a stable compound with diffusion coefficient D cm²/day, then (after the source has been in position for some time) the concentration c of the compound at the distance r from the center of the base of the hemisphere is given by

$$C = \frac{Q}{2\pi D} \quad \frac{1}{r} \tag{1}$$

Equation 1 is derived in essentially the same way as equation 20 on page 17 of *Mathematical Biophysics* by Rashevsky ('38).

Let r_1 and r_2, $r_1 > r_2$, be any 2 different values of r, $\Delta r = r_1 - r_2$, and Δc be the difference between the concentrations at r_1 and r_2. Then if r is between r_1 and r_2 and c is the concentration at some point r^1 also between r_1 and r_2 we have from equation 1.

$$\frac{-\Delta c}{c} = r^1 \left(\frac{1}{r_2} - \frac{1}{r_1} \right) = \frac{\Delta r}{r} \quad \frac{r r^1}{r_1 r_2} \tag{2}$$

From equation 2 we conclude that if Δr is small compared with r_2, then

$$-\frac{\Delta c}{c} \simeq \frac{\Delta r}{r} \qquad (3)$$

More precisely, we evaluate $-\Delta c/c$ thus:

$$-\frac{\Delta c}{c} \leq \frac{\Delta r}{r} \; \frac{r_1^2}{r_1 r_2} = \frac{\Delta r}{r} \; \frac{r_1}{r_2} = \frac{\Delta r}{r} \left(1 + \frac{\Delta r}{r_2}\right), \quad (4)$$

and

$$-\frac{\Delta c}{c} \geq \frac{\Delta r}{r} \; \frac{r_2^2}{r_1 r_2} = \frac{\Delta r}{r} \; \frac{r_2}{r_1} = \frac{\Delta r}{r} \left(1 + \frac{\Delta r}{r_2}\right)^{-1} \quad (5)$$

Summarizing inequalities 4 and 5

$$\frac{\Delta r}{r}\left(1 + \frac{\Delta r}{r_2}\right)^{-1} \leq \frac{-\Delta c}{c} \leq \frac{\Delta r}{r}\left(1 + \frac{\Delta r}{r_2}\right) \qquad (6)$$

by way of a numerical example, suppose $r_2 = 585 \; \mu$, $\Delta r = 30 \; \mu$, and $r = r^1 = 600 \; \mu$, then $\Delta r/r = .050$ and inequality 6 guarantees that $.0476 \leq - \Delta c/c \leq .0526$.

LITERATURE CITED

Arndt, A. 1937 Untersuchungen über Dictyostelium mucoroides Brefeld. Roux' Arch. Entwmech., **136**, 681-747.

Bonner, J. T. 1944 A descriptive study of the development of the slime mold Dictyostelium discoideum. Amer. Jour. Bot., **31**, 175-182.

Blum, H. F. 1935 An analysis of oriented movements of animals in light fields. Cold Spring Harbor Symposia on Quantitative Biology, **3**, 210-223.

Hahnert, W. F. 1932 A quantitative study of reactions to electricity in Amoeba proteus. Physiol. Zool., **5**, 491-526.

Harper, R. A. 1926 Morphogenesis in Dictyostelium. Bull Torrey Bot. Club., **53**, 229-268.

———————— 1932 Organization and light relations in Polysphondylium. Bull. Torrey Bot. Club., **59**, 49-84.

Mast, S. O. 1929 Mechanism of locomotion in Amoeba proteus with special reference to the factors involved in attachment to the substratum. Protoplasma, **8**, 344-377.

Oehler, R. 1922 Dictyostelium mucoroides (Brefeld). Centbl. Bakt. (etc.), **89**, 155-156.

Olive, E. W. 1902 Monograph of the Acrasieae. Proc. Boston Soc. Nat. Hist., **30**, 451-513.

Potts, G. 1902 Zur Physiologie des Dictyostelium mucoroides. Flora (Jena), **21**, 281-347.

*This work was carried out at Harvard University, under the auspices of the Society of Fellows, to which the author wishes to express his sincere gratitude.

Raper, K. B. 1935   Dictyostelium discoideum, a new species of slime mold from decaying forest leaves. Jour. Agric. Res., **50**, 135-147.

——————— 1940a   The communal nature of the fruiting process in Acrasieae. Amer. Jour. Bot., **27**, 436-448.

——————— 1940b   Pseudoplasmodium formation and organization in Dictyostelium discoideum. Jour. Elisha Mitchell. Sci. Soc., **56**, 241-282.

——————— 1941   Developmental patterns in simple slime molds. Growth (third Growth Symposium), **5**, 41-76.

Rashevsky, N. 1938   Mathematical Biophysics. Chicago.

Runyon, E. H. 1942   Aggregation of separate cells of Dictyostelium to form a multicellular body. Collecting Net, **17**, 88.

Schuckmann, W. von 1924   Zur Biologie von Dictyostelium mucoroides Bref. Centbl. Bakt. (etc.) (I), **91**, 302-309.

——————— 1925   Zur Morphologie und Biologie von Dictyostelium mucoroides Bref. Arch. Protistenk., **51**, 495-529.

Weiss, P. 1929   Erzwingung elementarer Strukturverschiedenheiten am in vitro wachsenden Gewebe. Die Wirkung mechanischer Spannung auf Richtung und Intensität des Gewebewachstums und ihre Analyse. Roux' Arch. Entwmech., **116**, 438-554.

——————— 1934   In vitro experiments on the factors determining the course of the outgrowing nerve fiber. J. Exp. Zool., **68**, 393-448.

——————— 1945   Experiments on cell and axion orientation in vitro; the role of colloidal exudates in tissue organization. J. Exp. Zool., **100**, 353-386.

2

nucleo-cytoplasmic relationships in the development of acetabularia

J. HAMMERLING

Max Planck Institut für Meeresbiologie, Wilhelmshaven, Germany

INTRODUCTION

The following account of experiments with *Acetabularia*, performed by my co-workers and myself, is based on a paper given at the Seventh International Congress of the International Society for Cell Biology held at New Haven, Connecticut in September, 1950.[1] It has been brought up to date by an addendum, and results by Brachet and his collaborators, based on new, promising methods, have also been taken into consideration.

The first part contains experiments on the influence of the nucleus on morphogenesis. In Section III the development of the nucleus and cytochemical work are described, partly as introduction for Section IV, in which the influence of the rest of the cell on the nucleus is considered. The necessary brevity of presentation should not cause the many as yet unsolved problems to be overlooked.

The *Acetabulariae* are green marine algae of subtropical and tropical waters (class *Siphonocladales*, family *Dasycladaceae*, subfamily *Acetabulariae*). The three main species dealt with in this review are the following:

Algae	Abbreviation	Origin
Acetabularia mediterranea	*med*	Mediterranean
Acetabularia crenulata	*cren*	Santo Domingo
Acicularia Schenckii	*Acic*	Curaçao

---

[1] I am very grateful to Dr. Beerman (Wilhelmshaven) and Dr. Lorch (London) for the translation of this paper.

All experiments were performed on plants cultured in the laboratory. In these no calcification takes place; growth may be quicker than in their natural habitat. (For culture methods, see Hämmerling, 1944; Beth, 1953).

A fully developed *Acetabularia* consists of the rhizoid, the stalk, and the cap, Fig. 1). The length of the stalk reaches 4 to 6 cm in *med* and *cren*; the cap diameter may be up to 1 cm (the *med* stalks in Figs. 1a and c are shorter than normal since they have been regenerated). The formation of the cap is preceded by the development of deciduous whorls (Figs. 1d and 2a).

Fig. 1. *Left: (a)* and *(c)* Young and adult caps of *med*, regenerated from nucleated posterior parts, hence stalks shorter than normal.

Right: caps of *cren*. *(b)* Two caps, stalk growing out above upper cap and beginning of whorl formation (between two caps a whorl is generally formed). Spurs well formed but only partially seen in reproductions. *(d)* Young cap with pointed rays, remains of old whorl seen. Note that *med* usually forms only one cap, *cren* always forms several. *(a)* 4×, *(b)* 7×, *(c)* 4×, *(d)* 10×.

c.s. = corona superior; r = rhizoid; w = whorl.

THE INFLUENCE OF THE NUCLEUS ON MORPHOGENESIS

Nucleated and Anucleate Parts

All the species of the *Acetabulariae* examined are not only unicellular but also uninucleate (Hämmerling, 1931, 1944; Schulze, 1939; Maschlanka, 1943a). The nucleus lies within the rhizoid. Thus, cutting off the rhizoid produces anucleate parts. These are not only long living (several months) but also display greatly varying morphogenetic capacities. Apical differentiations will be described first. They may go as far as the formation not only of a new stalk and one or several whorls but also of one or even two caps (Fig. 2).

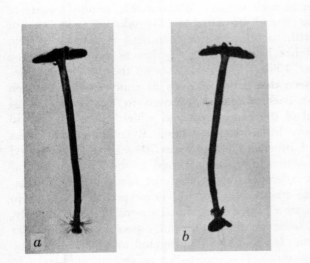

Fig. 2. Anucleate portion of a *med* plant with cap. Posteriorly a whorl and cap are formed; the latter grows. The anterior cap also increases in size. (a) 13, (b) 25, and (c) 71 days after amputation. (For details of polarity reversal, see Hämmerling, 1934a, 1936.)

The morphogenetic capacity of long pieces from a given region of the stalk is greater than that of short pieces from the same region. Anucleate portions from the anterior part of the stalk have a greater morphogenetic capacity than portions of equal length from more posterior regions, even if they are very short (0.1 cm). However, nucleated portions always possess full morphogenetic powers and can be made to regenerate repeatedly. These and other results lead to the following interpretations:

1. The morphogenetic capacity of an anucleate part is determined by the amount of nucleus-dependent morphogenetic substances stored in it.

2. There is an anterior-posterior concentration gradient of these substances.

3. In nucleated parts these substances are continually produced (Hämmerling, 1934a, b, 1943a).

The capacity of anucleate portions shows that the nuclear influence on morphogenetic processes is only indirect. In this connection it should be pointed out that, as a condition for morphogenesis in anucleate portions, at least partial formation of cytoplasm, plastids, and cellular membrane must take place in such regions. Without this, neither anucleate nor nucleated portions would be capable of producing, e.g., one or even two new caps with their numerous chambers. Regarding protein synthesis, direct proof has been obtained by Brachet and Chantrenne (1951, see also Brachet, 1952a) in experiments on the uptake of radio-active $C^{14}O_2$. It has been demonstrated even in anucleate parts which had been kept in the dark and were exposed to light only for 24 to 38 hours at the end of the experiment and which, therefore, should have shown no, or very little, morphogenesis. Even after five weeks the synthetic activity of anucleate portions was 70% of that of nucleated ones. The use of radioactive isotopes as started in the Brussels laboratories opens up a new approach to the study of many different metabolic processes in these plant cells. It will, however, be necessary to direct special attention to a hitherto neglected source of error, namely, the fact that bacteria settle on the stalk, and especially on the older regions of the membrane. It should be investigated to what extent they take up the labeled molecules. The surest—but as yet untested—way to eliminate this factor would naturally be a sterile culture method, e.g., by the addition of antibiotic substances.

Rhizoids, i.e., posterior ends, were also formed by anucleate portions, but only rarely and incompletely. Their production, therefore, does not depend on the presence of a nucleus either (Hämmerling, 1934a, b). According to unpublished observations on nucleated portions, nucleus formation occasionally takes place in the stalk or even in the cap. In such cases, a rhizoid always develops in the neighborhood of the nucleus. This means that favorable conditions for rhizoid formation are created, preferably near the nucleus. Thus it seems that in normal development the rhizoid is formed posteriorly because the nucleus is situated in this region. It is not known whether external factors are also concerned.

Interspecific Grafts

A.MEDITERRANEA AND A.CRENULATA

The mode of action of the morphogenetic substances has been examined by making grafts between different species. We shall first consider four kinds of grafts between the two species *cren* and *med* containing one, two, or three nuclei. Schemes of the grafts and the results are shown in Fig. 3 (Hämmerling, 1943b. 1946b).

Only certain differences in the structure of the caps are considered. The caps of both species are well characterized morphologically, for instance with respect to number of rays, number of small hair scars on the so-called corona superior, and presence or absence of a spur (Figs. 1 and 5).

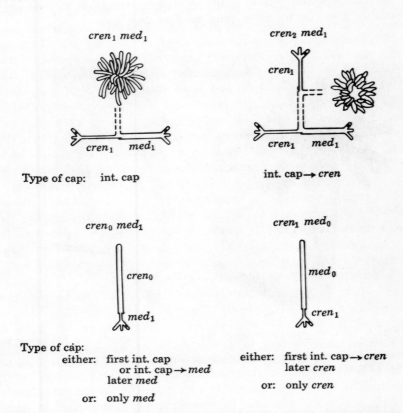

$cren_1\ med_1$

$cren_1$ med_1

Type of cap: int. cap

$cren_2\ med_1$

$cren_1$

$cren_1$ med_1

int. cap $\rightarrow$ *cren*

$cren_0\ med_1$

$cren_0$

med_1

Type of cap:
  either: first int. cap
         or int. cap $\rightarrow$ *med*
         later *med*
  or: only *med*

$cren_1\ med_0$

med_0

$cren_1$

  either: first int. cap $\rightarrow$ *cren*
         later *cren*
  or: only *cren*

Fig. 3. Diagram showing the four types of *cren med* transplants and the resulting caps. The subscripts 2, 1, and 0 indicate the number of nuclei. The dot in the rhizoid (shown as three branches) indicates the nucleus. Dotted line = regeneration.

The grafting procedure for binucleate grafts is as follows: two pieces including the rhizoid, and thus containing the nucleus, are pushed into one another with their cut ends. If the graft has been successful, the two cytoplasms will fuse completely and the graft will grow out at the point of fusion and form a new stalk with whorls and caps (Fig. 4). In trinucleate transplants the third rhizoid is grafted onto the cut end of the regenerated binucleate transplant. In mononucleate transplants the nucleated rhizoid is grafted onto an anucleate stalk. In these cases, regeneration usually occurs at the upper end of the stalk. In view of the size of the plants, all these operations can be carried out under a binocular dissecting microscope.

The operations can be classified into four groups:

1. Intra-specific control grafts, containing from one to four nuclei, invariably give rise to either pure *med* or *cren* caps.

Fig. 4. (a) Cren, med_1 transplant. Stalk with intermediate cap has grown out from point of fusion. (b) $Acic_1$ med_1 transplant. Left, the *Acic;* right, the *med* component. From their point of fusion a stalk with two intermediate caps has grown out. (a) 12×, (b) 6×.

2. Binucleate grafts, containing one *med* and one *cren* nucleus, form caps, which we will call briefly, if not quite correctly, intermediate

caps. Of their individual characters some tend more toward *med,* and some toward *cren,* as may be seen from Table 1. For instance, with respect to the number of rays and the hair number of the coronae they come close to *cren,* whereas with respect to the presence of spurred or pointed rays they tend more toward *med.* Other characters seem to be nearly intermediate *sensu stricto,* but it is difficult to say if they really are. The general appearance of intermediate caps is fairly similar to that of the *cren* caps with isolated rays (Figs. 5*b* and *d*). This, however, is due to secondary reasons not to be explained here.

3. Trinucleate grafts containing two *cren* and one *med* nucleus give rise to caps coming much closer to *cren* than those developing from binucleate grafts (Figs. 3*b* and 5*c*). We shall call them "*cren*-like intermediate caps." That they are not pure *cren* caps is shown especially by a lesser degree of spur development. Figure 6 shows a series of

TABLE 1

Some Characters of *cren,* Intermediate, and *med* Caps

| Character | Caps | | | Tendency |
	cren	Intermediate	med	
Number of rays	$30.68 \pm 2.79c$	42.23 ± 4.77	80.80 ± 3.21	$\rightarrow$ *cren*
Hair number of corona superior	1.94 ± 0.03	2.08 ± 0.04	3.43 ± 0.06	
Rays with spur or pointed	Yes	Very rarely pointed	No	$\rightarrow$ *med*

$c = M \pm 3m.$

isolated rays leading from pure *med* to pure *cren,* with several intermediate degrees of ray shape and spur development. Thus bi- and trinucleate grafts form different but characteristic and constant types of caps.

4. On the other hand, uninucleate grafts containing a *med* nucleus (anucleate *cren* part without caps) form various types of caps, representing two kinds of intergrades as well as pure *med* caps. (Fig. 3*c*). The intergrades can be either "*med*-like intermediate caps" or intermediate caps, much resembling those of binucleate grafts, but on the average tending somewhat more toward *med* than the latter.

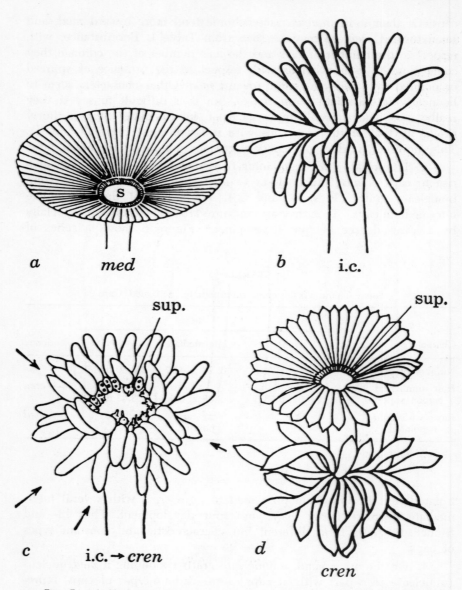

Fig. 5. (a) Med cap, 72 rays, united, without spurs. (b) $cren_1$ med_1 intermediate cap (i.c.), 33 rays, isolated, slim, without spurs. (c) "Cren-like intermediate cap" (i.c. $\rightarrow$ cren) of a $cren_2$ med_1 transplant, 34 rays, partly united, some
pointed (arrows). (d) Two cren caps, the lower with isolated rays (only 18 shown),
the upper with rays still united (35). Both with spurs. (a) 7×, (b) 17×, (c) 18×,
(d) 11×.

s and sup = corona superior. Hair scars shown only in (c). Semidiagrammatic.

If a graft forms several caps after the first cap is cut off, and if the first cap has been an intergrade, the second will be a pure *med* cap. This sequence is a fixed rule.[2]

The frequency of intergrades depends on the length of the anucleate *cren* part (Table 2). If this is long, an intergrade will develop first in most cases, followed by a pure *med* cap (provided that more than one cap is formed), but if it is short, the first cap will frequently be a *med* one.

Finally, the reciprocal combination—*cren* nucleus plus anucleate *med* part—will give rise either to *cren*-like intermediate caps followed by pure *cren* caps or immediately to pure *cren* caps (Fig. 3d).

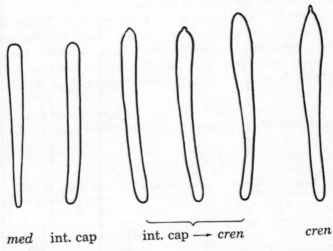

med   int. cap   int. cap ⟶ cren   cren

Fig. 6. Single rays showing transition from *med* to *cren*. Semidiagrammatic. 20×.

----

[2]A considerable number of the transplants showed reversible damage or died after formation of the first or second cap, even if this was a pure *med* cap. It is interesting that the incompatibility was manifested here only after a previous morphogenesis. Incompatibility between the two species was also evident from the fact that so far all cysts which had formed after apparently normal nuclear division from interspecific caps of one-, two-, or three-nucleate grafts soon died off. Since gametes are formed in the cysts no further generations could be obtained from transplants with intergrades. If, however, mononucleate transplants gave rise to pure *med* caps corresponding to the nucleate portion, the cysts were viable; they produced pure *med* plants. It should be added also that mononucleate grafts, the anucleate *cren* stalk of which already had a cap, were produced, as well as reciprocal transplants with *cren* nucleus and *med* cap. In both cases the transplanted caps remained unchanged. Again, the cysts produced were not viable, and strains therefore could not be obtained (1940, unpublished).

TABLE 2

$cren_0\ med_1$

Type of First Cap in Relation to Length of Anucleate *cren* Component
(in All Grafts from the Posterior Region of the Stalk)

cren component	First cap intergrade		First cap *med*	Total of grafts
Long (0.75—1.92 cm.)	21	:	1	22
Short (0.15—0.6 cm.)	7	:	9	16

Thus, both uninuclear graft series lead to the formation of various intergrades, but in all surviving grafts caps eventually appear which are characteristic of the transplanted nucleus.

The results of the four series are summarized in Tables 3 and 4. Table 3 clearly shows the tendency toward *cren* of the trinucleate caps as compared with the binucleate ones. Table 4 shows the tendency toward *cren* or *med,* respectively, of the uninucleated caps. (The numbers in Table 3 refer to the number of *caps,* and in Table 4 to the number of *grafts.*)

The experimental data show that the type of cap formed in each case depends on the combination of the nuclei and of the nucleus-

TABLE 3

Grafts between *cren* and *med* with Two and Three Nuclei

Type of grafts	Type and number of caps			
	cren	"*cren*-like i.c."	i.c.	*med*
$cren_1\ med_1$	(3)[a]	(3)	180	(3)
$cren_2\ med_1$	0	$\geqslant$76[b]	(4)	0

[a]Numbers in parentheses are exceptions, in most cases to be explained by special conditions.

[b]Minimum number; exact number not available owing to loss of data.

controlled morphogenetic substances present within the graft. These results may be interpreted as follows:

1. The nucleus-controlled morphogenetic substances differ from species to species.

2. Hence in binucleate grafts a definite ratio between the substances controlled by both nuclei will be established and maintained. This explains the formation of intermediate caps of constant types.

TABLE 4

Grafts between *cren* and *med* with One Nucleus

Type of grafts and total	Number of grafts with type of caps				
	Only *cren*	First "*cren-*like i.c." later partly *cren*	First i.c. later partly *med*	First "*med-*like i.c." later partly *med*	Only *med*
$cren_0\ med_1$ (39)	(1)[a]	0	25(9)	3(2)	10
$cren_1\ med_0$ (19)	12	7(4)	0	0	0

[a]Case not certain.

Note: A number of transplants with intergrades died before more caps were formed. Values for surviving specimens which later formed pure *cren* and *med* caps respectively are given in parentheses.

3. In trinucleate grafts containing two *cren* nuclei and one *med* nucleus, a shift of this ratio would be expected in favor of the *cren* substances. This is obviously the reason why their caps tend more toward *cren* than they do in binucleate grafts (*cren*-like intermediate caps).

It must be concluded that the type of cap forming in each case is determined by the ratio of the two morphogenetic substances.

4. In uninucleate grafts the following situation will result: Like all anucleate parts, the anucleate component of the graft has stored a certain quantity of morphogenetic substances of its own species. In the component containing the nucleus the substances of the other species are not only stored but continue to be produced. The two kinds of substances compete with one another and thus give rise to an intergrade cap, provided that the anucleate component has stored enough substances.

In this connection it may be emphasized that, from the experiments with anucleate parts, it was concluded that the longer parts of the posterior region of the stalk contain more morphogenetic substances than shorter ones of the same region. This explains why the frequency with which the various intergrades appear in the uninucleate grafts depends on the length of the anucleate component (Table 2). Furthermore, the results obtained with anucleate parts led to the assumption that once the stored substances are used up they will not be produced anew, whereas in parts containing the nucleus their production continues. This presumably is the reason why uninucleate interspecific grafts always eventually give rise to a cap characteristic of the nucleated component.

Moreover, it becomes clear why, in mononucleate transplants, *med*-like intermediate caps occur only in transplants with *med* nuclei, and *cren*-like intermediate caps only in those with *cren* nuclei (Fig. 2). In view of the variable amounts of substances stored, it may be expected that, in transplants with *med* nuclei, the ratio may be in favor of the *med* substances, whereas in transplants with *cren* nuclei it may be in favor of *cren* substances. However, the latter type never formed pure intermediate caps. This may be due to the small number of transplants, or the anucleate *med* parts may store less morphogenetic substance than the equivalent *cren* parts in the reciprocal transplants. Or possibly nucleated *cren* parts produce more morphogenetic substance in a given time than nucleated *med* parts.

5. So far, we have dealt only with the mode of action of the morphogenetic substances. As to their *origin,* the results permit more than the general statement that they are nucleus controlled.

According to our interpretation, the effect of the *med* substances is the development, not only of a cap, but of a cap characteristic for *med*—the effect of the *cren* substances is the development of a *cren* cap—and both kinds of substances combined will lead to the development of intergrades. Thus we must conclude that they do not just induce a development already fixed in its direction, but that they determine this direction itself. Hence their effect is of the same order as that of the genes controlling the cap characters. Therefore, they have to be considered as products of gene action, which stand between the gene and character. Any attempt to avoid this interpretation leads to great difficulties. It is indispensable, even though it has not yet been possible to confirm this conclusion by an additional genetic analysis, because so far no interbreeding species or mutations have been found. Neither have any of the morphogenetic substances been extracted from the plants. Thus all information with respect to these substances can only be gained indirectly, and a specific statement as to their true relations to genes is impossible for the time being. The gene dependence of certain characteristics of the cap may be considered certain, but it must be pointed out that in interspecific grafts of nucleated parts cytoplasm as well as the nucleus is transferred. It is, therefore, impossible to say more about the course of processes resulting in a cap of a certain shape. The question also remains unanswered whether or not the morphogenetic substances are associated with specific self-reproducing but gene-determined plasma particles.

Although earlier the behavior of anucleate parts seemed evidence in support of the first alternative, mono- and multinucleate interspecific grafts show that both explanations are feasible. If the first alternative is true, even that possibility of a temporary multiplication of the specific plasma particles in anucleate parts cannot be ruled out. In any case, however, their reproduction capacity would be limited, so that in mononucleate grafts $a_1 b_0$, only the production of a-particles would finally be maintained. Theoretically, such hypotheses of plasma particles can be applied to microsomes as well as has been done by Brachet (1952a).

The interpretations given may be summarized as follows: under the influence of the genes controlling the characters studied, chemical compounds are synthesized within the nucleus and released into the cytoplasm. They direct metabolism in such a way that, from protoplasm as the substrate of morphogenesis, eventually a cap of definite shape is formed. An essential point in this interpretation is the assumption that these compounds react effectively with the cytoplasm of other species, e.g., the morophogenetic substances of *mediterranea* cause formation of a *med* cap from *cren* cytoplasm.

ACICULARIA SCHENCKII AND OTHER SPECIES

Considerable progress in a new direction was made through experiments with transplants between *Acic* and *med* (Beth, 1943a, b, c).

The *Acic* caps are spurred and can hardly be distinguished from the *cren* caps in their other characters also. Accordingly, the intermediate stages resulting from $Acic_1 med_1$ and $Acic_0 med_1$ transplants resemble those described for *cren med* transplants. Also in the frequency and kind of intergrades, no difference was detected: in binucleate $Acic_1 med_1$ transplants only intermediate caps were formed; in the mononucleate $Acic_0 med_1$ transplants, *med*-like intermediate caps, or pure *med* caps, in addition to intermediate caps, were produced. In transplants giving rise to intergrades and *med* caps, the *med* cap was always the last cap formed. Figure 4b shows $Acic_1 med_1$ intermediate caps. It should be pointed out that these caps, like the $cren_1 med_1$ caps, were without spurs (cf. Figs. 4a and b). However, when binucleate $cren_1 Acic_1$ transplants were made, the resulting intermediate caps had spurs, and in this and all other respects they were indistinguishable from the two pure species (Fig. 7; compare with the *cren* caps in Fig. 1) (Maschlanka, 1943b). It may be concluded that the absence of spurs

Fig. 7. $Cren_1$ $Acic_1$ intermediate cap with spurs. Indistinguishable from pure *cren* and *Acic* caps; cf. Figs. 1 and 4. 20×.

in $cren_1$ med_1 and $Acic_1$ med_1 caps is due not to some unspecific inhibition but to a specific *med* influence.[3]

Up to now these transplants confirmed the results with *cren med* transplants. Nevertheless, the results are very surprising. For, under conditions which constantly led to cap formation in *cren* and *med* cultures, the *Acic* plants never formed caps, and of the *Acic* regenerates from nucleated parts only 15% produced caps.

Since $Acic_1$ med_1 transplants always form intergrades, and $Acic_0$ med_1 form them at least to the same extent as $cren_0$ med_1 transplants,

---

[3]Also, the remainder of the previously mentioned cap characteristics showed little or no disturbance. However, marked disturbances and malformations of the caps resulted from binucleate transplants between systematically distant genera: *A.wettsteinii* and *polyphysoides* on the one hand, and *med* and *cren* on the other (Hämmerling, 1946b, and unpublished work; Wolf, unpublished). These disturbances are probably caused by too great a genetic difference between the two nuclei. Thus mononucleate transplants between *med* and *Wettsteinii* resulted in normal pure *Wettsteinii* and *med caps* (Hämmerling, 1934b). Some differently formed med_0 $Wett_1$ ps were then interpreted as disturbed but pure *Wettsteinii* caps. It is possible that they were really intergrades.

it follows that the *Acic* nucleus produces morphogenetic substances which are stored in the stalk, but which cannot have their full effect in pure *Acic* plants, owing to a missing substance. This substance becomes functional when a nucleated *med* part is combined with a nucleated or anucleate *Acic* part. Hence we have to distinguish between two types of morphogenetic substances.

1. Species-specific substances, controlling the shape of the caps.[4]

2. Non-species-specific substances. The latter are necessary for the effectiveness of the former. *Med, cren,* and *Acic* produce (and store) the first type of substance in sufficient quantity; the second substance is also produced sufficiently by *med* and *cren,* but only rarely by *Acic.* Thus it becomes comprehensible why pure *Acic* parts rarely form caps, whereas combinations of *Acic* parts (nucleated or anucleate) with nucleated *med* parts form intergrades. Species-specific substances from *Acic* and *med* are both made effective by non-species-specific substances from *med.*

The behavior of med_0 $Acic_1$ transplants (anucleate *med* + nucleated *Acic*) is in full agreement with this interpretation; e.g., these transplants act according to the presence of the *Acic* nucleus in failing to form caps, either at once or after regeneration of an intergrade. (Theoretically, 15% cap formation would be expected, as in pure *Acic* parts, but the material was insufficient to test this.)

Recent experiments by Beth (1953), especially on *cred* and *med,* have shown that the ability of the *Acetabulariae* to form caps depends on the quantity of light received daily. Under certain conditions of weak illumination the stalk continues to grow normally, though slowly, yet no cap is formed. Thus there is no *general* inhibition of development, but, as in *Acicularia,* certain specific factors essential for the formation of a cap are absent, despite adequate cytoplasmic increase. If anucleate anterior portions are prepared from such capless *cren* plants and normal illumination restored, then they develop caps at about the same rate and to the same extent as similar portions from plants whose illumination was never reduced! The controls, anucleate portions under weak illumination, formed no caps.

At present a possible special interpretation is that the non-species-specific morphogenetic substances reach a precursor stage only when the illumination is weak, and these stored precursors are converted to

----

[4]It has to be taken into account that these may be a group of different substances. In this case it would be more correct to say that every species has a characteristic specific combination of substances. The German expressions are "hutgestaltende" and "hutbildende" substances. Whether the second type are really "morphogenetic" substances is not certain.

the active product when normal illumination is restored. These experiments on *cren* suggest that *Acicularia* requires particularly high light intensities for this activation in view of its non-species-specific substances. At present, experiments to verify this point cannot be carried out, owing to loss of the *Acic* cultures through deficient reproduction.

Some species differ also in the shape of the stalk and whorls, e.g., *A.Wettsteinii* and *polyphysoides* on the one hand, and *med* and *cren* on the other. Hence binucleate grafts between these species would also be expected to show intermediates with respect to these characters. At least in the case of the stalk, intergrades seem to develop. On the other hand, stalk and whorl characters have wide and overlapping ranges of variability, so that precise information on this point could not be gained. In contrast to the cap, stalk and whorls of these transplants develop without malformation (see footnote, p. 487).

Thus it is merely by way of analogy if we conclude that the differentiation of all morphological characters—in other words, the development of patterns of organization—is controlled by the action of morphogenetic substances.

DEVELOPMENT OF NUCLEUS: CYTOCHEMICAL WORK

The development of the plant from the germination of the zygote to the formation of a cap of maximum size takes several months. During this period the nucleus shows a marked development, especially with regard to its nucleolar material. The species differ in some minor details. As an example we have chosen *med*.

In the germinating zygote the nucleus and the single nucleolus are small and spherical. Then they grow considerably. The nucleus assumes an ellipsoid or ovid shape, and the nucleolus divides into several parts and eventually exhibits the structure seen in Figs. 8a, b, e, f. Compared with the nucleus of a gamete (diameter $\approx 4\ \mu$) or zygote, the nucleus of a plant with a cap of maximum size is a giant nucleus (long diameter up to 80 μ), but compared with the whole plant it is very small. It is likely that the "giant nucleus" of an adult plant is still a normal diploid nucleus (Hämmerling, 1931; Schulze, 1939). The morphological appearance alone suggests a strong activity of the nucleolar material. Recently Stich (1951a, b) began a cytochemical study of this and other points. Applying the usual tests he found protein, polysaccharides, and a high content of ribonucleic acid (RNA) (Figs. 8a, b) as well as a high alkaline phosphatase activity within the nucleolus (Fig. 8e). Moreover, in *living* cells small vacuoles present within the nucleolus can be seen to burst from time to time and release their contents into the nuclear cap. The chemical content of these vacuoles is not known.

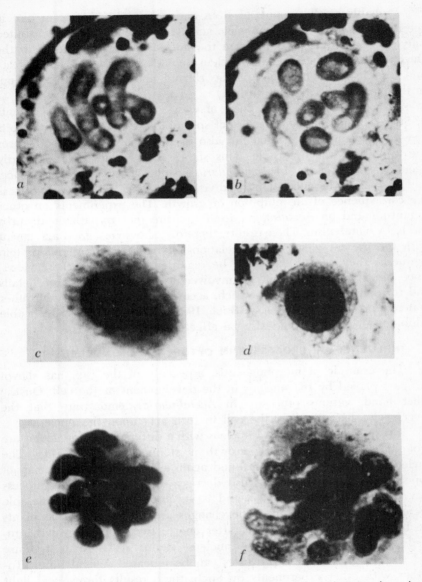

Fig. 8. Nuclear changes induced by dark treatment (A. mediterranea): a, b, d sections, toluidine blue (test for RNA; a and b, two sections through the same nucleus); c and e, total mounts, Gomori reaction (test for alkaline phosphatase); f, total amount, gallocyanine. Nucleolar vacuoles partially seen in b and f.

(a) 26 weeks old; (b) 26 weeks old; (c) after 7 weeks in dark; (d) after 9 weeks in dark; (e) 5 weeks after restoration to normal conditions; (f) 9 weeks after restoration to normal conditions. (a-f) 750×.

Probably small amounts of RNA and polysaccharides occur also in the nuclear sap. Desoxyribonucleic acid (DNA) could be demonstrated only in young nuclei. Apart from the nucleus, RNA was found in the rhizoid branch containing the nucleus (Vanderhaeghe; Brachet, 1952a) and also in other branches of the rhizoid and in the stalk, but not in the plastids (Stich, unpublished).

From the cytochemical point of view, the trypaflavin experiments of Stich (1951c) on *med* are also of special interest. Trypaflavin inhibits growth not only in nucleated but also in anucleate parts; in both cases the inhibition was reversible. This shows that it does not necessarily occur via the nucleus. In *Acetabularia* no nuclear divisions take place, and therefore the inhibition of division observed in other objects is the consequence of an inhibition of growth. The experiments on other organisms and on *Acetabularia* itself indicate that trypaflavin disturbs the RNA metabolism. Their results, therefore, show very good agreement with the present views on the relationship between RNA and protein synthesis; they cannot, however, be regarded as proof of these views, since other processes might be involved as well as RNA (for details and for damage to the DNA which, according to experience with other material, presumably occurs, see Stich, 1951c; Brachet, 1952a). Reversible inhibition of growth could also be effected by streptomycin.

INFLUENCE OF PROCESSES IN CYTOPLASM ON NUCLEUS

The example of morphogenesis, especially of the cap, has shown the part played by the nucleus in the development of the cell. On the other hand, various processes in *Acetabularia* demonstrate that the reverse also happens; i.e., the cell in turn acts upon the nucleus.

If plants already having a nucleus with a differentiated nucleolus are brought into the dark, their growth is stopped (Stich, 1951a). The nucleoli rapidly decrease in size and again assume a spherical compact appearance. Apparently they also decrease in substance. This process may take as little as ten days and is accompanied by a considerable decrease of nuclear volume. The changes are reversible; if the plants are brought back into the light, after one to two months, growth proceeds normally again and the nucleus attains its normal structure and size (Fig. 8). These processes can be repeated several times. Together with other experiments by Stich, these results throw new light on the old problem of the nucleoplasm. Size, structure, and functional capacity probably depend less on the cell volume than on the extent of synthetic processes of the cytoplasm. According to experiments by Brachet (1952a) the effect of dinitrophenol and of usnate upon the nucleus is the same as that of darkness.

A second example of the effect of the rest of the cell upon the nucleus is provided by the division of the primary nucleus (Hämmerling, 1939). Normally the nucleus does not divide until the cap has obtained maximum size. Then, by successive divisions, numerous small secondary nuclei are formed and carried into the cap by protoplasmic streaming. There a so-called cyst is formed around each nucleus, later giving rise to the gametes.

In *A. mediterranea*, the nuclear divisions do not begin until the cap has reached a diameter of 0.55 to 1.0 cm (Fig. 9). If such a cap is cut

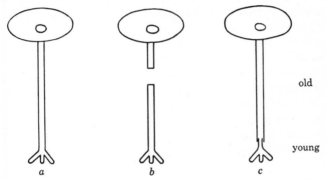

Fig. 9. Suppression and induction of division of the primary nucleus. *(a)* Division at stage of cap with maximum diameter—*a normal case*. (b) No division if cap is cut off. *(c)* Division of young nucleus if grafted on anucleate part having cap of maximum diameter.

off, the divisions are suppressed. Then new morphogenetic processes are initiated, and division does not take place until a new cap of maximum size has been completed. Thus the division could be delayed as long as two years.

On the other hand, division of the nucleus may be induced prematurely by making grafts between young and old parts. The young components of the grafts were rhizoids, containing a nucleus and obtained from plants still without a cap. Their nucleus normally would have remained undivided for at least two months. The rhizoids were transplanted onto anucleate anterior parts of plants having a cap of maximum size. In some of these experiments division began as early as two weeks after grafting, in others a little later.

Delayed and premature divisions take a normal course, as judged by the formation of normal cysts in all cases.

Thus the development of the nucleus is not an autonomous one. Whether or not it divides depends on the state of the rest of the cell.

The nature of the principles inducing nuclear division has still to be investigated. They cannot be species-specific, as premature divisions also occur in interspecific *cren med* grafts (Hämmerling, unpublished).

The realization that nuclear division is dependent on the conditions prevailing within the cell is, of course, not new. The peculiarity of the case of *Acetabularia* is due to the fact that it could be shown that a young nucleus divides under normal physiological conditions when transplanted into a cell system "ripe for division" and that nuclear division can be postponed indefinitely when the necessary conditions are removed. Moreover, the conditions which initiate nuclear division are the indirect outcome of the previous influence of the nucleus on the rest of the cell.

In the third and last example we return again to the problem of morphogenesis. As mentioned at the beginning, anucleate parts still possess a certain partly high morphogenetic capacity. It is most pronounced in anucleate anterior parts, but it changes according to the age of the cell from which the anucleate part has been cut off in such a way that, during development after an initial increase, it decreases again. This rule applies not only to the number of structures formed in each part but also to their qualitative character (Table 5).

TABLE 5

Morphogenetic Capacity of Anucleate Anterior Parts of *A.mediterranea*
(Formation of Whorls and/or Caps)

Stage of development	Investigated parts	Number of whorls and/or caps formed, total : per part		% typical : atypical (incomplete forms)		
0.3-1.0 cm	82	0	0	0	:	0
1.5-shortly before cap form	284	444	1.6	64	:	36
Cap diameter, 0.2-0.35 cm	173	116	0.7	45	:	55
Cap diameter, 0.4-1 cm	79	29	0.4	14	:	86

Data from material published in Hämmerling (1934a).

Parts containing a nucleus, however, show a more or less complete and typical morphogenesis during all stages; that is, they always form stalk and whorls, and older parts also form a new cap in most cases, even repeatedly.

The differences between the anucleate parts and the parts containing the nucleus lead to the following conclusions:

1. The changes in the morphogenetic capacity of anucleate parts are not due to changes of the reactivity of the protoplasmic substrate but apparently are a consequence of changes in the activity of the nucleus during normal development.

2. These changes are not autonomous ones but depend on the state of the cell system. Thus in old plants the nucleus is less active than in younger ones, but becomes fully active if the cap is cut off.

It is of special interest that, in the older plants, the conditions established by the morphogenetic activity of the nucleus in turn react upon itself, controlling just this activity.

SUMMARY

The investigations described in the first section lead to the interpretation that the nucleus of *Acetabularia* controls the pattern of organization, especially of the caps, by the production of morphogenetic substances (action of the nucleus on the processes in the cytoplasm). In the second section the development of the nucleus and cytochemical work is described. From the experiments described in the third section, it follows that the size, the structure, and the functional intensity of the nucleus and other nuclear processes e.g., mitosis and morphogenetic activity, depend on the conditions of the other cell components (action of the processes in the cytoplasm on the nucleus).

ADDENDA

1. Recently Beth (1953) confirmed that the cap-forming capacity of anucleate parts is not dependent on the length of the stalk, i.e., upon the amount of cytoplasm, plastids, etc., but only on the amount of "factors" specific for cap formation, to which we gave the very general term "morphogenetic substances." This capacity is fixed at the moment of enucleation and is not changed by different external conditions, e.g., at 21° or 27° or with weak or strong illumination. Only the speed of cap formation is changed, not the number of caps.

2. With respect to researches on the biochemical level there are the following additions to make:

(*a*) After three months the respiration of anucleate *med* parts was not reduced (Chantrenne-van Halteren and Brachet, 1952), whereas the uptake of P^{32} was much diminished at that time (Brachet, 1952). Apparently the absence of the nucleus influences phosphorylations much more than the functioning of the respiratory enzymes. These results agree with the experiments of Brachet and co-workers on anucleate amebae (see Brachet, 1952a, d). The situation becomes more complicated, since Hämmerling and Stich (1953a) sometimes found an *increase* of P^{32} uptake occurring even two weeks after enucleation. The reasons for these differences are still unknown.

(*b*) In the dark, with anucleate parts only a decline of P^{32} uptake has been observed. It is partly reversible: with anterior and posterior *med* parts after three weeks in darkness followed by seven days of illumination, that is, four week after enucleation, the P^{32} uptake was much higher than with two-week-old parts which were continually illuminated.

This reactivation is independent of growth processes, at least within certain limits, for anterior parts growing out after re-illumination showed reactivation of P^{32} uptake to the same degree as nongrowing posterior parts (Hämmerling, and Stich, 1953a).

(*c*) The P^{32} once taken up is not exchanged against the phosphorus of the culture medium, at least for a certain time after activation. This is in agreement with the findings on other unicellular organisms with very different types of metabolism (Labaw *et al.*, 1950, on *Escherichia coli;* Freidrich-Freksa and Kaudewitz, 1951, on *Amoeba proteus*). Non-exchange of P is found with (1) growing nucleated parts; (2) illuminated growing and nongrowing anucleate parts of the anterior and posterior stalk region; and (3) nucleated and enucleated parts brought into darkness, where growth is stopped (Hämmerling and Stich, 1953b).

(*d*) Stich (1953) found that metaphosphates are localized in distinct small globules in the cytoplasm. If the photosynthesis is suspended by darkness for four to eight weeks and consequently growth is stopped, then the metaphosphate bodies are consumed in nucleated and enucleated parts. Both nucleated and enucleated parts, if re-illuminated, again synthesize new metaphosphates to the same extent. Thus the presence of the nucleus is not necessary for these endothermal processes.

In *illuminated* anucleate parts, whether capable of growth or not, the processes of synthesis probably exceed those of consumption, for the metaphosphate bodies increase considerably in size (not in number). The possibility that this is due to a hydration is not yet excluded. The stopping of growth of anucleate parts after a given time is not caused by a lack of metaphosphates. Increase of size of the metaphosphate bodies occurs also if the growth is stopped by trypaflavine.

(*e*) The dry weight of *regenerating* anucleate parts also increases. The very interesting question whether the dry weight of nonregenerating anucleated parts is also increasing is not yet tested.

The results described under (a) to (e) show clearly, from a new angle, that the capacity or noncapacity of anucleate parts to grow is not due to a general alteration of metabolic processes but originally only to specific substances present or absent at the time of enucleation.

3. Additions concerning interspecific grafts.

(a) The conclusions about an anterior-posterior concentration gradient of the morphogenetic substances were recently confirmed also (Werz unpublished): anterior parts of 2.5- or 5-mm length taken as anucleate components of $cren_0$ med_1 transplants gave rise to intergrades only, whereas 5-mm and 10-mm long parts of the posterior region gave rise to quite pure med caps only. Thus there is a concentration gradient of the species-specific substances. It may be added that probably the nonspecies-specific substances also are distributed in a concentration gradient (Hämmerling, 1943b).

(b) In former experiments with tri- and tetranucleated grafts caps were formed only in the already described $cren_2$ med_1 grafts (Maschlanka, 1946, and unpublished). But recently Werz (unpublished) showed that cap formation can take place in *all* combinations from 2 to 4 nuclei. It was confirmed that the type of caps depends on the ratio of nuclei.

(c) If we consider all results of intra- and interspecific grafts as well as isolated anucleate parts, we can state that there is *evidence* for species-specific and non-species-specific *actions* of the nucleus. The species-specific actions in the interspecific grafts are interpreted by the assumption that "morphogenetic substances," dependent on a nucleus A and responsible for the formation of an A cap, can also react with a B cytoplasm and bring out of it an A cap. It may be added that this fundamental assumption is supported also by the following facts: (1) pure *Wettsteinii* caps which were formed from med_0 $Wettst_1$ transplants contained med chloroplasts; (2) in these transplants the cellulose membrane of the anucleate med component took the properties of *Wettsteinii* membranes, e.g., the med membrane shrank after cap formation. In these cases it is very tempting to assume that the med cytoplasm present in the grafts had participated in the formation of *Wettsteinii* caps and membranes, i.e., that the med cytoplasm was converted into a *Wettsteinii* cytoplasm under the influence of a *Wettsteinii* nucleus. Nevertheless there is no proof that this interpretation is right. For up to now it has not been possible to make pure transfers of nuclei without cytoplasm. Therefore an alternative explanation could be based on the assumption that in interspecific grafts a nucleus A can react only with cytoplasm A and that this species-specific action consists only in inducing the synthesis of new A cytoplasm with irreversibly determined properties. This assumption is more complicated and needs additional assumptions, especially for mononucleate transplants. Furthermore, researches on a modification of *med* gave strong arguments against this explanation (Hämmerling, 1945). Nevertheless, it cannot at present be excluded. For further discussion see Hämmerling, 1934c, e; 1943b; 1946a.

4. Function of the nucleolus. More concrete knowledge of the nucleolus could be gained by experiments with P^{32}. Not only the fixed and stained giant nucleolus but also its nucleolar substance can already be isolated under the dissecting binocular. Consequently it is possible to examine the uptake of P^{32} by the whole nucleus and by the nucleoli alone. P^{32} was added to the seawater as inorganic phosphate. It is very quickly taken up by the nucleus and nucleoli. About 75% of the uptake is incorporated within the nucleolus and probably the greatest part within its RNA. We may conclude from these results: (*a*) that the nucleolar RNA is synthesized in the nucleolus itself. (*b*) According to our present knowledge, we must assume that the DNA of the interphase chromosomes has a relatively weak metabolism and that in dividing nuclei the amount of DNA between two divisions is only doubled. We may suppose this also for *Acetabularia*, which probably contains a normal diploid nucleus. The RNA of the nucleoli, however, probably has vigorous metabolism; furthermore the increase of its amount is extremely high from the zygote up to a fully grown nucleolus. Therefore we have to account for strong differences in synthetic activity and turnover between the chromosomal DNA and the nucleolar RNA; (*c*) Nowadays a correlation between RNA-turnover and protein-synthesis in the *cytoplasm* is supposed to exist. Therefore the conclusion seems to be justified that the same is the case in the nucleolus, which would thus be a center of protein synthesis in the nucleus (Stich and Hämmerling, 1953).

REFERENCES

Beth, K. (1943a) *Naturwissenschaften*, **31**, 206.
Beth, K. (1943b) *Z. indukt. Abstamm.-u. VererbLehre*, **81**, 252.
Beth, K. (1943c) *Z. indukt. Abstamm.-u. VererbLehre*, **81**, 271.
Beth, K. (1953) *Z. Naturf.*, **8b**, in press.
Brachet, J. (1952a) Le rôle des acides nucléiques dans la vie de cellule et de l'embryon, *Actualités biochim.*, **61**.
Brachet, J. (1952b) *Experientia*, **8**, 347.
Brachet, J. (1952c) *Biochim. biophys. Acta*, **9**, 221.
Brachet, J. (1952d) *Symp. Soc. exp. Biol.*, **6**, 173.
Brachet, J. and Chantrenne, H. (1951) *Nature*, **168**, 950.
Brachet, J., and Chantrenne, H. (1952) *Arch. int. Physiol.*, **60**, 547.

Chantrenne-van Halteren, M., and Brachet, J. (1952) *Arch. int. Physiol.*, **60**,187.

Friedrich-Freksa, H., and Kaudewitz, F. (1951) *Z. Elektrochem.*, **55**, 575.

Hämmerling, J. (1931) *Biol. Zbl.*, **51**, 633.

Hämmerling, J. (1932) *Biol. Z.*, **52**, 42.

Hämmerling, J. (1934a) *Arch. EntwMech. Org.*, **131**, 1.

Hämmerling, J. (1934b) *Biol. Zbl.*, **54**, 650.

Hämmerling, J. (1934c) *Arch. EntwMech. Org.*, **132**, 424.

Hämmerling, J. (1934d) *Arch. Protistenk.*, **83**, 57.

Hämmerling, J. (1934e) Naturwissenschaften, **22**, 829.

Hämmerling, J. (1936) *Zool. Jb., Abt.*, 3, **56**, 439.

Hämmerling, J. (1939) *Biol. Zbl.*, **59**, 158.

Hämmerling, J. (1940) *Note 1st Biol. mar. Rovigno*, **2**, 1.

Hämmerling, J. (1943a) *Z. indukt. Abstamm.-u. VererbLehre*, **81**, 84.

Hämmerling, J. (1934b) *Z. indukt. Abstamm.-u. VererbLehre*, **81**, 114.

Hämmerling, J. (1944) *Arch. Protistenk*, **97**, 7.

Hämmerling, J. (1945) *Biol. Z.*, **64**, 266.

Hämmerling, J. (1946a) *Naturwissenschaften*, **33**, 337, 361.

Hämmerling, J. (1946b) *Z. Naturf.*, **1**, 337.

Hämmerling, J. and Stich, H. (1953a) *Z. Naturf.*, **8b**, in press.

Hämmerling, J. and Stich, H. (1953b) *Z. Naturf.*, **8b**, in press.

Labaw, L., Mosley, V., and Wycoff, R. (1950) *J. Bact.*, **59**, 251.

Maschlanka, H. (1943a) *Naturwissenschaften*, **31**, 548.

Maschlanka, H. (1943b) *Naturwissenschaften*, **31**, 549.

Maschlanka, H. (1946) *Biol. Zbl.*, **65**, 167.

Schulze, K. L. (1939) *Arch. Protistenk.*, **92**, 179.

Stich, H. (1951a) *Z. Naturf.*, **6b**, 320.

Stich, H. (1951b) *Chromosoma*, **4**, 429.

Stich, H. (1951c) *Naturwissenschaften*, **38**, 435.

Survey not mentioned in the text.

Stich, H. (1951d) *Z. Naturf.*, **6b**, 259.

Stich, H. (1953) *Z. Naturf.*, **8b**, 36.

Stich, H., and Hammerling, J. (1953) *Z. Naturf.*, in press.

Vanderhaeghe, F. (1952) *Arch. int. Physiol.*, **60**, 190.

Hämmerling, J. (1946) *Naturwissenschaften*, **33**, 337 and 361.

3

the effect of hydrogen ion concentration upon the induction of polarity in fucus eggs
III. gradients of hydrogen ion concentration*

D. M. WHITAKER

From the School of Biological Sciences, Stanford University and the Hopkins Marine Station, Stanford University

INTRODUCTION

It has been shown (Whitaker (1)) that the tendency of the *Fucus* egg to form a rhizoid on the side toward a neighbor, or in the resultant direction of neighbors ("group effect"), is greatly intensified or augmented when the sea water medium is acidified to pH 6.0. When single eggs are placed near one end in a close fitting tube of glass or quartz 10 or 20 egg diameters long so that substances diffusing from the egg escape more rapidly from one side than from the other, the egg develops in a gradient of its own diffusion products. It has been shown (Whitaker and Lowrance (2)) that in this case also acidification of the medium increases the tendency of the egg to form the rhizoid on the side of greatest concentration of substances diffusing from the egg. The polarity of the egg is determined by the concentration of substances diffusing from the egg itself, just as it may be determined by concentration gradients brought about by a neighboring egg.

A general or uniform increase in the concentration of hydrogen ions, which intensifies the response of the egg to gradients, should not be confused with gradients of concentration of hydrogen ions or of other substances across the developing eggs. Groups of eggs or even two eggs alone in a dish developing in close proximity in the dark, or single eggs near one end in glass tubes undoubtedly produce pH

Reprinted from the Journal of General Physiology
July 20, 1938, Vol. 21, No. 6, pp. 833-845

gradients across the developing eggs as a result of the diffusion patterns of CO_2 and perhaps other acid metabolites. However, these pH gradients, which may be presumed to exist under conditions which result in the group effect, coincide with concentration gradients of any and all substances diffusing into or from each egg cell. In order to separate the effects of hydrogen ions from the effects of other substances except CO_2 (see discussion), the effect of pH gradients has been tested directly in the experiments now to be reported. A preliminary report of a part of the results has been published (3).

METHOD

Ripe fruiting tips of *Fucus furcatus f. luxurians* were collected at the same locality and by methods which have previously been described (4). The fruiting tips were kept for a few days at 4°C. When gametes were obtained they were kept in the dark except for brief exposure during parts of the experiment to red light, which does not affect the polarity of *Fucus* eggs. All work was carried out in a constant temperature room at 15 ± ¼°C., and no eggs were used which did not appear to be spherical at the start. Material was collected and the experiments were carried out in March, April, May, and June, 1935.

Diffusion pipettes were made of Pyrex glass. Each pipette was drawn with a very steep taper from 10 mm stock. The finished pipette consisted of a tube of Pyrex 10 mm in diameter and about 5 cm long, but at one end within approximately 1-2 cm of length the tube was tapered to an overall diameter of about 25 microns, and a lumen of about 8-20 microns diameter. The tapers were drawn at an angle of about 45° with respect to the long axis of the primary tube. Pipettes of similar size and shape were matched in pairs and the tips were cut off so that the lumens were of similar diameter. The tips were cut off with a diamond mounted in a Taylor micromanipulator.

The pipettes were filled from the tips to the bases of the tapers with 1 per cent agar-sea water so that the main body of the pipette could be refilled with liquid without leaving an air bubble between the liquid and the inner surface of the agar. Two matched pipettes were used in each experiment. One of the pipettes was filled with normal sea water and the other was filled with acidified sea water. To equilibrate the agar in the tip with the solution to be used in the experiment each pipette was filled and refilled several times, and the tip was also soaked in the same solution. The level of the solution in the pipette was several centimeters above the solution in which the tip was maintained so that some pressure supported the diffusion. The agar in the tips of the pipettes was equilibrated over a period of 11-16 hours before the start of an experiment.

In each experiment a single egg was reared in a pH gradient. The egg was placed in a square Petri dish of normal sea water on the levelled stage of a microscope on a concrete table. These precautions were necessary to keep the egg from moving. Sea water from the same supply was used in the Petri dish and in the normal sea water pipette. The two pipettes were freshly filled with fluid to the same level which ranged from 3 to 15 mm above the level of the sea water in which the egg was placed, so that the diffusion was supported by some pressure. The agar plugs apparently adhered firmly to the glass and no detectable volume of fluid passed from the pipettes into the culture dishes during the experiment. About 2 hours after fertilization the two pipettes, which were mounted in a Taylor micromanipulator at an inclined angle so that the finely drawn tapers were approximately horizontal, were approached toward the egg on opposite sides until the tips were level with the egg and were about an egg diameter from it. Fig. 1 shows photomicrographs of the eggs and pipette tips at a later stage of development. The two tips were originally equidistant from the spherical egg, and this relation usually persisted although in some cases the egg moved slightly at some time during development. In earlier experiments the egg rested on the glass bottom of the dish. In later experiments a level layer of sea water agar was placed in the bottom of the dish to reduce breakage of pipettes at the time of set up. Four micromanipulators were available and four experiments were run simultaneously.

The normal sea water pipette provided a control for the glass, agar, etc. of the pipette. The need for this control was suggested by collateral observations that *Fucus* eggs may be affected by a nearby glass surface, probably because of its interference with diffusion of products from the eggs.

In selecting an agent for acidifying the sea water in the acid pipette it was regarded as desirable to have enough buffer capacity to be sure that the acid diffusing from the very small lumen of the pipette would not too readily be neutralized by the sea water. On the other hand, it would be undesirable to have so much buffer capacity that acidity would be maintained in high degree when the buffer diffused around to the other side of the egg. From these considerations, a mixture of 4 or 5 parts of McIlvaine's[1] buffer to 96 or 95 parts of sea water was selected. As pointed out in the first paper of this series (Whitaker (1)), such mixtures provide enough buffer capacity to hold the pH constant

---

[1] A mixture of 0.1 M citric acid and 0.2 M secondary sodium phosphate, in such proportions as to give the desired pH.

for 24 hours to within 0.1 pH unit when eggs are growing in them, but they contain the least amount of buffer which will do so. Upon dilution with sea water the buffer capacity and the hydrogen ion concentration decrease rapidly. Since the mixture diffusing from the acid pipette would be very greatly diluted before reaching the far side of the egg, these conditions should be favorable to an effective pH gradient.

After definite and convincing results had been obtained, it was thought desirable to carry out a few more experiments using another buffer system involving neither citrate nor phosphate to be sure that the results could not be attributed to these ions. For his purpose acidification was carried out by means of a mixture of HCl and $NaHCO_3$ added in such amount as to give a buffer capacity which was empirically found to be approximately the same as the buffer capacity of the 4 per cent or 5 percent McIlvaine's mixture. After acidification with either buffer system the sea water was equilibrated with atmospheric CO_2, and the osmotic pressure of the mixtures was readjusted if necessary with glass distilled water.

TABLE 1

The conditions of the experiments (see Figs. 1, 2, and 3 for results). The pH of the sea water as given is the initial pH at the start of each experiment. Under the heading "buffer," McIlv. refers to McIlvaine's buffer. See text.

Experiment No.	Sea water pH	Acid pipette pH	Acid pipette Buffer	Experiment No.	Sea water pH	Acid pipette pH	Acid pipette Buffer	Experiment No.	Sea water pH	Acid pipette pH	Acid pipette Buffer
			per cent				per cent				
1	7.8	6.4	McIlv. 4	22	8.0	6.0	McIlv. 4	43	8.1	5.9	McIlv. 4 per cent
2	7.7	6.2	" 4	23	7.5	6.0	" 5	44	7.7	6.2	HCl—NaHCO₃
3	8.3	6.0	" 5	24	7.5	6.2	" 4	45	7.7	6.2	" "
4	7.5	6.0	McIlv. 5	25	7.5	6.0	McIlv. 5	46	7.6	6.1	HCl—NaHCO₃
5	7.5	6.0	" 5	26	7.4	6.0	" 5	47	7.6	6.1	" "
6	7.5	6.2	" 4	27	7.4	6.0	" 5	48	7.6	6.1	" "
7	8.1	5.9	McIlv. 4	28	7.7	6.2	McIlv. 4	49	7.7	6.2	HCl—NaHCO₃
8	8.1	5.9	" 4	29	7.5	6.0	" 5	50	7.7	6.2	" "
9	7.7	6.2	" 4	30	7.7	6.2	" 4	51	7.6	5.5	McIlv. 4 per cent
10	8.3	5.8	McIlv. 5	31	7.6	6.0	McIlv. 4	52	7.6	5.5	McIlv. 4 " "
11	7.8	6.4	" 4	32	8.3	5.8	" 5	53	7.6	5.6	" 4 " "
12	7.7	6.2	" 4	33	7.5	6.0	" 5	54	7.6	5.6	" 4 " "
13	7.8	6.4	McIlv. 4	34	8.3	5.8	McIlv. 5	55	7.6	5.6	McIlv. 4 " "
14	8.1	5.9	" 4	35	7.4	6.0	" 5	56	7.6	5.5	" 4 " "
15	7.7	6.0	" 5	36	7.4	6.0	" 5	57	7.6	5.5	" 4 " "
16	7.5	6.2	McIlv. 4	37	8.0	6.0	McIlv. 4	58	7.6	5.6	McIlv. 4 " "
17	7.7	6.0	" 5	38	8.1	5.9	" 4	59	7.8	5.7	HCl—NaHCO₃
18	7.8	6.4	" 4	39	8.3	5.8	" 5	60	7.8	5.7	" "
19	7.5	6.0	McIlv. 5	40	7.8	6.4	McIlv. 4	61	7.8	5.7	HCl—NaHCO₃
20	7.6	6.0	" 4	41	7.5	6.2	" 4	62	7.8	5.7	" "
21	8.1	5.9	" 4	42	8.3	6.0	" 5	—	—	—	—

RESULTS

After setting up the pipettes, the dish containing the egg was covered to reduce evaporation, and the assembly was ordinarily left undisturbed for 24 hours or longer. By this time the rhizoid protuberance was well developed and the first cell division was usually completed. The results were sketched and photographed.

Figs. 1, 2, and 3 show photomicrographs of all eggs reared in pH gradients, except that the result of experiment 7 (Fig. 1) is shown as a drawing from the original because the photograph failed. In all cases the right hand pipette in each boxed figure, which is also the pipette under which the number of the experiment appears, is the acid pipette. For convenience in considering the results shown in the figures, the numbers of the experiments are given not in the order in which they were carried out, but in the order of the type of result. Table I gives the conditions of each experiment.

Fig. 1 shows all eggs which were reared with McIlvaine's buffer used as the acidifying agent in the acid pipette. The data in Table 1 show that the pH of the normal sea water at the start of these experiments (experiments 1-43) ranged from 7.4 to 8.3 and that the pH of the medium in the acid pipette ranged from 5.8 to 6.4. Of the 43 eggs, 39 or 91 per cent formed rhizoids on the acid half of the egg, and 21 or nearly half formed them within 10° of the most acid point of the egg surface.

7 more eggs were then reared with HCl–NaHCO$_3$ used as the acidifying agent in the acid pipette, and the results are shown in Fig. 2. In these experiments (44-50) the initial pH at the tips of the pipettes ranged from 7.6 to 7.7 (basic) and from 6.1 to 6.2 (acid). All of the eggs formed rhizoids on the acid side. The results are thus essentially the same regardless of which buffer system is used. Considering experiments 1-50 together, 46 eggs or 92 per cent formed the rhizoid on the acid side of the egg.

While most of the eggs formed rhizoids quite close to the most acid point of the egg surface (Figs. 1 and 2), a considerable number which formed them on the acid side did so at some distance from the most acid point. A number of considerations suggested that this might be due to slightly greater than optimum acidity at the most acid point of the egg surface resulting from greater acidity of the solutions, greater diameter of the pipette tips, closer proximity of the tips to the egg, or a combination of such factors. To test this, experiments 51 to 62 were arranged with still greater acidity of the acid pipette. The results are shown in Fig. 3.

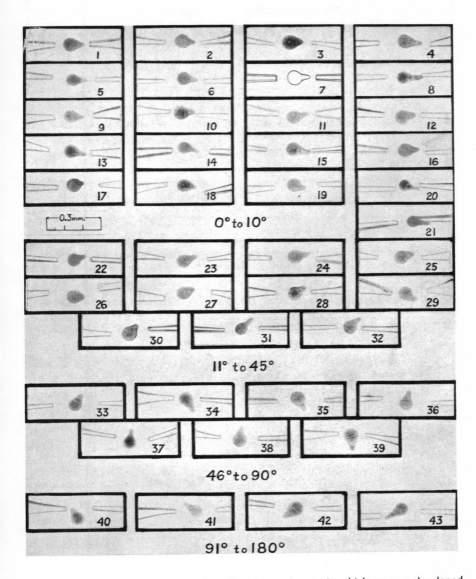

Fig. 1. Photomicrographs of results of experiments in which an egg developed in a pH gradient and in which McIlvaine's buffer was used to acidify the sea water in the acid pipette. In each photograph the pipette is shown on the right hand side, above the number of the experiment. See Table 1 and text for conditions of each experiment. The result of experiment 7 is shown as a drawing.

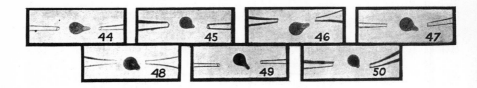

Fig. 2. Photomicrographs of results of experiments in which an egg developed in a pH gradient and in which HCl-NaHCO$_3$ was used to acidify the sea water in the acid pipette. In each photograph the acid pipette is on the right hand side, above the number of the experiment. See Table I and text for conditions of each experiment.

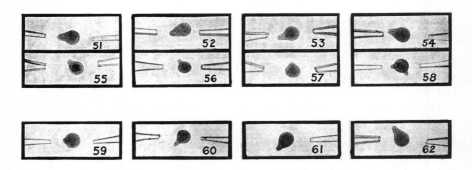

Fig. 3. Photomicrographs of experiments in which an egg developed in a pH gradient and in which the sea water in the acid pipette (shown on the right hand side in each photograph, above the number of the experiment) was acidified to pH 5.7-5.5. This is slightly more acid than in the cases shown in Figs. 1 and 2. In experiments 51-58 inclusive McIlvaine's buffer was used to acidify, and in experiments 59-62 inclusive a mixture of HCl and NaHCO$_3$ was used. See Table I and text for conditions of each experiment.

In experiments 51-58 (Fig. 3) the medium in the acid pipette was acidified to pH 5.5–5.6 with McIlvaine's buffer. In experiments 59-62 it was acidified to pH 5.7 with HCl–NaHCO$_3$. The results show that when the pH of the medium in the acid pipette is lowered to 5.5-5.7 the rhizoid forms on the side of the egg away from the acid pipette.

At the end of the experiments a small amount of almost transparent deposit was quite often observed attached to the tip of the acid pipette, extending out from it for about 5 to 20 microns. This material was not identified. It may have been a precipitate of buffer ingredients, or possibly a growth of microorganisms. It never formed on the basic pipette. This deposit was variable in amount, and it was entirely absent in quite a number of experiments with McIlvaine's buffer and in all experiments in which HCl-NaHCO$_3$ was used to acidify. No correlation could be found between its presence and the result, and it is therefore regarded as inconsequential.

In four experiments the pipettes were not maintained in place until the end as in all other experiments, but instead they were withdrawn at 15 hours after fertilization. At this time no rhizoid protuberances or any other external indications of polarity had yet appeared. The rhizoid protuberances later formed near the regions of the egg surfaces which had formerly been most acid. So far as this evidence goes, therefore, it indicates that the pH gradient may determine the developmental polarity some time before the morphological response takes place.

DISCUSSION

The results appear to show quite conclusively that the developmental polarity and the pattern of differentiation of the *Fucus* egg can be determined by a gradient of hydrogen ion concentration across the developing egg in sea water. Since the sea water contains carbonates, a diffusion gradient of hydrogen ion concentration may be expected to produce a gradient of CO_2 tension by chemical action on the sea water. Even when all the excess CO_2 resulting from acidification of the sea water is successfully removed by aeration from the fluid used in the acid pipette, CO_2 would be produced again when the acid sea water diffused into more basic sea water. So long as a gradient of hydrogen ion concentration is maintained in carbonate bearing sea water, a coincident gradient of CO_2 tention is a corollary. The experiments therefore do not show whether the physiological effects are due directly to the hydrogen ions or to the CO_2 which they produce in the medium.

It is not known whether an earlier polarity exists in the egg[2] which is superseded by the effect of the gradient, or whether polarity is first established under the influence of the gradient. The former is perhaps more probable, especially since an egg develops normally with no external gradient of any sort. In any event, any region of the cytoplasm may be caused to give rise to rhizoid or thallus, depending on this external factor.

The rhizoid tends to form at or near the most acid point on the surface of the egg unless this is too acid, in which case it forms at a more basic region. In extreme cases it forms at the most basic point on the egg surface. Since eggs will develop rhizoids in medium buffered

---

[2]Knapp (5) reports that the rhizoid normally forms at the entrance point of the sperm in *Cystosira*.

at pH 5.5 (1), although with some delay, it cannot be supposed that rhizoid formation is impossible at the absolute pH of the most acid point of the egg surface under conditions resulting in reversal. The reversals were obtained when the acid pipette was at pH 5.5-5.7. The rhizoid forms at a more basic point on the egg surface when one is available. It is clear that what happens at a given region of the egg depends not only on the pH at that region but also on the pH at other regions of the egg surface. In other words, it depends on the gradient as well as upon the absolute pH. This is in harmony with Child's theory of physiological gradients (6 and 7). The specific mechanism by which the gradient of hydrogen ion (or CO_2) concentration determines the morphogenesis remains as the principal problem. A *Fucus* egg which apparently is not subjected to any external pH gradient develops normally and forms one rhizoid over a wide pH range. The differentiation therefore appears to be controlled by an internal system which is readily altered or shifted by a number of external factors, including the pH gradient.

The actual pH values at the egg surface which result in the particular responses are of course not known precisely. The effect of metabolites on the pH at the surface can only be guessed at, and the acid diffuses around the egg to acidify the the basic side to an unknown extent. There is no doubt, however, about the relative pH values and the directions of the pH gradients. Even when the pH of the solutions is reproduced there is, of course, a considerable variation in the pH effect of the acid pipette depending on its diameter, distance from the egg, steepness of taper, etc. Since reversal of the developmental response takes place when the pH of the acid pipette is lowered only slightly (from 5.9 to 5.7), the variation seen in the position of the rhizoids with respect to the most acid point, even when the pH of the pipettes is reproduced, may be due to considerable part to slight differences in the effectiveness of the pipettes. Some differences in the eggs are also to be expected, and possibly there is some residual effect of an earlier polarity.

The group effect phenomenon (see introduction) and the response of an egg in a capillary to its own diffusion products (2) can be accounted for adequately on the basis of acid metabolites, acting through diffusion patterns of hydrogen ions or CO_2. It has been pointed out earlier (1 and 2) that there are reasons for suspecting that a growth substance may be involved in the responses of the *Fucus* egg and that a number of agents which determine polarity may act by affecting growth substance. Since the known growth substances are acids which are physiologically active in the undissociated molecular form, hydrogen ions increase the activity of growth substance (8-10). Growth substance (auxin) softens cellulose walls, and it has further been shown by Thimann and Went and others (9) that auxin initiates and induces root differentiation. The rhizoid formation in *Fucus* involves softening of the cellulose wall, and at least by analogy the differentiation resembles root differentiation.

Recently du Buy and Olson (11) have succeeded in extracting an unidentified growth substance from eggs of *F. vesiculosus* with chloroform. Dr. du Buy informs me that the volume of the agar gel blocks which they used in the oat test was 8 mm³. They obtained positive results using test blocks containing egg extract in a concentration approximately equivalent to 0.85 cc. eggs per cc. agar gel. In January, 1936, Drs. Went, Skoog, and van Overbeek, at the California Institute of Technology, were so kind as to test extracts which Dr. Lowrance and I made from recently fertilized eggs of *F. furcatus*. The tests were made with 4 mm³ agar blocks on seeded and de-seeded oat seedlings. Our extracts were made with purified chloroform, and separate extractions were repeated on the same material with chloroform and HCl. The products of the primary neutral extractions were tested in equivalent concentrations of approximately 0.38, 2.4, and 3.8 cc. eggs per cc. agar gel. The acid extractions were tested in equivalent concentrations of approximately 0.9, 2.4, and 3.8 cc. eggs per cc. agar gel. The results were negative, and in May, 1936, Dr. van Overbeek tested some more extracts which we prepared at the Hopkins Marine Station from eggs reared in light (40 watts at 1 meter) until just before and just after rhizoid protuberances began to form. Chloroform partition extracts from the sea water medium were also added in. These extracts were tested in a similar manner. The concentrations of the products of neutral extraction were approximately equivalent to 0.4 and 1.7 cc. eggs per cc. agar gel, and the concentration of the products of a second acid extraction was 1.7. Again the results were negative, but negative results do not mean much in a case of this sort as special procedures are often necessary for the extraction of growth substance. It is also possible that oxidative destruction took place during the 30 to 48 hours required to transport the iced extracts to Pasadena and start the tests.

Olson and du Buy (12) recently report that rhizoids tend to form on the sides of developing eggs of *F. vesiculosus* to which the potassium salt of indole acetic acid (hetero-auxin) is applied in sufficient concentration. As they point out, their results strengthen the hypothesis that growth substance in the egg induces rhizoid formation and that a number of agents which determine polarity may act by affecting the activity of growth substance. Most of the effects of the pH gradient can be interpreted on this basis very well. To explain the formation of the rhizoid on the basic side of the egg when the pH of the acid pipette is lowered to pH 5.7-5.5, it would probably be necessary to suppose that in this case so much growth substance is present in the molecular form at the most acid point that it is inhibitory. It may instead be that other effects of the hydrogen ions predominate at this concentration. It is more difficult to explain the rôle of hydrogen ions in terms of their effect on growth substance in the case of the egg developing near one end in a capillary tube, which tends to form the rhizoid on the side away from its own diffusion products (which is also presumably the basic side) when the pH of the medium is initially high; *i.e.*, 8.1-8.4 (2). It is probable that hydrogen ions or CO_2 also affect the underlying rhizoid forming processes in other ways than through the pH effect on the activity of growth substance.

The results reported in this paper show that hydrogen ions and CO_2, produced as metabolites, are adequate to explain the group effect. They probably act, at least in part, through their effects on growth substance in the egg. Whether the effect is supported in addition by the diffusion of growth substance from neighboring eggs to form effective concentration gradients in the medium is undetermined.

SUMMARY AND CONCLUSIONS

1. Gradients of hydrogen ion concentration across *Fucus* eggs growing in sea water determine the developmental polarity of the embryo.

2. Gradients may determine polarity even if removed before the morphological response begins.

3. The rhizoid forms on the acid side of the egg unless this is too acid, in which case it develops on the basic side of the egg.

4. Since gradients of hydrogen ion concentration in sea water produce gradients of CO_2 tension, as a result of chemical action on the carbonate buffer system, it is not proven whether the physiological effects are due to the hydrogen ions, or to the CO_2 which they produce in the medium.

5. The developmental response of the eggs to gradients of hydrogen ion (or CO_2) concentration provides an adequate but not an exclusive explanation of the group effect in *Fucus*.

6. Hydrogen ions may exert their effect by activating growth substance. Hydrogen ions or CO_2 probably also affect the underlying rhizoid forming processes in other ways as well.

The author is indebted to Dr. Edward Lowrance for assistance in carrying out the experiments.

BIBLIOGRAPHY

1. Whitaker, D. M., 1937, The effect of hydrogen ion concentration upon the induction of polarity in *Fucus* eggs. I. Increased hyrdogen ion concentration and the intensity of mutual inductions by neighboring eggs of *Fucus furcatus*, *J. Gen. Physiol.*, **20**, 491.
2. Whitaker, D. M., and Lowrance, E. W., 1937, The effect of hydrogen ion concentration upon the induction of polarity in *Fucus* eggs. II. The effect of diffusion gradients brought about by eggs in capillary tubes, *J. Gen. Physiol.*, **21**, 57.
3. Whitaker, D. M., 1935, Induction of polarity in *Fucus furcatus* by a localized concentration of hydrogen ions, *Proc. Soc. Exp. Biol. and Med.*, **33**, 472.
4. Whitaker, D. M., 1936, The effect of white light upon the rate of development of the rhizoid protuberance and the first cell division in *Fucus furcatus*, *Biol. Bull.*, **70**, 100.
5. Knapp, E., 1931, Entwicklungsphysiologische Untersuchungen an *Fucaceen*-Eiern. I. Zur Kenntnis der Polarität der Eier von *Cystosira barbata*, *Planta*, **14**, 731.
6. Child, C. M., 1929, The physiological gradients, *Protoplasma*, **5**, 447.
7. Child, C. M., 1936, Differential reduction of vital dyes in the early development of echinoderms, *Arch. Entwcklngsmechn. Organ.*, **135**, 426.
8. Went, F. W., 1935, Auxin, the plant growth hormone, *Bot. Rev.* **1**, 162.
9. Thimann, K. V., 1935, Growth substances in plants, in Luck, James M., Annual review of biochemistry, Stanford University, **4**, 545.
10. Bonner, J., 1934, The relation of hydrogen ions to the growth rate of the *Avena* coleoptile, *Protoplasma*, **21**, 406.
11. Buy, H. G. du, and Olson, R. A., 1937, The presence of growth regulators during the early development of *Fucus*, *Am. J. Bot.*, **24**, 609.
12. Olson, R. A., and du Buy, H. G., 1937, The rôle of growth substance in the polarity and morphogenesis of *Fucus*, *Am. J. Bot.*, **24**, 611.

*This work has been supported in part by funds granted by The Rockefeller Foundation.

4

electrical control of morphogenesis in regenerating dugesia tigrina
I. relation of axial polarity to field strength

GORDON MARSH AND H. W. BEAMS
Zoological Laboratories, State University of Iowa

INTRODUCTION

Externally applied electric fields of appropriate strength have been shown to exert polar control over growth direction, growth rate, and growth quality (differentiation) in developing or regenerating biological systems. The materials have been biologically simple and few in number, being confined to regenerating hydroids (Lund, '21, '24, '25, '47, p. 231; Barth, '34), the first cleavage of the egg of *Fucus* (Lund, '23b), and rhizoid formation in *Griffithsia* (Schechter, '34). Attempts to demonstrate similar phenomena in developing eggs and embryos of higher organisms have met with no success (Gray, '39; Needham, '31, pp. 537-538, 831-833).

Analysis of electrical control of morphogenetic processes offers fundamental contributions, potential and actual, to the nature of organic polarity, to various aspects of growth phenomena, and to the difficult problem of the nature of self-regulation in embryonic systems. There is need therefore for a more extensive body of factual data, with respect to both number of experiments and variety of type of material. It is also desirable to develop the details of control of systems differentiating along more than a single primary axis. These ends are partially served by the present series of experiments on electrical control of regeneration in one of the simpler triploblastic animals, the platyhelminth, *Dugesia tigrina*.

Reprinted from the Journal of Cellular and Comparative Physiology
Vol. 39, No. 2, April, 1952

MATERIAL AND METHOD

The material was obtained primarily from commercial sources, secondarily from local habitats. The two populations differed in size and pigmentation, but were indistinguishable on the basis of regeneration and other characteristics, and corresponded to the specific criteria proposed by Kenk ('44) for D. tigrina. A limited number of D. dorotocephala and C. foremani were employed; none survived exposure to current.

The head was severed behind the auricles and the tail cut through the tips of the posterior intestinal branches. Small animals were divided into thirds: anterior, middle (with pharynx) and posterior. Large animals were divided into fourths: anterior, anterior midpiece, posterior midpiece, and posterior, the center cut dividing the pharynx. Piece length varied from 2 to 5 mm. The width never exceeded the length in the resting, relaxed piece and no pieces were small enough to develop two heads spontaneously (Child, '41, and references there). A few heads and tails with one regenerating surface were used; no heads survived. A short longitudinal anterior or posterior slit was made in each piece to assure subsequent recognition of the original polarity. The slit usually healed rapidly, leaving a relatively unpigmented streak and refractile scar. If the scar could not be recognized throughout the regeneration period the piece was omitted from the results. If healing occurred, no effect of this procedure on regeneration could be detected. From 0.5 to 26 hours elapsed between cutting and exposure to the current. In general, mortality was lower for the longer healing times.

Since cut pieces show pronounced cathodal galvanotropism and galvanotaxis, they were imbedded in 3% agar near its setting temperature on tissue paper fragments tied with fine thread to glass slips about $10 \times 5 \times 1$ mm. While this did not produce complete immobilization, it did prevent free turning for pieces with length: width ratios greater than one. Pieces which turned (from the anode) infrequently were reoriented; some which turned freely were reoriented, others were allowed to remain oriented to the cathode. Movement was often sufficient to turn the axis of the piece at an angle to the current or to produce the equivalent effect through bending. While these were reoriented as observed, many pieces spent only a part of the exposure time parallel to the current. Also, pieces were mounted at, or moved to, small angles from the horizontal. Since the axial component of the current is proportional to the cosine of the angle between the piece axis and the current direction a number of pieces must have been recorded as at current densities higher than that effectively operating. This undoubtedly contributed to the wide range of values and the magnitudes of the standard errors of current density shown in Table 1.

The experimental chamber was diamond-shaped, 17.5 cm long, 13.2 cm wide at the center, and 1.5 cm wide at the outlets. Its wall was a continuous glass tube, looped over one outlet, and connected to a cold bath. The outlet tubes were so bent that the fluid level of the outlet vessels was that of the chamber. Thoroughly aerated one-twentieth Ringer's fluid in tap water passed continuously into the chamber from a supply vessel. The outflow was equalized at the two ends by adjustment of constant level siphons discharging from the outlet vessels through funnels into a waste jar. The velocity of outflow was maintained at or above the transference velocity of hydrogen ion at the potential gradient obtaining in the outlet tubes. That this was a more than adequate safeguard against contamination of the chamber by electrode products was shown by absence of toxic effects, following accidental reduction or even cessation of flow for several hours. The specific resistance of the medium at 21°C was 1031 ohm-cm.

By controlling the rate of flow through the perimeter coil the temperature in the chamber was held at $21 \pm 1°C$. In a few cases the temperature passed beyond these limits for short intervals without producing detectable effects. Temperature gradients within the chamber were generally small.

Current was supplied from a D.C. power unit with a reversing switch, an adjustable range milliammeter, and a variable resistance in series. Zinc: zinc sulfate electrodes completed the circuit at the outlet vessels through large area zinc sulfate-agar bridges. Current densities in microamperes per square millimeter were computed from the measured current and the appropriate cross-sectional area of the chamber, deducting the area of the glass slips, and were averaged on a time-weighted basis when these factors varied. Fluid height was measured with an adjustable gauge having a reading error between 2 and 5%. A sheet of millimeter cross-section paper was fixed beneath the base plate of the chamber to facilitate measurements of width and to guide the setting of the pieces.

Through carelessness, a systematic error was introduced into the calculations of current density. The pieces set at any position on a cross-line of the chamber were recorded as at the same current density. Their distance from the chamber center line was not noted. In reality, because of the diamond shape, the isopotential, or constant current density, lines were curved. Although known academically, this point was not appreciated practically until after the experiments were com-

pleted. The error along the center line varied from zero at the middle
to plus 17% at the ends; the error at the edges varied from zero at the
middle to minus 9% at the ends. The errors were thus partially self-
compensating, particularly since fewer pieces could be set along the
center line than at other positions. They tended to be restricted to
the lower values because, as the effect of lower current densities became known, the current was increased for succeeding runs, most of
the data thus being obtained in the midregion of the chamber. It is
apparent, however, that the extent of error is unknown, and that this
partly accounts for the magnitude of the standard errors in Table 1.

The regenerating pieces were placed in known orientation in the
electric field and exposed to current 4 to 5.7 days (average 5.1 days),
by which time the regeneration axis was determined, although complete
symmetry was not attained. Approximately one-half the pieces were
maintained at the same position throughout the experiment. About 40%
spent from a few hours to approximately one day at low current before
being moved to high current for the remainder of the regeneration
period, partly in an attempt to reduce mortality and partly to replace
pieces dying at the higher current densities. About 10% were exposed
to low current densities for 2.8 to 3.6 days or were shifted gradually
from low to high density in order to test the limits of effect of duration of exposure. The pieces were examined at frequent, but irregular,
intervals through a binocular microscope and a running record kept
of their position, orientation, and condition, as well as of the height
of the medium, temperature, and chamber current. Adjustments were
made at these times; current and temperature were also adjusted at
other intervals. At the end of the run regenerated individuals were
freed from the agar and examined under binocular and compound microscope for details of polarity, gross structure, and behavior. One bipolar
regenerant was fixed in Bouin's fluid and stained with hematoxylin. No
animals were sectioned. Three animals were treated with dilute formic
acid to bring out the details of the nerve cords.

RESULTS

Cathodal orientation

Seventy-four pieces regenerated with their original anterior ends
oriented to the cathode at current densities ranging from 1.6 to 24.4
$\mu a/mm^2$. Eleven were tail pieces with a single cut surface. All regenerated in accordance with their original axis, and were similar to
control animals at the same temperature. Body symmetry and responses
were essentially normal, save in one piece in which the marking slit

(posterior) had healed incompletely and in two pieces which developed vesicular swellings about the remnant of the old pharyngeal cavity.

Anodal orientation: two regenerating surfaces

Pieces oriented with their original anterior ends to the anode showed morphogenetic responses varying with the current density, as shown in Table 1, sections 1 to 6. The first column shows the average current density producing the morphogenetic effect noted in the last column. The average is derived from the final current densities, ignoring the lower values applied during initial conditioning or duration test periods. The validity of this procedure will be apparent from section D below. The second column shows the range of final current densities applied to the number of pieces recorded in the 4th column. By Ohm's law, the potential gradient imposed upon the regenerating piece in millivolts per millimeter is 10.31 times the current density. The values of the mean potential gradients are shown in the third column of the table.

At or below 16.5 μa/mm^2 the pieces regenerated in their original axis. The animal showing temporary bipolarity at 16.43 μa/mm^2 in section 3 is the single real exception to this generalization. The values in parenthesis in sections 1 and 2 each include two animals exposed for insufficient time to the high current density (section D below). The exception in section 2 was a piece mounted approximately 20° from the horizontal so that the axial component of the current was less than the recorded 17.21 μa/mm^2.

The regenerants of section 2, while possessing no visible controls. The average current densities calculated for this group, while significantly different from those of sections 2 to 6, have no very useful meaning, since there is no lower limit to the density which will permit normal regeneration.

The regenerants of section 2, while possessing no visible gross structural differences from controls, showed head behavior in the tail. This consisted of any, or all, of the following: (1) locomotor competition, representing attempts of the tail to crawl in the posterior direction, producing accordion-like stretching and contraction of the animal, or adherence of the tail to the substratum, producing checking of the normal forward progress followed by uncoordinated squirming or accordion movements; (2) competition with the head or assumption of the lead, in the righting response; (3) avoiding reaction, wherein the tail withdraws when mechanically stimulated, then extends, often in a new direction; (4) testing movements, in which the tail is elevated with the tip approximately horizontal and moved in various directions

TABLE 1

Relation of (average final) current density to polarity of regenerated Dugesia oriented to the anode; 5.1 days' average exposure. 1-6, pieces with two regenerating surfaces; 7-8, tails with one regenerating surface

	Current Density in $\mu a/mm^2$		Potential Gradient	Number of Cases	Morphogenetic Effect
	Average ± S.E.	Range	mv/mm		
1	7.92 ± 0.74 (8.49 ± 0.81)	1.6 –15.2 (1.6 –18.99)	81.6 (87.5)	32 (34)	Normal regeneration
2	13.28 ± 1.21 (14.68 ± 1.42)	8.35–17.21 (8.35–24.4)	136.8 (151.4)	10 (12)	Normal axis; head behavior in tail
3	17.81 ± 0.38	16.43–18.92	183.5	7	Bipolarity with regression to normal
4a	19.45 ± 0.57	17.55–21.62	200.4	7	Bipolarity with anode dominance
b	18.97		195.5	1	Bipolarity without dominance
c	19.14 ± 0.58	16.88–22.67	197.2	13	Bipolarity with cathode dominance
d	19.24 ± 0.39		198.3	21	All permanent bipolars
5	19.92 ± 0.41	18.48–23.03	205.2	11	Bipolarity with progression to reversal
6a	22.09 ± 1.89 (20.3 ± 0.73)	18.92–31.05 (18.92–23.03)	227.4 (209.2)	6 (5)	Reversal of axis; head behavior in tail
b	21.28 ± 0.62	18.02–23.03	219.1	8	Reversal of axis
c	21.62 ± 0.85 (20.9 ± 0.4)		222.7 (215.3)	14 (13)	All reversed animals
7	13.05 ± 1.54	1.84–21.17	134.5	14	Normal regeneration
8a	18.94 ± 1.94	14.46–24.49	195.1	3	Acephalic
b	22.76 ± 1.58	21.17–24.34	234.3	2	Acephalic; head behavior in tail
c	20.47 ± 1.93		210.1	5	All acephalic animals

as if sampling the environment, generally in response to mechanical stimulation, but sometimes spontaneously following a period of loco-motor competition; or extension of the tail and application of its ventral surface to a probe, followed by movement of the tip over and about the probe. Head behavior persisted 2 to 3 days after exposure to the current, followed by resumption of normal tail responses. The range of current densities producing this result was approximately equivalent to the upper half of the range in section 1. The mean current densities for sections 1 and 2 are significantly different, but it is evident that other factors contribute to appearance of head function in the tail, since 18 of the 32 cases in section 1 fall within this range of current densities without appearance of the phenomenon.

Section 3 of the table shows the effect upon 7 regenerants of an average current density of 17.81 $\mu a/mm^2$ from a much narrower range. Animals of this group possessed a typical head on the anode end, and, in addition, an apparent head on the cathode end, so that they resembled the bipolar forms in section 4a of the table, differing principally in their subsequent development. The "eyes" on the cathode head tended to have pigment spots smaller than normal and frequently multiple, and to lack the clear, vesicular region. The difference from the normal eye was of the same character as the difference between Figure 1 E, e_2, and Figure 1 A. The cathode head tended to be narrower than the anode head, but broader than a typical tail. The intestine had a single branch into the anode head, and a pair of branches encircling the pharynx, which opened toward the cathode. In two animals the posterior branches remained separate, in two they appeared to join in a closed ring, and in three they were apparently joined with a short single branch extend-ing into the cathode head. The head behavior of the cathode ends was more marked than that of regenerants of section 2, but of the same character; in addition, the responses to light involved both ends of the animals. The cathode head showed only competition with the anode head, never cooperation as was the case with some regenerants of section 4. Within three days the cathode head reorganized into a tail, the "eyes" disappearing and the intestine separating into two typical pos-terior branches. The changes were similar to those shown in Figure 1, E vs. F, G vs. H. The mean current density for the regressive bipolars is not significantly different from those of sections 4b, c and d, although it is from all the other means.

At a mean density of 19.24 $\mu a/mm^2$, section 4d, 21 pieces regenerated a complete head on each end. The intestine in these forms consisted

of a single anterior branch into each head joined to a ring surrounding
the pharyngeal region (Fig. 1, A, B, C, D). Nineteen individuals had
a single pharynx (Fig. 1 A); two individuals had two pharynges
(Fig. 1 D). In several animals the alimentary canal contained protozoa,
from whose movements it was observed that the lumina of the main
branches were continuous. A single pair of nerve cords was present, with
a brain in each head (Fig. 1 D). These were plainly revealed in two
bipolars by treatment with 4% formic acid after about one minute.
The cords showed little, if any, change in diameter between the brains;
differentiation was sufficiently sharp to show the lateral connections
and larger nerve branches. These latter were also observed in treated
normal animals as a check upon method.

Unlike the regenerants in sections 3 and 5, the bipolar condition
was permanent. No tendency toward division was observed. Fourteen
of the regenerants lived two weeks or longer; 7 lived 4 weeks or longer.
The longest survival was 41 days. All apparently succumbed to accidental overheating or drying of the medium. Two unsuccessful attempts
were made to induce the animal shown in Figure 1 D to feed, once
on yeast and once on minced liver.

All but one of the regenerants of this section, immediately after removal from the agar, showed dominance of one head in extent of response to mechanical stimulation and to light, and in determination
of direction of locomotion. Seven regenerants (section 4a) showed
dominance of the anode head (Fig. 1 A), developing on the original
anterior end, at an average current density of 19.45 $\mu a/mm^2$. This was
a higher density than the average at which 13 regenerants (section 4c)
showed dominance of the cathode head (Fig. 1 B, C), although a
lower value might have been anticipated. The difference in the means
is not significant. The mean density for all permanent bipolars shown
at 4d is significantly different from the other means in the table except
those of sections 3, 4, 5, and 6a. In general, the dominant head was
larger and more symmetrical, had larger eye spots and a longer intestinal branch, and controlled the position of the pharynx, which opened
toward the subordinate head.

For 10 of the animals no subsequent record was kept. In 6 the
dominance persisted or became more pronounced over a period of
5 to 41 days, as in Figure 1 B, C; this includes the animal showing no
dominance at the end of the run in which the anode head developed
dominance in 13 days. In 5 animals dominance disappeared in 3 to 13
days with the achievement of bipolar symmetry (Fig. 1 D). In animals

showing dominance locomotion was primarily in the direction of the dominant head, with the subordinate head interfering. Occasionally the subordinate head was drawn about at an angle, but the direction (Fig. 1 B) was still that of the dominant head. In animals without head dominance the two heads cooperated smoothly in locomotion, the typical body position being a V of 60 to 80° angle with direction along the bisector. In 9 bipolars a protrusion developed at the midregion, varying from a slight bulge (Fig. 1 D) to a tail-like extension rounded at the tip (Fig. 1 C), which in one animal achieved a length 50% greater than that of the combined head regions. In all these the pharynx was forced into the protrusion and opened toward its tip. The intestine, however, still formed a closed ring about the pharynx. In animals without head dominance the protrusion was posterior in locomotion. In those showing dominance (4 animals) it was typically carried at right angles to the direction of locomotion (Fig. 1 C). That the protrusion was sometimes created by muscular contraction was shown by several animals in which it was occasionally withdrawn; the animal of Figure 1 A had such a protrusion equal to about one-sixth the body length three days before the photograph was taken.

Eleven pieces regenerating at a mean density of 19.92 $\mu a/mm^2$ (section 5), emerged as apparent bipolars with strong cathode dominance. Two were actually tripolar, two heads having formed to the anode on either side of the incompletely healed marking slit. In each animal the pharynx opened to the anode. The intestine in one was double at the anode end, in 4 apparently was joined in a closed ring about the anode end of the pharynx, while in 6 was joined and had a single branch extending into the anode head. Head shape, eye condition, behavior and subsequent development were similar to that of animals of section 3, save that the polar axis was reversed. In 3 to 5 days after removal from the chamber the anode head reorganized into a tail and the animals assumed normal symmetry, but with the original axis reversed. One such animal is shown in Figure 1 E at the end of 4.6 days exposure to 19.5 $\mu a/mm^2$. The narrower anode head contained a single intestinal branch and two eye spots, marked e_2 in the figure; the left-hand one is partially obscured by superficial pigment. Figure 1 F was taken three days later, at which time the anode end had lost its eye spots and most of its head behavior, and the intestine had separated into two branches. Figure 1 G and H are line drawings from the prints E and F respectively. In Figure 1 F the superficial pigment spots may be inventoried against those in 1 E. The mean current density for this group is not significantly different from the means of the permanent bipolars in section 4 of Table 1, nor from those of the reversed animals of section 6. It is significantly different from the means of sections 1 to 3.

Fourteen pieces regenerated heads on the original posterior end and tails or potential tails on the original anterior end at an average current density of 21.62 μa/mm^2 (section 6c). The mean, as well as that in parenthesis, is significantly different from those in the upper portion of the table, save for 4a and 5. The animals were distinguishable into two groups. Six regenerants, section 6a, upon removal from the chamber showed head behavior in the anode end which disappeared within three days. The average current density for this group was 22.09 μa/mm^2. One animal was at the extreme density employed, 31.05 μa/mm^2. As there is no assignable upper limit to the current strength capable of producing reversal, the means in parenthesis were calculated omitting this value. Eight individuals, section 6b, showed no detectable head function in the tail at 21.28 μa/mm^2, which is higher than the mean of 6a if the extreme value is omitted. Neither mean in 6a is significantly different from that of 6b and the ranges of values are closely similar. As in the case of the animals of section 2, it is evident that factors other than the applied current are involved in persistence or appearance of head function in the morphological tail. Figure 1 I shows one of the regenerants of section 6b after 4.6 days exposure to 20. μa/mm^2; s indicates the scar of the marking slit made in the original anterior end of the piece. The individuals of section 6 were distinguishable from normal regenerants only by the position of the marking slits.

No differences were encountered at any current density which were associated with the size of the pieces or with the body level from which they came.

Anodal orientation; one regenerating surface

Nineteen tail pieces having only an anterior cut surface, and oriented to the anode, regenerated as shown in the last two sections of Table 1. Fourteen animals, section 7, regenerated normally at a mean density of 13.05 μa/mm^2. Head behavior was not displayed by the uncut ends. The range of current densities is comparable to that of sections 1 and 2 combined. The mean for section 7 is significantly different from those of sections 1 and 3 to 6, but not from that of section 2; it is also significantly different from those of sections 8b and 8c, but not from that of section 8a.

The 5 animals of section 8 developed no head structures during exposure to the current. One was lost by spilling, one was subsequently overlooked, two died within the first 15 hours, and one of the two in section 8b died 6 days after removal without further reorganization. Thus no reliable information is at hand as to whether the condition would be permanent.

The two animals of section 8b, in addition to the acephalic condition, also showed strong head function in the uncut tail. The mean density at which this occurred is significantly different from the means of sections 1 to 5, but not from those of section 6. The mean density of 18.94 μa/mm^2 for the three animals of section 8a is significantly different from the means of section 1 only.

Duration of exposure

Although the healing times allowed before exposure to the current varied from 0.5 to 26 hours, no differences were produced in the effect of the current upon the subsequent regeneration. Plots of the final current densities producing a given morphological effect against healing time showed in all cases random distribution about the mean. Provided the current is applied 4 or more days the healing time has the character of an indifferent period.

Approximately 40% of the regenerants were exposed to current densities at or below the level of the mean for section 2, Table 1 for 2.5 to 25 hours, then moved to a high density position where they remained for 4 to 5.5 days longer. As with healing time, plots of the final current densities producing a given effect against time spent at either low or high current showed random distribution, indicating an additional indifferent period, or that the current produced delay in reorganization.

To test the limits of the exposure time necessary to produce a definitive morphogenetic effect 13 pieces were exposed to low current 2.8 to 3.6 days and to high current 1.8 to 1.86 days. The currents were of the order of the mean for section 2, or less; the animals tested were among those of sections 4, 5, and 6. In every case the morphogenetic effect was that of the final high current, and the groups at short exposure showed no consistent or reliable differences in the mean final current densities compared to those of longer exposure times.

Four animals were exposed to densities just larger than the mean for section 1, then shifted in 10 steps to final densities of from 16.3 to 24.4 μa/mm^2. The intermediate exposures were of less than one day duration; the final exposure varied from 0.36 to 1.15 days. All regenerated in the original axis. Two showed head function in the tail. These had spent respectively 1.34 and 1.64 days at densities above the mean for section 2. The two which regenerated normally had spent 1.15 and 1.7 days respectively at densities above this level.

The data appear to define the limits of the necessary exposure time (provided previous exposure to moderate current had obtained) at between 1 and 1.8 days. It may be questioned whether it is sufficiently reliable to place it between 1.7 and 1.8 days. In any case it provides the justification for the use of the final current density rather than a time-weighted average density for those pieces exposed to high current 1.8 days or longer. No inhibition of reorganization was found at any current density, except that described in connection with section 8, Table 1, and that implicit in the fact of control of differentiation quality.

Mortality

In all, 1053 pieces were mounted and exposed to the current. The over-all mortality was 81.8%. Mortality was least for tail pieces and greatest for midpieces, presumably because of the presence of the old pharynx. Anterior pieces showed a mortality similar to that of the entire population.

The plot of percent survival of all the pieces against current density descends rapidly to become nearly flat at $6\mu a/mm^2$ then drops appreciably at 21 $\mu a/mm^2$ and above. Over the greater part of the current density range mortality is nearly independent of the current. The corresponding curves for different body regions show considerable variability. Tail pieces and midpieces show a steady decline in percent survival over the entire range. Posterior pieces give a bell shaped curve with a maximum at about 19.5 $\mu a/mm^2$. Anterior and anterior-midpieces give v-shaped curves with their minima at 6 $\mu a/mm^2$. Lack of uniformity of shape of these curves suggests that the mortality is not due to direct damage by the current. Presumably it is a complex result of adverse conditions of temperature, desiccation, and trauma during the cutting and mounting, extent of healing of cut surfaces, and conditions during exposure to the current. Qualitatively it was noted during the experiments that pieces which failed to heal completely before exposure to the current generally disintegrated from one or both ends, and that mortality was uniformly higher for pieces introduced into the chamber immediately after mounting than for those allowed to heal for several hours. It was also observed that mortality was higher for those pieces which showed active movement during exposure. Upon rare occasions pieces were observed to contract with sufficient violence to rupture a healed surface. Disintegration showed no polar relation to the current, and the latter appeared to act principally as an indifferent stimulus. Occasionally a piece was able to heal and regenerate after degeneration of a considerable portion.

Although abnormalities appeared in the regenerants, such as body asymmetries, abnormal swellings, unequal eye size, their frequency was no greater than that commonly observed in control animals, and they were often attributable to conditions of cutting. They never showed polar relationships, and are believed not due to the current.

DISCUSSION

Electrical control of the polar axis and the differentiated quality of tissues is complete in Dugesia, and more delicately graded with the strength of the electric field than that of any material reported in the literature. This is probably due in part to the strong inherent polarity of the cut pieces, and in part to the design of experiments on the other forms. For Dugesia the cathode is a head-determining pole and the anode a tail-determining pole, and their respective "potencies" are unequal, head determination being the stronger. This follows from the facts that (1) bipolar individuals are always two-headed, never two-tailed; (2) head behavior and head structure appear in original posterior ends at lower field strengths than those producing tail behavior and tail structure in the original anterior end (Table 1, sections 2-6); and (3) that head suppression, but not tail-determination could be produced in the original anterior end of uncut tail pieces (Table 1, section 8) while head behavior could be induced in the uncut tail. In the present experiments there is no evidence that had and tail determining forces resident in the piece itself are quantitatively different.

If apicobasal and anteroposterior polarity be considered analogous, the pole determining power of the electric field for regenerating Dugesia is similar to that for Fucus (Lund, '23b) and Griffithsia (Schechter, '34), in which rhizoids regenerate to the anode and thalli to the cathode (in Schecter's experiments the fate of the shoots is not entirely clear). On the other hand in Obelia (Lund, '21, '24) the cathode is clearly a base-determining, the anode an apex-determining pole. This is probably also true for Tubularia (Barth, '34), although no basal structures were reported toward the cathode, whose principal action appeared to be growth inhibition. Barth's ('34) data for Eudendrium and Pennaria do not permit a decision. It is evident that in the action of the electric field as a morphogenetic field the power of a given electrical pole to determine a particular morphological pole is an aspect of tissue competence.

Within the limits of the current densities employed there was observed no tendency toward reorganization of the cells of the end of a piece unless a cut surface was present. This would suggest that the electric field operates upon cellular processes rather than upon cellular states, although the data presented are not adequate to make this generalization conclusive.

The fact that animals exposed for 3.6 days to moderate current densities insufficient to produce polar structural changes, would develop at suitable high density in 1.8 days to the morphogenetic state attained by other animals exposed to the same high density for 5 days, suggests that the lower current may have produced delay or inhibition of the regeneration process. The maximum healing time plus low current time was 4.17 days. Regeneration delay was found by Lund ('23a, b) for Obelia and Fucus and by Barth ('34) for Tubularia, Eudendrium, and Pennaria. The results of the present experiments do not exclude this since detailed observations necessary to precise determination of this point were not made. The normal variation in regeneration time of controls is sufficient to make a delay of 1 to 2 days difficult to determine with certainty, although a delay of 3 to 4 days should be observable. No obvious differences in developmental state were found in our experiments between cathodally and anodally oriented regenerants and control pieces, except those associated with regressive or progressive bipolarity and the acephalic condition. Head or tail determination under these conditions appear to be very nearly all-or-nothing phenomena, and the first (approximately) 3 to 4 days to be an indifferent period, rather than one of delay or inhibition.

The fact that the morphogenetic state produced by a given field strength is substantially independent of the total time of exposure, provided exposure be longer than a critical time of about 1.8 days, would seem to indicate that electrical control is not effected through the extensive properties of total charge transported or total electrical work performed. Indeed, because of variation in exposure time individual pieces regenerating normally were subjected to the action of slightly greater total charge transported through them than some pieces whose axis was reversed. The control would appear to be established through the attainment of critical energy levels, which are properly characterized by the potential gradient rather than the current density, as was shown by Lund ('25) for Obelia. In succeeding papers of this series direct proof of dependence upon the potential gradient and substantial independence of the current density will be presented.

In Obelia (Lund, '25) the potential fall across the ectoendoderm necessary to produce cathodal inhibition and reversal of the polar axis, proved to lie between 1.88 and 10 mv, the range of magnitudes of the inherent potential of the tissue. This is obviously not the case in Dugesia, where the controlling potential gradients are about two orders of magnitude greater than the erratic potential differences measurable on either normal or regenerating animals. This discrepancy may possibly be resolved by the following considerations: In Obelia the apico-basal axis is overwhelmingly predominant, differentiation in the other two dimensions being uniform and of minimum complexity. A single external bipolar field corresponds in its properties reasonably well to the prospective organismic polarity and to the presumed character of the inherent morphogenetic field. In a bilaterally symmetrical organism such as Dugesia, while the anteroposterior axis is still predominant, the lateral and dorsoventral axes are relatively complex and are not uniform at different positions along the anteroposterior axis. The morphogenetic field of a regenerating Dugesia piece partakes of Weiss' ('39, p. 293) field property no. 3: "Fields, at least in the most specialized forms, are *heteroaxial*, . . . and *heteropolar* . . ." An external field must control all three axes simultaneously to produce symmetry and viability. The electric field does work upon the dorsoventral and lateral axes under the extreme disadvantages imposed by the cosine law. In order to produce symmetrical control the potential fall along the subordinate axes would presumably have to reach some limiting value, which would inevitably magnify the field strength along the parallel axis. If the average angle of orientation of the subordinate axes to the longitudinal field axis were 89° the potential gradient along them at the field strengths given in Table 1, sections 3 to 6, would vary between 3.2 and 4.1 mv/mm. In the absence of further experimental evidence and other clarifying concepts we incline to this explanation.

In this connection it is of some interest that the narrow range of effective field strengths producing recognizable modifications of normal axial regeneration in Dugesia should be nearly identical in extent with the corresponding range in Obelia (Lund, '24, '25). The potential gradient producing regressive bipolars is 82.5% of that producing reversal (Table 1, sections 3 and 6c). In Obelia the potential gradient threshold for cathodal inhibition, above which apical structures were no longer developed on the cathodal ends of internodes regardless of orientation, was 22.4 mv/mm. This is 80.3% of the potential gradient of 27.9 mv/mm above which growth toward the cathode ceased during current flow. Between these values reversal of polarity became more frequent the higher the potential gradient.

SUMMARY

1. Cut pieces of *Dugesia tigrina* of known original polarity were imbedded in 3% agar and exposed to direct current for 5.1 days (average) at $21 \pm 1°C$ in a continuous flow chamber.

2. Pieces oriented with their original anterior end to the cathode developed normally at all current densities.

3. Pieces oriented to the anode (a) developed in accordance with the original axis below 16.5 $\mu a/mm^2$ current density (7.92 $\mu a/mm^2$ average), but showed temporary development of head behavior in the tail (to cathode) in the higher range (13.28 $\mu a/mm^2$ average); (b) developed temporary head structures and behavior to the cathode at 17.81 $\mu a/mm^2$ (average); (c) developed two permanent heads (bipolarity) at 19.24 $\mu a/mm^2$ (average). and (d) underwent reversal of original polarity at 21.62 $\mu a/mm^2$ (average).

4. Tail pieces with a single cut surface oriented to the anode became acephalic at 20.47 $\mu a/mm^2$ (average), with no structural alteration, but with occasional head behavior appearing, in the uncut tips.

5. The potential gradient in mv/mm was 10.31 $\times$ current density. An explanation of the large magnitude of the potential gradient is offered in terms of the difficulties of triaxial control by a uniaxial external field.

6. The first 3 to 4 days of regeneration have the character of an indifferent period. The minimum effective exposure time to a given current density was about 1.8 days. No regeneration delay or inhibition was observed other than that implicit in control of the polar axis.

7. The morphogenetic effect of the current was not related to piece length or original body position.

LITERATURE CITED

Barth, L. G., 1934, The effect of constant electric current on the regeneration of certain hydroids. Physiol. Zool., **7**: 340-364.

Child, C. M., 1941, Patterns and problems of development. Univ. of Chicago Press.

Gray, P., 1939, Experiments with direct currents on chick embryos. Arch. f. Entw. mechan., **139**: 732-779.

Kenk, R., 1944, The fresh-water triclads of Michigan. Misc. Pub. Mus. Zool., Univ. of Mich., No. 60.

Lund, E. J., 1921, Experimental control of organic polarity by the electric current. I. Effects of the electric current on regenerating internodes of Obelia commissuralis. J. Exp. Zool., **34**: 471-493.

————————, 1923a, III. Normal and experimental delay in the initiation of polyp formation in Obelia internodes. J. Exp. Zool., **37**: 69-87.

————————, 1923b, Electrical control of organic polarity in the egg of Fucus. Bot. Gaz., **76**: 288-301.

————————, 1924, IV. The quantitative relations between current density, orientation, and inhibition of regeneration. J. Exp. Zool., **39**: 357-379.

————————, 1925, V. The nature of the control of organic polarity by the electric current. J. Exp. Zool., **41**: 155-190.

Lund, E. J., et al., 1947, Bioelectric fields and growth. Univ. of Texas Press.

Needham, J., 1931, Chemical embryology. Cambridge Univ. Press.

Schechter, V., 1934, Electrical control of rhizoid formation in the red alga, Griffithsia bornetiana. J. Gen. Physiol., **18**: 1-21.

Weiss, P., 1939, Principles of Development. Henry Holt and Co., New York.

PLATE 1. *Explanation of Figures.*

1 Dugesia regenerants after exposure to current. Cathode to left in A, right in B and C, up in D-I. e, eye spot; p, pharynx; s, scar of marking slit. A: permanent bipolar, anode dominance, 16 days old (after cutting; 5 days' exposure, 18.1 μa/mm^2. B: permanent bipolar, cathode dominance, 5.3 days old; 4.7 days' exposure, 17.7 μa/mm^2. C: same animal as B, 10.3 days old; anode eyes present, but indistinct. D: permanent bipolar, cathode dominance (gone at 13 days), 21 days old; 1.86 days' final exposure to 19 μa/mm^2, 3.6 days' exposure to 12.9 μa/mm^2; fixed in Bouin's fluid and stained with Delafield's hematoxylin. E: bipolar with progression to reversal, 5.2 days old; 4.6 days' exposure to 19.5 μa/mm^2; eyes, e_2, and superficial pigment on anode head, intestine joined with single anode extension. F: same animal as in E, 8.2 days old; anode eyes gone, superficial pigment remaining, intestine in two branches. G, H: line drawings from E and F respectively. I: reversed animal, no head function in tail, 5.2 days old; 4.6 days' exposure to 20 μa/mm^2; s shows scar of marking slit in original anterior end.

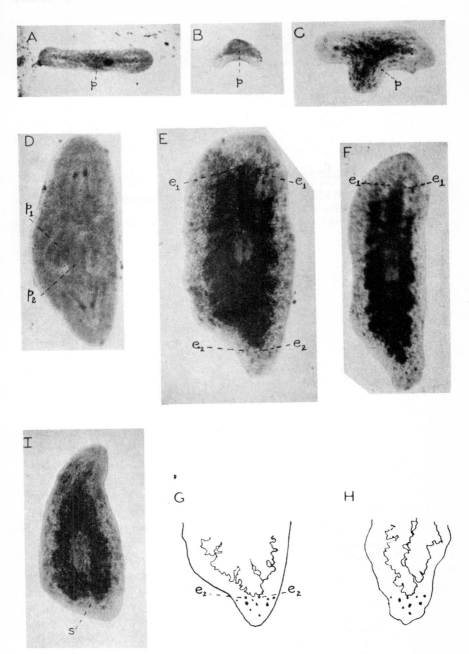

PLATE 1

5

cytological aspects of information transfer in cellular differentiation

W. BEERMANN
Max-Planck-Institut für Biologie, Tübingen, Germany

The embryonic development of higher, multicellular organisms, especially animals, offers some of the most striking examples of cellular specialization. The diverse forms and functions of cells, all of which by virtue of their common descent from the zygote must contain identical sets of genes, demonstrate that, at least in the higher organisms, very effective control mechanisms exist which must be capable of activating some of the genetic potencies of the cell and of suppressing others. More specifically, since the structural as well as the functional character of a cell will ultimately depend on its protein composition, differentiation may be described as a controlled process whereby cells of identical genetic constitution develop different protein patterns. This view has some obvious implications from the point of view of biochemical genetics. Since we know that the structural information for the sythesis of proteins is laid down in a coded form in the nucleotide sequences of the informational DNA units of the genome (the classical "genes") we are led to postulate the existence of a mechanism which reads the genetic information differentially in different types of cells. In looking for mechanisms which, on the basis of a given genotype, would bring about the development of different protein patterns, several possibilities may be envisaged. The transfer of information from the DNA of the gene to the protein involves two main steps: first, the transcrip-

Reprinted from Am. Zoologist
3:23-32 (1963)

tion of the nucleotide sequences of the DNA into nucleotide sequences of RNA molecules (synthesis of "messengers") and, secondly, the transcription of the nucleotide sequences of the RNA messengers into the amino acid sequences of the protein. The first of these processes, messenger synthesis, would have to take place at the site of the genes themselves. The second could take place anywhere in the cell, most probably at the site of the ribosomes in the cytoplasm. With respect to the regulation and control of these processes, we are therefore left with several possibilities. One could take the extreme stand of those embryologists who, in the past, tended to ignore entirely the nucleus and the Mendelian factors in assuming that there is no differentiation at the level of the chromosomes, or, in modern terms, that all genes are producing messenger molecules at the same rate all the time. Under these circumstances a change in the pattern of protein synthesis can only be produced by a specific inhibition or activation of specific messengers, or by a differential self-reproduction of some species of messenger molecules. Both types of control would meet with certain *a priori* limitations from the theoretical standpoint, that is they could only be effective to a limited extent. The drastic changes accompanying the actual differentiation of cells seem to require a direct involvement of the genes in the control mechanism such that the initial production of the messengers can be regulated. The well known results of Jacob and Monod (1961) show that this type of gene regulation is actually realized in bacteria. In the course of our own work on dipteran giant chromosomes we have collected data of a quite different nature which, however, lend further support to the hypothesis of differential gene control as outlined above.

VISIBLE DIFFERENTIATION OF
GIANT POLYTENE CHROMOSOMES IN INTERPHASE

Giant interphase chromosomes occur in the highly differentiated giant cells of dipteran larval and imaginal tissues. They attain a length of at least 10 times, and a cross section of up to 10,000 times that of normal univalent interphase chromosomes. According to the generally accepted views of Koltzoff (1934), Bauer (1935), and Bridges (1935), these chromosomes are to be considered as being "polytene," i.e., multivalent in a cable-like fashion, as a result of progressive replication of the chromatids without mitotic splitting. The most conspicuous feature of the polytene chromosomes is their banding pattern which, according to the concept of polyteny, reflects the ultimate chromomeric organization of the mitotic chromosomes of the individual. In other words, it is commonly taken for granted that the "phenotype" of the giant chromo-

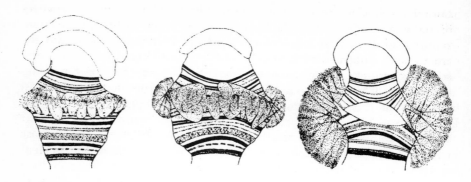

Fig. 1. One of the three large puffs ("Balbiani's rings") of the 4th chromosome characteristic for all salivary gland nuclei of *Chironomus tentans* and *Chironomus pallidivittatus*. Three different stages of puffing are shown. Magnification approximately 1000.

somes—in most instances salivary gland chromosomes—is directly representative of the underlying genetic organization of the constituent strands and is not subject to phenotypic variation. However, if one actually studies the banding pattern of homologous chromosomes in different tissues of the same individual it is quite obvious that the statement of constancy needs further specification. Although it is not true that the pattern varies in the sense of actual variations in the number, the distance, and the arrangement of the bands relative to each other, specific differences can be observed with respect to the fine structure of individual bands in different tissues. The same band may appear as a sharply defined disc of considerable density and DNA concentration or it may have the appearance of a "puff." Sometimes the puffing may be rather inconspicuous, with the locus in question still forming a band-like coherent structure of only slightly changed texture and dimensions. In other cases a single band may be blown up into a huge ball-like, diffusely staining structure, called a Balbiani-ring (Fig. 1). From our investigation on *Chironomus,* where polytene chromosomes in four different tissues may be studied on a comparative basis, one elementary fact emerged quite early (cf., Beermann 1956, 1959): The variations in the puffing behavior of the bands are not random but strictly correlated to cellular differentiation. Different tissues are characterized by different puffing patterns in their chromosomes, and developmental changes are always paralleled by characteristic changes in the puffing pattern as well. The statement is therefore justified that cellular differentiation regularly involves chromosomal differentiation, at least on the morphological level. Before we go on from here to discuss the possible physiological meaning of the observed chromosomal differentiation, the process of puffing as such needs to be defined in terms of chromosome fine structure and chemistry. The unchanged chromomere, i.e., the ultimate unit composing each band, may be considered as a tightly folded-up portion of the constituent DNA-histone fiber of the chromatid. Puffing in terms of the single chromomere would mean the unfolding, or uncoiling, of the DNA-histone fiber into a long, loop-like thread. This has actually been observed to be so in the case of Balbiani's rings, both by light and electron microscopy (Beermann and Bahr, 1954). The cytochemistry of puffing strengthens the structural interpretation. The intensity of the Feulgen reaction diminishes as the puffing of a band increases. The diffuse, peripheral regions of large puffs no longer show any visible Feulgen reaction. This would be expected on the basis of a progressive unfolding of the DNA which is equivalent to a structural dilution. On the other hand, cytochemistry shows the presence in large amounts of non-histone proteins in the puffs. The role of these proteins in the formation of puffs, i.e. in the unfolding of the chromomeric DNA fiber, may be a decisive one but has not yet been elucidated. All puffs contain RNA, but it is doubtful whether RNA plays any structural role at all. As will be seen presently, the RNA of the puffs seems to be exclusively concerned with genic activity.

On cytochemical as well as structural criteria, about 10% of all the bands appear to be in a more or less puffed condition in each tissue but, as has been already pointed out, as a rule these are not the same bands, the puffing pattern being specifically different from tissue to tissue and from stage to stage. Even the size attained by any one puff is usually quite characteristic for the cell type studied, the most outstanding example being Balbiani's rings which are characteristic for the polytene chromosomes of the salivary glands in all Chironomids. It has actually been demonstrated that puffing is a completely reversible phenomenon and does not involve any permanent change in the structure of the chromosome. Mention should be made, however, of an exceptional situation found in some puffs of polytene chromosomes of *Sciarid* flies. Here, in a few loci, puffing is always accompanied by the accumulation of large amounts of DNA (Rudkin and Corlette, 1957). If, as it seems, extra replications of the constituent chromomeres are involved, this may indeed lead to an irreversible structural and functional change of the locus.

PUFFING PATTERNS AS PATTERNS OF GENIC ACTIVITY, IN TERMS OF RNA SYNTHESIS

A *priori*, there is little doubt that the chromosomal differentiation observed in polytene chromosomes is primarly a functional phenomenon. A fruitful working hypothesis may be based on the assumption that puffing is an expression of, or the actual mechanism which causes enhanced genic activity whatever this may mean in precise biochemical terms. For, if we consider the puffs to be activated gene loci, then the observed differentiation with respect to puffing patterns would be equivalent to differentiation with respect to patterns of genic activity —in other words, it is exactly what one would expect if differential gene activation occurred in embryonic development. This interpretation implies that those loci which are puffed in any one tissue, or stage of development, contain genetic information which is of special importance to the cells under consideration. One should expect, for instance, that the bands forming the giant puffs of the Balbiani ring type in the salivary glands contain genes which specifically control the structure or the function of the salivary glands, the more so since the same bands are not found in a puffed condition in other tissues of the *Chironomus larva*. Before we furnish direct genetic proof for this hypothesis, let us see what general physiological arguments we can adduce in favor of an interpretation of puffing in terms of genic activity.

On account of their large size, the polytene chromosomes lend themselves to autoradiographic studies. If radioactive (tritium-labelled) precursors of the nucleic acids or of the proteins are injected into *Chironomus* larvae, and if after a short incubation period the salivary glands are dissected, fixed, and squashed, then covered with auto-radiographic stripping film, the following results are obtained. Tritiated thymidine is exclusively incorporated into the DNA during the endomitotic replication of the chromosomes. On the average only 2 out of 50 cells are found in the replication phase, the chromosomes of all other cells remaining unlabelled. The pattern of labelling in the case of thymidine exactly deflects the pattern of banding as demonstrated by the Feulgen reaction. The results are radically different if tritiated uridine, a precursor of RNA, is injected. Fifteen minutes after injection, appreciable amounts of labelled RNA are found in all nuclei of the salivary glands, whereas little or none is found in the cytoplasm. Within the nucleus the labeled RNA shows a highly characteristic distribution: it is almost exclusively located in the puffed regions of the chromosomes and in the nucleolus. The radioactivity of these regions increases when longer incubation times are used, but the topography remains essentially unchanged. With longer incubation times the cytoplasmic RNA will also become labeled, indicating a transfer of labeled RNA from the nucleus, that is, from the puffed chromosome regions and from the nucleolus to the cytoplasm. Such a transfer is also indicated by the fact that the amount of label in the puffs cannot be increased indefinitely by prolongation of the incubation period. A maximal value is very soon reached (after 2 hours) while the activity of the cytoplasm still increases over the next 12 hours. The relationship is, however, not entirely clear because most of the cytoplasmic RNA label could also be derived not from the puffs but from the nucleolus. That non-nucleolar RNA from the nucleus is actually transported into the cytoplasm can only be inferred from an independent study of lethal embryos lacking the nucleolus-organizing regions (Beermann, 1960).

The incorporation studies with tritiated uridine show that puffs are active centers of chromosomal RNA synthesis. Since, in addition to RNA, large amounts of protein always occur in the puffed regions, one might expect to find a similar situation with respect to protein synthesis or turnover in the puffs. However, there is no indication of a rapid and strictly localized incorporation of tritiated amino acids into the chromosomes or the nucleolus of *Chironomus* salivary gland nuclei. In fact, the autoradiograph of a salivary gland cell one hour after injection of tritiated leucine looks almost like a negative of a uridine autoradiograph; no label in the nucleus and heavy incorporation in the cytoplasm. Although these observations by no means exclude nuclear and chromosomal protein synthesis as a possibility, they seem to rule out protein synthesis as a major function of the puffed chromosome regions. We are therefore left with the conclusion that the activity of the puffed chromosome regions consists entirely in the synthesis of RNA; in other words, the puffing pattern of the polytene chromosomes represents the pattern of RNA synthesis along the chromosomes. Are we justified in considering this type of a chromosomal activity pattern as being equivalent to a pattern of "genic activity" in the sense of a differential reading of the genetic information? In a very general sense this question can be answered in the affirmative since, as is well known from modern biochemical studies on protein synthesis, RNA molecules play a central role in the transfer of information from the DNA to the protein, as "messengers" or "templates" and, in the case of the so-called soluble RNA, as specific vehicles for the amino acids to direct them into their correct position on the templates. However, in order to prove the point directly, one would have to characterize the RNA produced in the puffs chemically and demonstrate that it actually plays one or the other decisive role in protein synthesis. A first attempt to characterize the RNA of the puffs of

Chironomus polytene chromosomes has been made in collaboration with Dr. Edström from Gothenburg, Sweden.

The largest puffs (the Balbiani rings) of the salivary gland chromosomes of *Chironomus tentans* are very suitably located in the short

TABLE 1

Base composition of the RNA extracted from different components of Chironomus salivary gland cells, as molar proportions in percent of the sum.
(From Edström and Beermann, 1962)

	Adenine	Guanine	Cytosine	Uracil	A/U	G+C%	n
Chromosome 1	29.4 ± 0.5	19.8 ± 1.0	27.7 ± 0.8	23.1 ± 0.6	1.27	47.5	4
Chromosome 4							
proximal (BR 1)	35.7 ± 0.6	20.6 ± 1.7	23.2 ± 1.2	20.8 ± 0.8	1.72	43.8	5
median (BR 2)	38.0 ± 0.6	20.5 ± 0.6	24.5 ± 0.6	17.1 ± 0.6	2.22	45.0	6
distal (BR 3)	31.2 ± 2.2	22.0 ± 2.0	26.4 ± 1.9	20.2 ± 1.4	1.54	48.4	3
Nucleolus	30.6 ± 0.8	20.1 ± 0.5	22.1 ± 0.6	27.1 ± 0.6	1.13	42.2	13
Cytoplasm	29.4 ± 0.4	22.9 ± 0.3	22.1 ± 0.4	25.7 ± 0.3	1.14	45.0	7
A/G ratio for DNA							
Chromosome 1	37.8	12.2				24.4	
Chromosome 4	35.9	14.1				28.2	

fourth chromosome which can easily be isolated with glass needles from the nuclei of formalin-fixed glands. These chromosomes are collected, individually placed on coverslips, and left to dry. They can then be cut into three pieces, each containing one of the three giant Balbiani-ring puffs. The RNA from a number of homologous pieces, i.e., RNA which practically represents the specific RNA of one single puff, is extracted by repeated RNAase digestion and then subjected to a microanalytic procedure involving hydrolysis in micropipettes, electrophoresis on a rayon fiber of 25 μ diameter, and UV microphotometry of the fractions separated on the fiber (cf. Edström, 1960). The sensitivity of the method is about 10^{-10} g RNA per analysis. This quantity roughly corresponds to 50 Balbiani rings, or 5 nucleoli, or half the cytoplasm of one salivary gland cell in *Chironomus*. The method leads to a characterization of the cellular RNA fractions in terms of their base ratios (adenine + uracil + cytosine + guanine = 100%). The results are shown in Table 1.

The information gained from base ratios is, of course, limited. Base ratios do not tell us anything about the size of the RNA molecules analyzed, nor do they reflect their nucleotide sequence. In our case, we cannot even decide whether we are dealing with pure RNA fractions; our fractions might be mixtures of several molecular species. Therefore, the observed similarity between the nucleolar and the cytoplasmic RNA's might be spurious although it agrees nicely with the idea that the structural ribosomal RNA in the cytoplasm is of nucleolar origin. However, if large, significant differences in the base composition are consistently found between the nucleolar and the cytoplasmic RNA's on the one hand, and the chromosomal and puff RNA's on the other, the idea of one being the precursor of the other becomes less likely. More specifically, our data speak against the possibility that the RNA produced at the puffs is collected in the nucleolus and/or is stored in the cytoplasm in the form of ribosomal stationary RNA. It could, however, represent a short-lived messenger type of RNA, or, perhaps, soluble transfer RNA, or a mixture of both. If we consider this chromosomal RNA as a direct copy of the chromosomal DNA, the specific way in which it differs in its base composition from the other RNA fractions becomes highly significant. The DNA molecules are generally known to be double-stranded, with the base composition of one strand complementary to the other, so that the ratios thymine/adenine and cystosine/guanine both equal 1. If both strands of the DNA molecules in the puffs were copied by the RNA at the same rate, then, obviously, one should obtain a mixture of two types of single-stranded RNA molecules complementary to each other, with an over-all base composition where uracil/adenine and cytosine/guanine again both equal 1. But this type of symmetry is approached only in the nucleolar and the cytoplasmic RNA fractions. The chromosomal RNA fractions are extremely asymmetric, with A/U more than 2 in the case of the Balbiani rings, and with large deviations from 1 also in the ratio G/C, especially in chromosome 1. It should be pointed out that RNA fractions of such an extreme asymmetry have never been detected before. If, as is very likely, we are dealing with copies of the chromosomal DNA we are faced with the following possibilities: (1) The DNA in the puffs may be effectively single-stranded so that only one type of RNA molecule is produced; this single-strandedness could have either a structural or a functional (enzymatic) basis. (2) The two complementary types of RNA copies are both actually formed, but one of the two is immediately removed from the site of synthesis, either by enzymatic destruction or by rapid transport mechanisms. In any case it would appear that either the production or the selection of only one, and a specific one, of the two possible RNA copies of the genic DNA is a necessary prerequisite for an unambiguous information transfer mechanism. Our data, then, support the hypothesis that the RNA of the puffs is either the messenger itself or its complementary counterpart, the "anti-messenger." This conclusion, in turn, once more strengthens our original view that the puffing pattern of the polytene chromosomes is an expression of differential gene activation.

GENETIC CHARACTERIZATION OF A SPECIFIC PUFFED REGION IN SALIVARY GLAND CHROMOSOMES

In *Chironomus* the salivary glands continuously produce a mucopolysaccharide secretion which hardens under water and enables the larvae to build from mud particles the tubes in which they live and feed. The protein moiety of the secretion rapidly incorporates radioactive amino acids. The rate of synthesis of the secretion protein must be high as compared to the rates of synthesis of any other cellular proteins. If there is any quantitative relationship between the rate of messenger production and the rate of protein synthesis at all, one should expect the locus, or loci, containing the information for the synthesis of secretion protein to be especially, and exclusively, active in the salivary glands. As judged by their giant size and their synthetic activity with respect to RNA, the Balbiani rings of the salivary gland chromosomes seem to represent such loci. The bands forming Balbiani rings are always few in number (2-5), and those forming Balbiani rings in the salivary glands never seem to form a puff in any other tissue. Moreover, whenever one lobe of the gland differs from the others in the composition of the secretion which it produces—as is the rule in Chironomid salivary glands—this differentiation on the level of cellular function is invariably accompanied by a differentiation on the chromosomal level, with respect to the pattern of bands forming Balbiani rings. This differentiation is often mutually exclusive so that different bands are transformed into Balbiani rings in different regions of the gland. In other instances the cells of the gland may all share two or three Balbiani rings, but specialized regions of the gland may have chromosomes with additional Balbiani rings of their own. If the general views outlined above are correct, a lobe-specific Balbiani ring would furnish the genetic information necessary for the production of a lobe-specific component of the secretion. Any change, genetic or other, which would prevent a lobe-specific Balbiani ring from being developed should, on our hypothesis, lead to the loss of a lobe-specific secretion component. We have been able to verify this correlation by cytogenetic methods (Beermann, 1961).

In *Chironomus pallidivittatus* and in many other *Chironomus* species a small specialized sector of the larval salivary gland, usually consisting of four cells, produces a secretion which, in contrast to the clear secre-

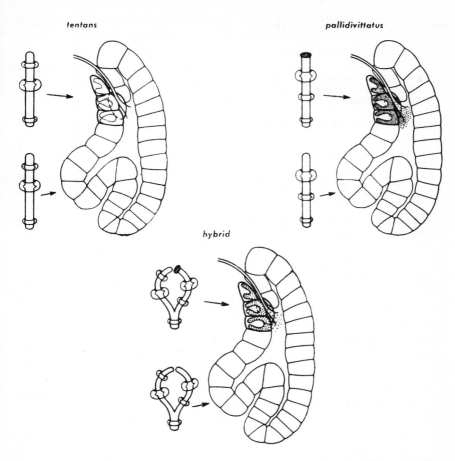

Fig. 2. The pattern of Balbiani rings in the two functionally different portions of the salivary gland in *Chironomus tetans, pallidivittatus,* and their hybrid. See text for further details.

tion of the major part of the gland, is granular in character. However, in *Chironomus tentans,* the closest relative of *C. pallidivittatus,* the granular component is not present in the secretion of the special cells. This difference between the two species does not seem to be due to a loss of structural differentiation in the salivary glands of *C. tentans,* since the special cells in the latter maintain the same fine structural details which characterize them in *C. pallidivittatus,* e.g., a cytoplasmic secretion zone of the brush border type which is not found in the normal gland cells of both species. The difference between the two species, then, must be due to the loss of a specific synthetic function from the special cells of *C. tentans*. The chromosomal situation is exactly what one would expect: In both species there are three Balbiani rings which are shared by all the cells of the glands, all in the small 4th chromosome, as mentioned earlier. In *C. pallidivittatus*, where the special cells regularly produce secretion granules, the small 4th chromosome always shows an additional Balbiani ring close to its centromeric end (Fig. 2). In *C. tentans*, on the other hand, there is no lobe-specific Balbiani ring so that, concomitant with the loss of the major, and distinctive, function of the special cells the only major distinguishing character on the chromosomal level is also lost. We may formulate the hypothesis, therefore, that the genetic information necessary for the production of the secretion granules is entirely or partially located in the band which forms the lobe-specific Balbiani ring in *C. pallidivittatus*, and that the transfer of this information to the cellular synthetic sites depends on the actual formation of the Balbiani ring in question. These postulates can be put to test by classical gene localization techniques. *C. tentans* and *C. pallidivittatus* produce fertile hybrids, and their chromosomes are marked by a number of species-specific rearrangements, mainly inversions, which prevent crossing-over in most chromosome regions. It was found that the "mutant character" in question, namely, the inability to produce secretion granules, is recessive, and that it is inherited as a simple Mendelian factor whose pattern of inheritance closely follows the inheritance of the 4th chromosome of *C. tentans*. Its location within the 4th chromosome was determined by crossing-over tests and found to coincide with the location of the lobe-specific Balbiani ring. In heterozygotes, the two allelic segments behave visibly differently so that the allelic segments originally furnished by *C. pallidivittatus* form the Balbiani ring whereas the homologous segment furnished by *C. tentans* fails to do so in the same nucleus. This permits a parallel scoring of crossovers both on the chromosomal level and on the level of the phenotype, always with identical results. Moreover, some exceptional cases have been observed in these hybridization experiments where the formation of the lobe-specific Balbiani ring was suppressed by modifying genetic factors. In all these instances a parallel decrease was observed in the amount of secretion granules in the special lobe of the salivary glands.

Apart from demonstrating that our interpretation of the puffing phenomenon is basically correct, these results also illustrate another general point, namely, the possibility of purely "operational" mutations as opposed to informational ones. No visible deficiency is present at the locus of the mutant which distinguishes *C. tentans* from *C. pallidi-*

vittatus. Thus, it is conceivable that the mutation did not involve the informational content of the locus at all but only its operational properties. These might be determined by a special segment immediately adjacent to the informational one, just as the operation of bacterial genes is controlled via a special "operator" site (Jacob and Monod, 1961). At any rate, since we know now that puffing is an operational phenomenon, we are in a position to use this phenomenon to define operational units or "operons" in polytene chromosomes. The question may then be raised whether or not the units thus defined always coincide with the units defined by other means, morphological as well as genetic ones. We will probably have to revise the statement that a puff as a rule represents only a single band which in turn could be considered as an informational unit. A combined study of position effects and puffing may throw further light on this problem.

THE INDUCTION AND CONTROL OF PUFFING

The existence of different activity patterns of the genes in different types of cells and in different stages of development must be due to the action of specific triggering and controlling factors in development. Unfortunately, the mechanism of puff formation as such is at present a complete mystery. When a puff is formed, the most conspicuous change from a chemical standpoint is the incorporation of large amounts of nonbasic proteins, presumably in an organized fashion. The same protein must be incorporated also wherever chromosomal replication occurs in a place where a puff is already present. With radioactive precursors, however, we have not been able to find evidence for a substantial net synthesis of protein, nor for that matter, for any kind of turnover during puff formation or puff growth. Probably the proteins are made elsewhere in the cells and become subsequently attached to the site of puff formation. The properties of this protein are not known in detail, nor do we know whether the protein is the same in all puffs. An attractive hypothesis would be that the protein represents RNA polymerase. As regards RNA, we have seen earlier that the bulk of the RNA in the puffs seems to be involved in information transfer but we can by no means exclude the presence in puffs of small amounts of RNA with an "inductive" function.

In the present state of ignorance about the puffing mechanism, the search for inducing or controlling agents is largely determined by the view that agents known to be effective as inducers in animal development might act via the activation of genes. This idea is generally supported by the fact that unspecific physical and chemical factors which are able to bring about specific changes in development, such as temperature or ionic strength of the medium, can also evoke specific responses in the puffing pattern of the chromosomes (Becker, 1959; Ritossa, 1962; personal communication). A much better clue to the understanding of the puffing mechanism should, of course, be derivable from the use of biological agents such as the hormones, which are known to be extremely specific both in their action and their chemical structure. In insects the molting process is initiated and can be experimentally induced by the molting hormone, "ecdysone," a product of the prothoracic glands. This hormone has been highly purified, but not yet chemically identified by Karlson (1956); there are indications that it is a cholesterol derivative. Clever (1961) in our laboratory has found that the injection of minimal doses of this hormone into *Chironomus* larvae leads within 30 minutes to the formation of a puff at a specific site in chromosome 1, and 30 minutes later to the formation of another puff in chromosome 4. The hormone, as judged by the puffing reaction, is active in concentrations as low as 10^{-7} μg/mg larval weight in the case of the first puff, and 10^{-6} μg/mg in the case of the second puff. These values are equivalent to a few hundred molecules per single chromatid in each nucleus. After molting has been induced, the first puff stays on until after the molting process is completed—as it should, since ecdysone is constantly present in the hemolymph during the molting period, owing to an induction of hormone production in the animals themselves. The second puff, however, invariably regresses after 2 days, a process which must be due to the action of a specific "repressor." The formation of the two primary puffs is followed, in normal development as well as in the experiments, by a chain of secondary puffing reactions, the amplitude of which does not, however, depend on the hormone concentration as it does in the case of the primary puffs. These data indicate that the hormone acts as a direct inducer of activity in two loci, an activity which in its turn triggers off the whole chain of secondary events which may include the production of several new enzymes. That the primary puffs probably only act as recipients for the developmental signal is further indicated by the fact that they are formed not only in the salivary glands but also in the Malpighian tubules and probably in all tissues. Jacob and Monod (1961) think that inducers, or repressors, of gene activity exert their function as co-factors by forming a molecular complex with an internal "apo-repressor," thereby changing its stereochemical affinity to the "operator" in the operon involved. It is possible that the hormone in our case is just such an "effector."

The fact that, in the case of the ecdysone, a hormone has been found to act as a specific inducer of puffing at a specific site of the chromosomes does not, of course, justify generalization in one way or the other. Neither must all hormones of necessity act as gene inducers, nor can the majority of substances that act in gene regulation be considered as hormones. On the contrary, the very fact that cellular differentiation can take place in a multicellular organism shows that most of the specific inducers or repressors of gene activities must remain limited in their effects to the cell in which they are produced. It is the search for these substances that may, in the future, prove to be the most illuminating approach to the problem of cellular differentiation.

REFERENCES

Bauer, H., 1935, Der Aufbau der Chromosomen aus den Speicheldüsen von Chiromomus Thummi Fiefer (Untersuchungen an den Riesenchromosomen der Dipteren I). Z. Zellforsch, **23**, 280-313.

Becker, H. J., 1959, Die Puffs der Speicheldrüsen-chromosomen *von Drosophila melanogaster*. 1. Mitteilung. Beobachtungen zum Verhalten des Puffmusters im Normalstamm und bein zwei Mutanten, *giant* und *giant-lethal-larvae*. Chromosoma (Berlin), **10**, 654-678.

Beermann, W., 1956, Nuclear differentiation and functional morphology of chromosomes. Cold Spr. Harb. Symp. Quant. Biol., **21**, 217-232.

——————, 1959, Chromosomal differentiation in insects. p. 83-103. *In* D. Rudnick, [ed.], Developmental cytology, Ronald, New York.

——————, 1960, Der Nukleolus als lebenswichtiger Bestandteil des Zellkerns. Chromosoma (Berlin), **11**, 263-296.

——————, 1961, Ein Balbiani-Ring als Locus einer Speicheldrüsen-Mutation. Chromosoma (Berlin), **12**, 1-25.

Beermann, W., and G. F. Bahr, 1954, The submicroscopic structure of the Balbiani-ring. Exptl. Cell. Res., **6**, 195-201.

Bridges, C. B., 1935, The structure of salivary chromosomes and the relation of the banding to the genes. Amer. Naturalist, **69**, 59.

Clever, U., 1961, Genaktivitaten in den Riesenchromosomen von *Chironomus tentans* und ihre Beziehungen zur Entwicklung. I. Genaktivierungen durch Ecdyson. Chromosoma (Berlin) **12**, 607-675.

Edström, J. E., 1960, Extraction, hydrolysis, and electrophoretic analysis of ribonucleic acid from microscopic tissue units (microphoresis). J. Biophys. Biochem. Cytol., **8**, 39-46.

Edström, J. E., and W. Beermann, 1962, The base composition of nucleic acids in chromosomes, puffs, nucleoli, and cytoplasm of *Chironomus* salivary gland cells. J. Cell Biol., **14**, 371-379.

Jacob, F., and J. Monod, 1961, Genetic regulatory mechanisms in the synthesis of proteins. J. Mol. Biol., **3**, 318-356.

Karlson, J., 1956, Chemische Untersuchungen über die Metamorphose-hormone der Insekten. Ann. Sci. nat. Zool., **11**, 125-137.

Koltzoff, N. K., 1934, The structure of the chromosomes in the salivary glands of Drosophila. Science, **80**, 312-313.

Rudkin, G. T., and S. L. Corlette, 1957, Disproportionate synthesis of DNA in a polytene chromosome region. Proc. Natl. Acad. Sci. U. S., **43**, 964-968.

6

serial transplantation
of embryonic nuclei*

THOMAS J. KING and ROBERT BRIGGS
Lankenau Hospital Research Institute
and Institute for Cancer Research, Philadelphia, Pennsylvania

Over the past many years genetical research has revealed large numbers of gene effects on cell differentiation. These are usually effects on the final phases of differentiation, but may also be manifested at early developmental stages (Gluecksohn-Waelsch, 1954; Hadorn, 1948, 1956; Poulson, 1945; and others). In principle, the analysis of these effects depends upon the permanent alteration or deletion of a chromosome segment, and the subsequent detection of a change in differentiation—usually a deficiency. The evidence so obtained permits the conclusion that a particular gene or gene set is required for a particular type of differentiation to proceed normally. However, in general it leaves unanswered the questions which are of greatest concern to students of development. First, the genetic evidence as yet provides no explanation of the orderly segregation of cell types during development—of the fact that a given gene comes to have one effect in one part of the organism while in another part it has no effect or a different one. This must, of course, involve interactions of the geneticist's nucleus with the embryologist's cytoplasmic localizations, but the nature of this interaction is unknown. Second, the available evidence fails to account for the stability or irreversibility of differentiation. In other words, while genes have particular functions in differentiation, in general, it is not known how they acquire them, nor whether they

Reprinted from Cold Spring Harbor Symposia on Quantitative Biology
Volume XXI, 1956

are themselves altered in the performance of these functions in such a way as to confer stability on the differentiated cells.

It has been apparent for some time that in order to obtain answers to the questions posed above it would be necessary to devise new methods for detecting changes in gene function in somatic cells. Essentially, such methods should yield recombinations of nucleus and cytoplasm and of different types of nuclei of somatic cells, comparable with the natural recombinations of germ cells from which most genetic information is obtained.

Experiments of the type mentioned above, involving artificial transfer of cytoplasm or nucleus, were accomplished with unicellular organisms some years ago. Hämmerling (1934, 1953), using the unicellular uninucleate alga, *Acetabularia*, grafted stalk pieces from one species to the nucleated rhizoidal ends of another and demonstrated that the form of the cap that regenerated from the grafted stalk was controlled by the nucleus. Later Hämmerling (1953) produced heterokaryons and showed that the form of the regenerated cap was intermediate between the forms characteristic of the species contributing the nuclei. This and other evidence led to the conclusion that the nucleus produces specific morphogenetic substances which pass into the cytoplasm and there control the differentiation of the cap.

Another instance in which new combinations of nucleus and cytoplasm have been produced artificially is provided by the studies of Danielli and co-workers on amoebae. Using a method devised by Comandon and deFonbrune (1939), these investigators transferred nuclei from one species of amoeba to another (Lorch and Danielli, 1950). In the best analyzed case, a combination of *A. proteus* nucleus with *A. discoides* cytoplasm, a clone was obtained which has survived more than six years. Some properties of the individuals in this clone (division rate, nuclear diameter) are determined by the cytoplasm, others (shape when migrating) are intermediate, while the type of antigen(s) produced is under nuclear control (Danielli, Lorch, Ord and Wilson, 1955). Similar experiments, involving transfers of nuclei between different species of *Stentor*, have been done by Tartar (1953). The ciliates, with their highly organized cytoplasmic structures, possess obvious advantages over amoebae for this type of study. Tartar was able to make successful intraspecific transfers, but unfortunately the interspecific combinations did not survive long enough to permit an analysis of the relative contributions of cytoplasm and nucleus in the control of cytoplasmic differentiation.

So far, we have restricted ourselves to those instances in which nucleo-cytoplasmic recombinations have been produced artificially in

unicellular organisms. There is, of course, a much larger body of information, not to be reviewed here, which is based on regeneration
studies in ciliates and on various naturally occurring genetic recombinations in a variety of microorganisms. In the majority of cases, it appears
that cell type is determined by nuclear genes, but cytoplasmic particu-
lates or conditions have also been shown to be a part of the genetic
system (Sonneborn, 1954; Ephrussi, 1953; Weisz, 1951). This work
with unicellular organisms is extremely valuable in revealing a larger
range of recombination mechanisms, both natural and artificial, than
had been suspected 25 years ago. It has also provided us with a set
of beautifully analyzed types of nucleocytoplasmic interactions, which
have led to several theories of metazoan differentiation. However, as
Lederberg (1956) has pointed out, the problems of embryology cannot be solved with microbes, and we should now pass to a consideration
of some of the attempts that have been made toward an analysis of
nuclear function in metazoan differentiation.

This subject was of intense interest in the early years of experimental embryology, largely as a result of the stimulus provided by
the somatic segregation theory of differentiation proposed by Weismann
and by Roux. The large literature of the period has been summarized
by Wilson (1925). Of this, we should like to mention only two experiments. The first, by Jacques Loeb (1894), involved placing fertilized
sea urchin eggs in diluted sea water, in which they swell and sometimes burst the egg membrane. When this happens a portion of the
cytoplasm protrudes as a hernia. This may not at first contain a nucleus, but after a few divisions of the main part of the egg one of
the cleavage nuclei may migrate into the herniated portion and initiate
its development, which then proceeds to the formation of either a
complete embryo or half a double monster. A similar result was obtained later in the famous constriction experiment of Spemann (1914),
who observed a delayed nucleation of one half of the newt egg resulting
from the migration into it of a nucleus from the other half after it attained the 16 to 32 cell stage. Again the part experiencing the delayed
nucleation developed into a complete embryo.

In both Loeb's and Spemann's experiments, as well as in numerous
other investigations, the results showed that the cleavage nuclei are
equivalent and "totipotent." However, the actual evidence was restricted
to the first few cleavages and, as Spemann (1938) later pointed out,
it remained undecided whether the nuclei might come to have different
properties in different tissues later in development. Spemann further
suggested that decisive information on the question might perhaps be
afforded if it were possible to transfer nuclei from cells of older embryos

to non-nucleated eggs, the development of which should then reveal the character of the trasnplanted nucleus. This type of experiment was also suggested independently by Schultz (personal communication, 1943; 1952), Ephrussi (1951), Rostand (1943) and perhaps others.

To the best of our knowledge, the transfer of nuclei (by pricking frog's eggs coated with embryonic brei) was first attempted by Rostand in 1943, with uncertain success. A few years later, we began to work on the problem, and after a considerable number of failures devised a different procedure for the transplantation of living nuclei from embryonic cells into enucleated eggs of the frog, *Rana pipiens* (Briggs and King, 1952). More recently transfers of embryonic nuclei have also been made by Waddington and Pantelouris (1953), Lehman (1955, 1956), Markert (referred to in Lehman, 1956) and Subtelny (1956). The method used is not without its difficulties and complications, but it appears to represent the most direct experimental approach for obtaining evidence of the genetic condition of nuclei in differentiating embryonic cells.

NOTE ON METHODS

A brief description of the nuclear transplantation procedure was given in previous papers (Briggs and King, 1952, 1953; King and Briggs, 1955). Since then, certain refinements, particularly in the construction and use of micropipettes, have been added, which will be described elsewhere. Here we wish to mention only the main features of the method—those which are essential to an appraisal of the significance of the results obtained with it.

The transplantation operation is carried out in two main steps. First, the recipient eggs (*Rana pipiens*) are activated with a glass needle and subsequently enucleated, following Porter's (1939) technique. With practice and care, the enucleation operation is 100 percent successful. The second part of the procedure involves the isolation of the donor cells and the nuclear transfer itself. Free donor cells may be obtained by the appropriate use of Versene (Ethylene diamine tetra acetic acid, Na salt) alone or in combination with trypsin, as previously described (King and Briggs, 1955). A given cell, in Niu-Twitty (1953) solution, is then drawn into the tip of a micropipette, the inner diameter of which is somewhat smaller than that of the cell. When this is properly done the cell surface is broken but the contents are not dispersed. In this way the nucleus is protected by its own cytoplasm until the pipette is inserted into the recipient egg and the broken cell ejected, liberating the nucleus into the egg cytoplasm. The technique sounds deceptively simple, but it takes practice to perform these operations consistently well.

Two features of the method that bear on the interpretation of results are first the inclusion of donor cell cytoplasm along with the injected nucleus, and second, the possibility of inadvertently damaging the nucleus in the course of the operation. Nuclear damage can be appraised by a study of control eggs injected with undifferentiated blastula nuclei, and by observations on cleavage patterns and chromosomes of test eggs. With reference to the donor cell cytoplasm, it should be mentioned that it represents in volume only $\frac{1}{40,000}$ to $\frac{1}{500,000}$ the volume of cytoplasm of the recipient egg. Still, the possibility that it might contain self-replicating units controlling differentiation must be considered, and where necessary, control transfers of cytoplasm from differentiating cells must be carried out—as will be mentioned in a subsequent section of this paper.

TRANSPLANTATION TESTS OF BLASTULA NUCLEI

The first successful transplantations were carried out with nuclei of mid- to late blastulae. The donor blastulae were 18 to 24 hours old (at 18°C) and consisted of approximately 8,000 to 16,000 cells (estimates of cell number based on Sze's (1953) determinations). Only nuclei of undetermined animal hemisphere cells were used. In the first set of experiments, about one-third of the transfers led to normal cleavage and blastula formation on the part of the recipient eggs, and the majority of these blastulae, some 75 percent, developed into complete embryos. Half of the embryos appeared to be perfectly normal while the remainder displayed minor abnormalities (Briggs and King, 1952). In more recent experiments, the number of transfers of this type leading to normal cleavage has been larger (40% to 80%) and the majority (ca. 80%) of the resulting embryos develop normally to larval or later stages (King and Briggs, 1955 and unpub.).

The proof that the nuclear transfers are successful, and that the test eggs contain only the transplanted nuclei, consists of the following:

1) Control operations for removal of the egg nucleus, performed on normally fertilized eggs, show that all eggs develop as androgenetic haploids. Failures would lead to the development of diploids, of which there were none in control series of more than 500 embryos during the past two years.

2) Sections of eggs which cleave following enucleation and nuclear transplantation reveal the egg nucleus outside the egg, in the enucleation exovate, while the blastomeres contain nuclei derived from the transferred nucleus (Briggs and King, 1952).

3) Enucleated eggs which were injected with diploid nuclei and which begin cleavage at the normal time after activation, develop into diploid embryos, ploidy being determined by cell size, nucleolar number, and chromosome counts (see Table 2 of this paper for chromosome counts). If the first cleavage is initiated one cleavage interval late, the resulting embryos are tetraploids.

4) Enucleated eggs injected with haploid nuclei develop into haploid embryos unless there is a delayed initiation of cleavage—in which case the embryos become diploids (Subtelny, unpub.).

5) When enucleated *Rana pipiens* eggs are injected with *R. catesbeiana* nuclei the resulting development duplicates exactly that of the normally produced lethal hybrid between these two species (King and Briggs, 1953).

The results summarized above proved that late blastula nuclei could be transplanted in undamaged condition, and since the test eggs developed normally it was further demonstrated that the nuclei were unchanged, that is, equivalent to the nucleus at the beginning of development.

This result has been independently confirmed in this Institute by Subtelny, who also worked with *Rana pipiens*. So far as we are aware, the only other work on this species which has been mentioned in the literature (by Lehman, 1956) is that of Markert and Freedman. From 256 transfers these workers obtained 32 blastulae of which 20 gastrulated and 9 neurulated. While this represents a positive result, the yield from the transfers is relatively low and it would be difficult on this basis to draw conclusions concerning the properties of the nuclei tested.

Some attempts have been made to transfer embryonic nuclei into newt's eggs. The newt embryo would seem to offer important advantages for this work, with its large cells, relatively small chromosome number, and ease of handling in the usual tissue grafting and explanation techniques. However, the results so far have been disappointing. Waddington and Pantelouris (1953) transferred nuclei from blastula and later stages of *Triturus* (*Triton*) *palmatus* into non-nucleated egg fragments, which had been previously produced by constricting normally fertilized eggs. About 12 percent of the fragments developed into blastulae which failed to gastrulate. No chromosome studies of these blastulae were reported and for this and other reasons the interpretation of the results was uncertain.

More recently, H. E. Lehman (1955) has reported on the transplantation of *Triton* blastula nuclei into enucleated eggs. Apparently the *Triton* egg cannot be activated with a glass needle and then enucleated in the manner which works so well with the frog's eggs. Furthermore, attempts to inject nuclei and then enucleate eggs also failed; eggs so treated did not cleave. Either the egg cytoplasm is damaged by these manipulations, or the injected nucleus for one reason or another fails to provide an effective cleavage center. In any event, Lehman was forced to resort to a more complicated procedure in which the eggs were first fertilized with heavily irradiated sperm (50,000 r), then pricked and enucleated, and finally injected with a blastula nucleus. About 65 percent of the recipient eggs cleaved, and one-third of these formed blastulae which failed to gastrulate. Since the enucleations were only 50 percent successful, and there was in addition some question of the survival of chromosome fragments from the irradiated sperm, the interpretation of this experiment depended on an accurate chromosome analysis. This Lehman did, finding haploid, diploid and hyperdiploid numbers. The occurrence of diploid, and particularly of hyperdiploid chromosome numbers, indicated that the injected nuclei or chromosomes therefrom were participating in the cleavage. As Lehman pointed out, the reasons for the failure of the embryos to gastrulate could have been a) irregular distribution of chromosomes during cleavage, leading to lethal chromosome imbalance (Fankhauser, 1934b), b) operative damage to the egg or the transferred nucleus or both, and c) nuclear determination at the blastula stage. In view of the fact that the blastula donor cells are not themselves determined, and in view of the results obtained with the frog, it seems likely that the failure of the recipient newt eggs to develop normally is due principally to their greater susceptibility to damage in the course of transfer.

NUCLEI OF EARLY GASTRULAE

As has been appreciated for a long time, the beginning of gastrulation is a crucial phase of development. At this time the regional localizations of materials present from the beginning in the egg cytoplasm have their first morphogenetic expression. For example, in the amphibian egg the gray crescent material, localized on the dorsal side of the egg shortly after fertilization, is known to determine the position of the dorsal lip of the blastopore, and consequently the point of origin of the chorda mesoderm and the whole axial organization of the embryo. While the position of the dorsal lip is thus determined by the gray crescent cytoplasm, it is also known that in order for it to invaginate and form chorda mesoderm, it must be provided with a "normal" set of chromosomes. Prior to gastrulation, cleavage and blastula formation may proceed with nuclei containing variable numbers of chromosomes (Fankhauser, 1934b), no chromosomes (Fankhauser, 1934a; Stauffer,

1945; Briggs, Green and King, 1951); or with various foreign genomes (see review by Moore, 1955). However, in all these cases development stops at or before the beginning of gastrulation, from which it is concluded that gastrulation and later phases of development require the participation of a balanced chromosome set. Furthermore, nucleus and cytoplasm must be of the same or closely related species. This and other information indicates that the nuclei come to have specific essential functions at the beginning of gastrulation. Whether they undergo irreversible or quasi-irreversible changes, and whether these are the same or different in different parts of the early gastrula, are questions we have approached by means of nuclear transplantation. The work is not quite finished yet, and will be described in full elsewhere. Here we may give only a brief account to provide a background for the following portions of this paper.

Nuclei from the following portions of the early gastrula were tested: 1) animal hemisphere, near the pole, 2) dorsal lip region, 3) endoderm including the floor of the blastocoel, and a region between the vegetal pole and the dorsal lip. The nuclei were transplanted to enucleated eggs in the usual way, giving the following results:

1) Animal hemisphere nuclei—39 per cent of 33 test eggs formed complete blastulae, 69% of the blastulae developed into tadpoles.

2) Dorsal lip nuclei—25 percent of 77 test eggs formed complete blastulae, of which 74 percent developed into tadpoles.

3) Endoderm nuclei—54 percent of 107 recipient eggs cleaved normally, 66 percent of the blastulae so produced developed into tadpoles.

These preliminary experiments provide no definite evidence of differences among the nuclei from the various regions of the gastrula. The proportion of recipient eggs forming complete blastulae was smaller in the case of animal hemisphere and dorsal lip nuclear transfers than it was in the case of the endoderm transfers, but this is probably due to differences in donor cell size and ease of isolation. With respect to the development of the complete blastulae, there was some indication (in one experiment) that blastulae containing endoderm nuclei were more frequently arrested in gastrula or post-neurula stages. However, in the majority of experiments endoderm, dorsal lip, and animal hemisphere nuclei appeared equally capable of promoting normal development to the early larval stage, at least.

This result, indicating equivalence of early gastrula nuclei, is to some extent to be expected. One of the donor regions, the animal pole, is definitely undetermined and would not be expected to contain differentiated nuclei. The dorsal lip area is, of course, determined to form chordamesoderm. However, the determination is on a regional

and not a cell basis, for if parts of the region are explanted they are
found to be capable of differentiating into neural and endodermal as
well as mesodermal structures (Holtfreter, 1938). The endoderm, on
the other hand, gives evidence of being already determined in the
early gastrula (Holtfreter, 1938). Whether the individual cells are irreversibly set in their path of differentiation appears uncertain, but the
endoderm cell mass and portions of it are apparently determined to
form gut and gut derivatives. Yet the endoderm nuclei, along with nuclei
of other regions, give no definite evidence of differentiation in the
transplantation experiments. This could mean either that the individual
endoderm cells are not irreversibly determined, or that if they are,
the determination does not involve irreversible nuclear changes. Since
our experiments involve the transfer of donor cell cytoplasm along with
the nuclei, the results also indicate that there are no genetic units in
the cytoplasm which are capable of directing the differentiation of
the recipient eggs.

The nuclear transplantation work summarized above emphasizes a
point which has been familiar to embryologists for some time; namely,
that the morphogenetic events in the early gastrula depend on the
regional localization of cytoplasmic materials present in the egg at
the beginning of development. Normal nuclei are essential for morphogenesis to proceed, but neither the nuclei nor the individual cells (except
possibly endoderm cells) are irreversibly specialized at this stage. In
other words, the intrinsic properties of the individual cells provide no
explanation of the morphogenetic events, which are directed by the
aforementioned cytoplasmic localizations. Thus, the role of the nucleus
in this early phase of development will eventually have to be studied
prior to fertilization, when these materials are being laid down in the
oocyte.

NUCLEI OF LATE GASTRULAE

During gastrulation the germ layers are established, and by the
late gastrula stage are determined in the sense that they cannot be
transformed, one into the other, by grafting to inductive sites. In order
to see if the determination of the layers involves detectable changes
in the nuclei, we have made transplantation tests of nuclei from chorda
mesoderm, presumptive medullary plate, and endoderm. The first tests
were done on nuclei of the presumptive plate and the chorda mesoderm.
These nuclei elicited normal cleavage in a considerably smaller proportion of the test eggs than had been the case with the blastula nuclei.
Furthermore, about half the normally cleaved eggs were arrested in
blastula and gastrula stages, and of the ones completing gastrulation

the majority displayed abnormalities later in development (King and Briggs, 1954). However, a few embryos did develop normally, indicating that at least some of the chorda mesoderm and medullary plate nuclei were undifferentiated. The significance of the cases in which development was arrested or abnormal remained in doubt because of the technical problems in handling the small donor cells. At the time, these cells were being isolated with glass needles with some risk of injury; and being small they were difficult to handle in the micropipette without some dilution of the cytoplasm with the Niu-Twitty medium and consequent damage to the nucleus. In order to circumvent these problems, we began to use trypsin as an aid in separating embryonic layers, and Versene to dissociate the cells (King and Briggs, 1955). In addition, it was decided to concentrate on the endoderm since this tissue appears to be definitely determined in the late gastrula, and still consists of large cells which are as readily managed in the transfer procedure as are those of mid- to late blastulae.

Late gastrula endoderm nuclei

In view of the considerations mentioned above, an extensive series of transfers of late gastrula endoderm nuclei has been made, the donor cells being taken usually from the presumptive anterior midgut region (King and Briggs, 1955 and unpub.). These nuclei elicited normal cleavage and blastula formation in about 40 percent of the test eggs, and were therefore equivalent to undifferentiated blastula nuclei in this respect. However, the later development of the "endoderm blastulae" differed from that of the controls. Approximately 80 percent of the control blastulae, containing transplanted blastula nuclei, developed into normal larvae. By contrast, the majority of the endoderm blastulae displayed pronounced abnormalities in their development. About one-third were arrested in late blastula or gastrula stages, one-half gastrulated normally but later displayed deficiencies, while the remaining minority developed normally into tadpoles.

The nature of the abnormalities in the endoderm embryos has been studied, and will be described in more detail elsewhere. In brief, the embryos had the following characteristics.

Arrested late blastulae or early gastrulae were uniformly cleaved, contained nuclei of uniform size, and possessed a normal blastocoel. Before the onset of arrest the cleavages occurred at about the normal rate, and the cells contained the normal number of chromosomes ($2N = 26$) although in some cases the form of the chromosomes was changed (see below). After the embryos were arrested the nuclei tended to become vacuolated, and some loose cells appeared in the blastocoel.

Abnormal post-neurula embryos

These embryos completed gastrulation in apparently normal fashion, but later showed in varying degrees the following conditions. First, there was a reduction, sometimes extreme, in size and degree of differentiation of the central nervous system, sense organs, and neural crest derivatives, accompanied by nuclear pycnosis in the affected organs. The inductor system (notochord and somites) was well developed and displayed no significant pycnosis. However, somites were usually abnormal in form. Other mesodermal organs (cardiovascular system, pronephros) were generally less well developed. Endoderm, in the stages studied, is not normally highly differentiated. In the endoderm embryos, its differentiation was retarded, in keeping with the general retardation in development, but it did not display significant numbers of pycnotic nuclei.

Endoderm nuclei from later stages

Nuclei from the anterior midgut region of mid-neurulae elicited normal cleavage and blastula formation in only 16 percent of the test eggs, compared with 40 percent or more in the case of the late gastrula nuclei. Of the blastulae obtained, a larger proportion (70%) were arrested early, in blastula or gastrula stages. The remaining embryos gastrulated, but the large majority later displayed the abnormalities mentioned above. Endoderm nuclei from the same region of tail bud embryos displayed a still further reduced capacity to promote cleavage of recipient eggs. Only seven percent of the test eggs developed into complete blastulae 9 in number. Seven of these blastulae were arrested in late blastula or early gastrula stages, and two were abnormal "endoderm embryos."

These results on endoderm nuclear transfers indicate that the nuclei are going through definite changes. Nuclei from the late gastrula show an undiminished ability to promote cleavage and blastula formation. However, in their subsequent development the endoderm blastulae fall into three general classes—(a) embryos which are arrested before or during the formation of chorda mesoderm, (b) embryos which complete gastrulation but later show deficiencies, especially in ectodermal derivatives, and (c) normal embryos. This suggests that in the late gastrula some endoderm nuclei are unchanged; others are limited in their capacity to promote ectodermal differentiation; and still others are incapable of participating in chorda mesoderm formation. Results of transfers of mid-neurula and tail bud endoderm nuclei indicate that as differentiation proceeds the number of unchanged nuclei decreases, and that some nuclei may lose their capacity even to promote cleavage of recipient eggs.

That the changes described above occur in the nucleus or some nucleus-associated structure is indicated by the fact that endoderm cytoplasm, injected into normally nucleated eggs, has no influence on their development. This does not exclude cytoplasmic participation in the effects observed, but does indicate that cytoplasmic factors would be nucleus-dependent in their activity. In what follows, we shall refer to the changes detected by the transplantation procedure as nuclear changes, with the understanding that these changes may actually involve either the nucleus itself or some perinuclear organelle, or both.

SERIAL TRANSPLANTATION OF ENDODERM NUCLEI

From the experiments described above, it looks very much as if there is, during development, a progressive restriction of the capacity of endoderm nuclei to promote the coordinated differentiation of the various cell types required for the formation of a normal embryo. The two most pressing questions concerning these nuclear changes are 1) are they specific? and 2) are they stable or irreversible? For various reasons it seemed that the question of specificity could be solved more readily if that of irreversibility were first settled. A method of doing this is illustrated in Figure 1.

The experiment consists of first making transfers of a series of endoderm nuclei to enucleated ggs. Each egg receives one nucleus as usual, and a sizeable proportion of the eggs then cleave and form complete blastulae. Each blastula will be, so to speak, populated by descendants of a single endoderm nucleus. Different blastulae contain nuclei derived from different endoderm cells, and develop in the different ways shown in the figure. Now, in order to test the descendants of any given endoderm nucleus we may sacrifice one of the original recipient eggs at the blastula stage, and make from it a new series of nuclear transfers. All of the new group of recipient eggs will contain descendants of one original endoderm nucleus. If the expression of the nucleus with respect to differentiation is uniform and not much affected by vagaries of experimentation all of this new generation of test eggs (called the 1st blastula generation) should develop in the same fashion. It will, in effect, represent the first generation of a clone of embryos all containing descendants of a single nucleus, and is referred to as a nuclear clone. The characteristics of the clone may be studied further by sacrificing an individual of the first blastula generation to provide nuclei for another group of test eggs, referred to as the second blastula generation. The development of this group of eggs will tell us not only how uniform is the differentiation-promoting activity of the nucleus but also, by comparison with the preceding generation, how stable.

The actual experiments were carried out in the following way. In any given experiment we first transferred approximately 15 endoderm nuclei to the same number of enucleated eggs. Anywhere from 6 to 12 of these eggs cleaved and formed complete blastulae. The first two or three cleavages were observed and recorded, and the eggs were then placed in a water bath at 14°C. On the following day (ca. 24 hours later) the blastulae were removed from the 14° tank to the 18° room, three donors were selected, and the remaining embryos were set aside for observation. The donors were always blastulae of perfectly normal appearance which had records of having initiated cleavage at the normal time. It was important to select the donors on this basis to avoid the complication of polyploidy. Nuclei from each of the three donors were transferred to ten enucleated eggs to give the first blastula generation of three nuclear clones. Again cleavages were observed and on the following day one of the resulting blastulae in each clone was selected as the donor for the second blastula generation, while the remaining blastulae were allowed to develop. Usually the experiments were not carried beyond the second blastula generation, and as outlined above, each such experiment, producing three nuclear clones, required at least 75 nuclear transfers. The work reported below on 27 nuclear clones (9 control nuclei, 18 endoderm nuclei) is based on a total of about 850 nuclear transfers.

RESULTS

Results of serial transplantation of nuclei are given in the form of actual records of representative experiments and in a summary table and chart (Figs. 1-8 and Table 1). The experimental records reproduced here include only the test eggs that cleaved completely forming normal blastulae. Not included are eggs that failed to cleave, or cleaved abnormally or partially, since for one reason or another these provide no test of the capacity of the transferred nuclei to promote differentiation.

Figure 1, illustrating the principle of the experimental procedure, is also an accurate record of the development of one nuclear clone. In this experiment, the original transfers of endoderm nuclei as usual led to quite different types of development, ranging from arrested gastrulae to normal embyros, as illustrated by the camera lucida drawings. One blastula was sacrificed to provide nuclei for transfer to a new group

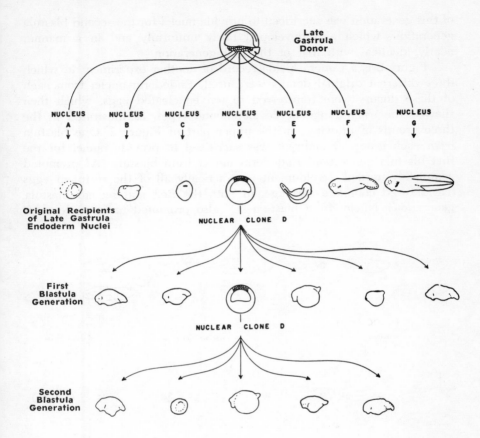

Fig. 1. Diagram illustrating serial transplantation of endoderm nuclei. Donor nuclei are actually taken from the presumptive anterior midgut region of the late gastrula. Transferred to enucleated eggs they promote the various types of development shown for the "original recipients" in the diagram. One of the original recipients, sacrificed at the blastula stage, provides nuclei for a single clone which shows the more uniform development illustrated for the first and second blastula generations. In this and subsequent figures the illustrations of embryos are in the form of either camera lucida drawings or photographs.

of enucleated eggs, giving rise to a nuclear clone which, in the first blastula generation, displayed a quite uniform type of development—in contrast to the wide variety of developmental types seen among the original recipients of the different endoderm nuclei. The embryos of this generation gastrulated normally, but later showed marked deficiencies, particularly in the ectodermal derivatives. One of the blastulae of this generation was sacrificed to provide nuclei for the second blastula generation, which also developed fairly uniformly and in a manner nearly identical with that of the first generation.

Figure 2 is a camera lucida record of another experiment in which three different original donors were used. Endoderm nuclei from each of these donors were transferred to ten enucleated eggs, which then showed the usual range of developmental types, as illustrated in the three groups of drawings in the upper part of Figure 2. One blastula from each group of embryos was sacrificed to provide nuclei for the first blastula generation. Endoderm nuclei from blastula "A" promoted completely normal development in practically all of the recipient eggs that showed complete cleavage, in both the first and second blastula generations. Nuclei from blastula "C" also promoted uniform develop-

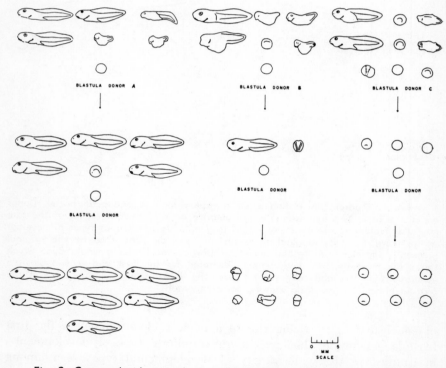

Fig. 2. Camera lucida record of serial transplantation experiment. Three late gastrula donors were used (not diagrammed in above record). Nuclei from these donors were transferred to 3 groups of enucleated eggs, which developed in the various ways illustrated in the upper part of the figure. The derived clones developed much more uniformly.

ment, stopping in late blastula or nearly gastrula stage. Nuclei from blastula "B," on the other hand, elicited normal blastula formation in only three of the test eggs, of which one developed normally, one arrested in neurulation, while one was sacrificed at blastula stage to provide nuclei for the second blastula generation. The second generation developed abnormally and displayed somewhat greater variability than usual. The variable development of this clone poses a problem of interpretation. Possibly some nuclei, chosen by chance at the time when they are beginning to undergo a change, will continue to change following transfer to egg cytoplasm. An alternative explanation would be that the variations in development within clone "B" are accidentally induced.

Another serial transplantation experiment is summarized in Figure 3. In this experiment all three nuclear clones were derived from a single donor. Descendants of nucleus "A" promoted development only to

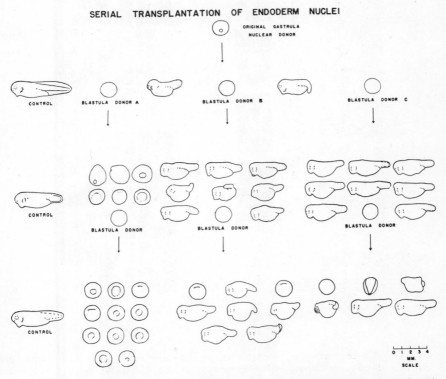

Fig. 3. Camera lucida record of a serial nuclear transplantation experiment. See text for description.

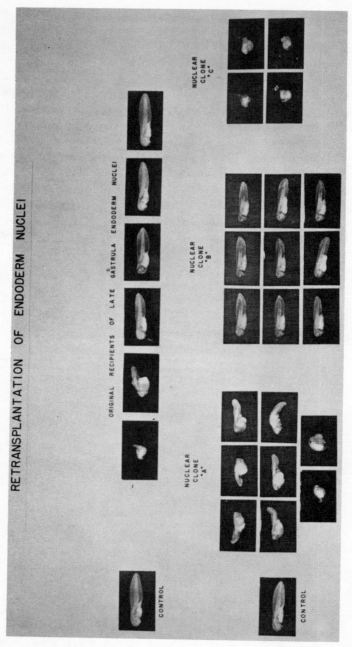

Fig. 4. Photographs of living embryos. Two generation serial transplantation experiment.

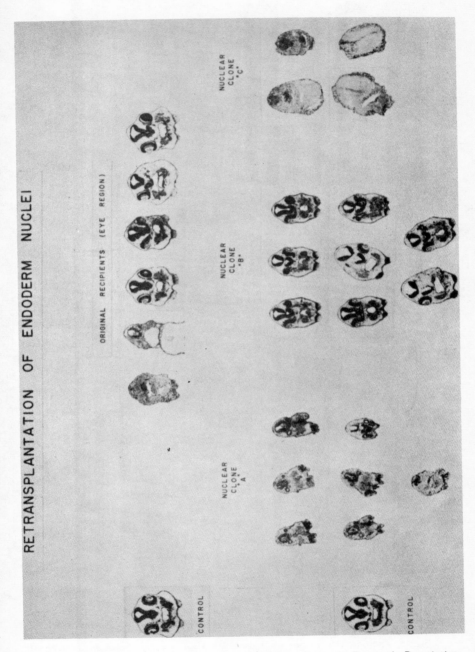

Fig. 5. Sections through eye region of embryos shown in Figure 4. Description given in text.

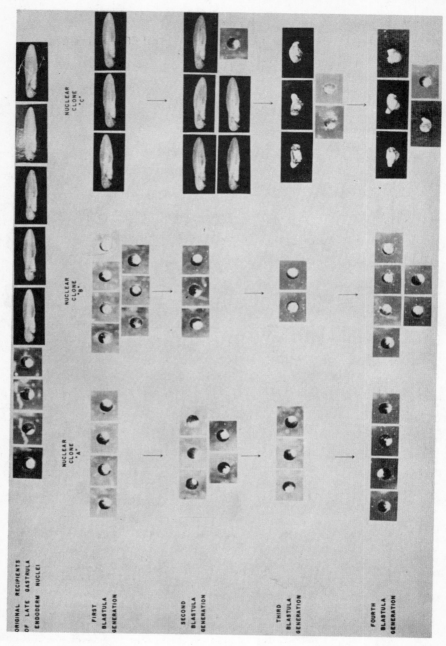

Fig. 6. Photographic record of 5 generation serial transplantation experiment. See text.

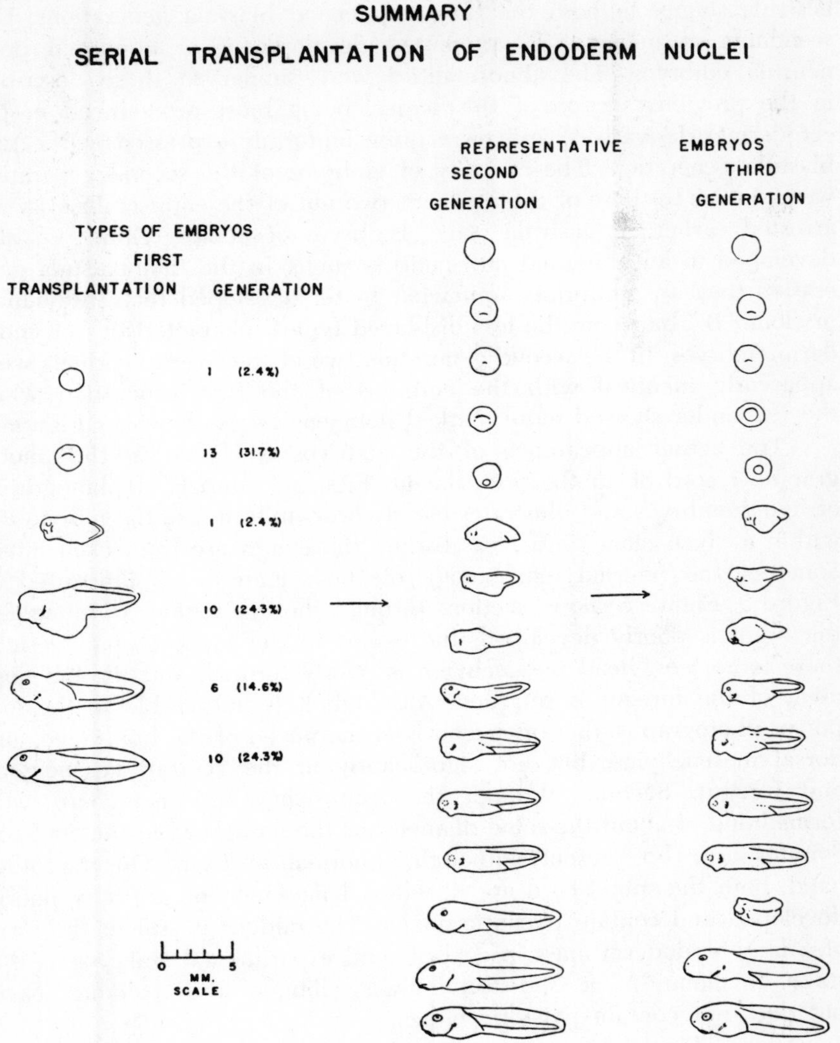

SUMMARY
SERIAL TRANSPLANTATION OF ENDODERM NUCLEI

Fig. 7. Summary of serial transplantation experiments including all endoderm clones except the ones shown in Figure 4 (not included because the experiment was carried on for only 2 generations). The row of drawings on the left illustrates the types of embryos developing from the original recipient eggs injected with endoderm nuclei. The middle row shows typical embryos from the clones in the second generation (referred to in text as the first blastula generation). Each embryo represents a single clone. The same clones in the third generation are represented in the right hand row of drawings. Note that in general the development in the third generation is similar to that in the second, with no evidence of change to a more normal type of differentiation.

gastrula stages, in both the first and second blastula generations. Descendants of nucleus "B" promoted development of abnormal post-neurula embryos. The abnormalities were similar to those described in the previous section of this paper, being most pronounced in the ectodermal derivatives, and were quite uniformly expressed in the first blastula generation. The majority of embryos of the second generation were similar to those of the first, but two out of the eight embryos were arrested earlier, at gastrula stage. Embryos of nuclear clone "C" also developed to an abnormal post-neurula stage. In the first blastula generation they are uniformly somewhat better developed than individuals in clone "B," but none the less displayed typical characteristics of endoderm embryos. In the second generation two of the five individuals were apparently identical with the embryos of the first generation while the remainder showed more marked deficiencies, as shown in Figure 3.

The actual appearance of the embryos is shown in the photographic record of another experiment. Figure 4 consists of photographs of living embryos and illustrates clearly how uniform are the individuals within a given clone, and how distinct the clones are from each other. Some of the internal morphology of these embryos is illustrated in Figure 5. Figure 5 shows sections through the eye region. In clone "A" the brain is poorly developed, the eye is in the form a small vesicle, there is no lens, head mesenchyme is poorly formed, and the development of the foregut is retarded. Although it is not visible in the low power photographs, there is pycnosis in the nuclei of the brain, eye, and dorsal mesenchyme, but not significantly in the ventral mesenchyme and foregut. Sections through the trunk show the notochord well formed and of about the same diameter as the notochord in the controls. Somites are also present, although abnormal in form. On the other hand, both the spinal cord and the dorsal mesenchyme are very poorly developed and contain pycnotic nuclei. The midgut is still in the form of a large endoderm mass in controls and experimental embryos at this stage. In clone "A" it is distorted by swelling of the coelomic space, but does not contain pycnotic nuclei.

Clone "B" displays more advanced differentiation than clone "A" but is still deficient compared with the controls. The deficiencies, although less pronounced, are of the same general character as those in clone "A." Brain and dorsal head mesenchyme contain numerous pycnotic nuclei. The eye cup has induced a lens which is still in the form of a simple vesicle whereas in the controls it has differentiated into the main body of the lens and the lens epithelium. Foregut and ventral mesenchyme are somewhat retarded but contain no significant number of pycnotic nuclei. Sections through the trunk show a modest but definite reduction in the size and degree of differentiation of the spinal cord.

Clone "C" shows extreme deficiencies, the brain and head mesenchyme being absent or very poorly formed and containing numerous degenerating nuclei. In the trunk the notochord and somite material is present. A rudimentary spinal cord is present in three of four cases examined. The gut is poorly developed, but contains no pycnotic nuclei.

Figure 6 gives the results of one experiment in which the serial nuclear transfers were carried on for a total of four blastula generations. The experiment was unique in that the original transfers of late gastrula endoderm nuclei led to only two types of development. The recipient eggs were either arrested in the very early gastrula stage, or they developed into perfectly normal postneurula embryos, as shown in the top line of photographs of Figure 6. There were no embryos of intermediate type. Correspondingly, clones derived from this group of embryos also expressed at first only the two types of development. Clones "A" and "B" showed uniformly an arrest of development in early gastrula stage, and even though the transfers were carried out for four blastula generations there was no evidence of reversal to a more normal type of development. Clone "C" embryos, on the other hand, developed normally for the first two blastula generations, but in the third and fourth generations the development changed, giving rise to abnormal postneurula embryos of the type commonly seen in the other endoderm experiments.

A summary of the serial transplantation tests of endoderm embryos is given in Table 1 and Figure 7. The main point to be emphasized concerning the data in Table 1 is that the same types of embryos occur in about the same proportions in both the original population of endoderm embryos and in the derived clones. Each clone displays a fairly uniform type of development and as a clone corresponds to one or another of the individual embryos in the original population. In other words, in the process of deriving the clones we obtain a faithful representation of the original types.

We have included also in Table 1 the data on serial transfers of undifferentiated blastula nuclei, for the purpose of showing that in the majority of experiments these give rise to clones of normal embryos. A detailed record of one of these experiments is given in Figure 8.

Figure 7 gives a comparison of the development of the endoderm clones in the successive blastula generations. Each generation of each clone is represented in the figure by a single typical embryo. The important fact emerging from this summary is that in no case so far studied is there a reversal to a more normal type of development in the second (or later) blastula generation compared with the first. In other words, the nuclear condition responsible for given deficiencies in differentiation is irreversible under the conditions of these experiments. However, it is possible that nuclear changes leading to more restricted development may sometimes progress in the course of repeated transfers. Two instances of a more restricted development in the later generations have been noted (Figs. 2 and 6) and it is possible, though far from certain, that endoderm nuclei may continue "differentiating" in egg cytoplasm.

CHROMOSOME STUDIES

Since it is known that embryos with unbalanced chromosome sets develop abnormally and are frequently arrested at early developmental

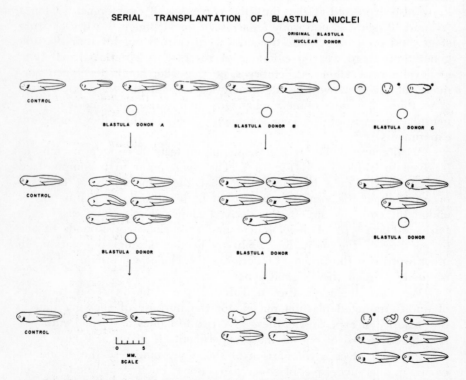

Fig. 8. Camera lucida record of serial transplantation experiment with nuclei of undifferentiated blastula cells. Embryos marked * died from some infectious or toxic process after developing normally to the stages shown.

TABLE 1

Development of Original Recipients of Endoderm Nuclei Compared with
Development of Endoderm Clones

Source of Nucle	Total No. Complete Blastulae	Development		
		Blastulae and gastrulae	Abnormal post-neurulae	Normal larvae
Endoderm (late gastrula) Original recipients (individual eggs)...	44	14 (32%)	20 (45%)	10 (23%)
Clones	18	5 (28%)	8 (44%)	5 (28%)
Control (blastulae) Original recipients (individual eggs)...	22	2 (9%)	2 (9%)	18 (82%)
Clones	9	0	2 (22%)	7 (78%)

stages (Fankhauser, 1934b), it was important to determine the condition of the chromosomes in the endoderm embryos described above. This was done as follows:

In each experiment portions of the original donor gastrula and of the blastula donor for each transplant generation were handed over to Miss Marie DiBerardino, who immediately prepared acetic-orcein squashes of the material. All the subsequent work on the chromosomes was done by Miss DiBerardino.

The preparation of satisfactory squashes of blastula chromosomes posed some problems. If the cells are squashed directly from the Niu-Twitty medium it is very difficult to obtain adequate separation of the chromosomes. A photograph of a typical metaphase plate is reproduced in Figure 9A, showing the long blastula chromosomes intertwined and impossible to count accurately. Adequate separation of chromosomes can be produced by pre-treating the cells with hypotonic medium and colchicine (Hungerford, 1955), but still better results can be obtained by pre-treatment for 30 minutes with a Niu-Twitty medium lacking Ca^{++} and Mg^{++}, and buffered to pH 7.5 with phosphate. A photograph of a plate from such a preparation is given in Figure 9B. The effect of pre-treatment with the modified Niu-Twitty medium is immediately reversed if the cells are returned to the normal medium

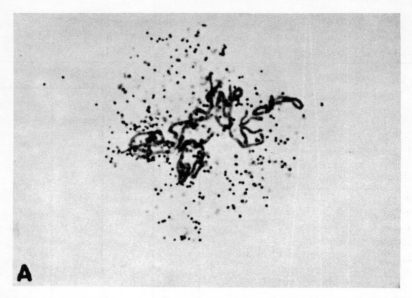

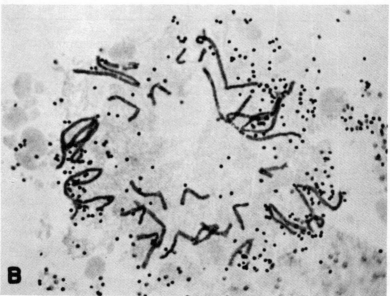

Fig. 9. A. Blastula metaphase plate. Prepared from cells transferred directly from Niu-Twitty solution to acetic-orcein stain- fixative. B. Blastula metaphase plate showing increased spreading of chromosomes resulting from pretreatment of cells with modified Niu-Twitty solution (lacking Ca^{++} and Mg^{++}). Black spots are pigment granules. Magnification, $\times$ 1370. Photographs by David A. Hungerford.

before squashing. The effect is also different for tissues from more advanced stages of development. These and other phenomena are being studied by Hungerford and DiBerardino and will be described elsewhere.

The results of the chromosome studies are presented in Table 2 and Figures 10 and 11. With respect to chromosome number the results are clear. In the majority of cases, the normal diploid number (26) was found, regardless of the type of development promoted by the nuclei. In one clone there was a shift from diploidy to a triploid or near triploid number between the first and second blastula generations. Otherwise the numbers remained at the diploid value throughout.

With respect to chromosome morphology there was also no detectable change in the majority of donors. However, in three clones the donor nuclei contained a few small ring chromosomes (see Figure 10) similar to those noted by Fankhauser (1934a) in one merogonic fragment of a salamander egg. These clones developed only to the late blastula or very early gastrula stage. In a fourth clone, displaying development to a mid gastrula stage, ring chromosomes were present

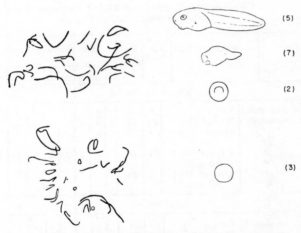

Fig. 10. Chromosome complements of endoderm embryos. Types and numbers of endoderm nuclear clones are illustrated by the drawings of representative embryos. The corresponding chromosome complements are shown in the form of camera lucida drawings of typical metaphase plates. Rings were present in clones displaying arrest of development in late blastula or early gastrula stage. Of two clones arresting at about mid-gastrula stage (*) one displayed rings in the first blastula generation but not in the second. Otherwise the chromosome complements appeared normal regardless of type of development.

in the first blastula generation but not in the second. In the remaining eleven clones studied chromosome morphology appeared to be normal even though the different clones developed in quite different ways.

Even though there were, for the majority of clones, no variations in chromosome number or morphology that could be correlated with type of development, it was still possible that deletions or translocations might have occurred that would have escaped detection. A rough attempt to detect such alterations was made in the following way. The lengths of the camera lucida drawings of chromosomes were measured with a Keuffel and Esser map reader. In order to put chromosome lengths in different figures and squashes on a comparable basis we calculated the relative length as the ratio: individual chromosome length/total length of all 26 chromosomes (L/Total L). The relative lengths of the chromosomes in any given figure were then plotted in the manner shown in Figure 11. From a comparison of such plots

TABLE 2

Chromosome Numbers of Donor Embryos Used in
Serial Transplantation Experiments

Type of Donor	Dev. of Test Eggs	No. of Embryos	No. of Metaphase Plates	Exact Chromosome Counts								Approximate Counts		
				12	13	20	23	24	25	26	27	13-14	21-28	35-45
Endoderm Nuclei														
Original donors (last gast.) Clonal donors (blastulae)	Variable	8	33		4					17			12	
	Normal	10	43	1	3				2	29			8	
	Abnormal post-neurula	14	55		2			1		34			13	5
	Arrested blast. and gast.	14	73		1	1	1	2	2	44	1	5	16	
	Arrested blast. and gast.*	7	26							26				
Blastula Nuclei														
Original and clonal donors (blastulae)	Normal	20	75						1	59			15	
	Abnormal post-neurula	2	15	2								8	5	

Original donors—late gastrulae: Donor cells from presumptive anterior mid-gut. For reasons of technical convenience chromosome counts were done on squashes of archenteron roof.

Clonal donors: Embryos derived from eggs injected with endoderm nuclei, sacrificed at blastula stage to provide nuclei (animal hemisphere) for establishment of clones. Counts done on part of animal hemisphere of these donors. In the table donors are grouped according to type of development observed in the derived clones. Listed separately (*) are 7 blastulae which were not used as donors. They were taken from the 4th blastula generation of two clones which consistently showed arrest in late blastula or early gastrula stage.

Controls: Original donors and clonal donors, both in blastula stage, grouped together. For further description see text and Figs. 10 and 11.

one can determine whether the distribution of chromosome lengths is the same or different in the different clones. The results of this analysis are illustrated in Figure 11. In general, the distribution of chromosome lengths did not appear to differ in the different types of clones. One of the clones containing ring chromosomes did differ from the others in displaying a wider range of chromosome lengths (Figure 11). Otherwise, there were no differences that could be definitely related to type of development. This does not eliminate the possibility that deletions, etc. may have occurred, but does suggest that they would have to be on a relatively small scale. It also does not mean that more

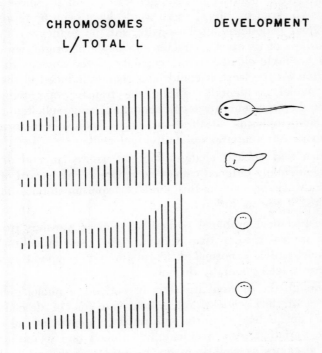

Fig. 11. Relative lengths of chromosomes were measured on a total of 78 metaphase plates from 14 endoderm embryos and 6 controls. The results shown above for endoderm embryos are representative. Differences in relative lengths, from embryo to embryo, are not significant being within the range observed in different plates from single embryos. The one exception, in which the range in relative lengths is greater than normal, is plotted at the bottom of the figure.

subtle types of chromosomal (or other) changes may not be occurring as a regular concomitant of differentiation.

DISCUSSION

The serial transplantation experiments described above show that the changes occurring in endoderm nuclei during differentiation are highly stabilized, in the sense that they are not reversed in egg cytoplasm. Each transfer is followed by cleavage of the recipient egg to produce a donor blastula consisting of approximately 8,000 cells, requiring about 13 divisions (or generations) of the original nucleus. In the majority of experiments, three such transfers were done serially and therefore involved about 39 nuclear generations. In the most extensive experiments (5 serial transfers) there would have been 65 reproductions of the original endoderm nucleus, with still no evidence of reversal. Thus, regardless of its exact character and mode of origin, we are dealing with a heritable change in the capacity of the nucleus to promote differentiation. At the least, it could be a change induced in the original endoderm nuclei accidentally during the transfer operation. At the most, it would represent a specific genetic change elicited somehow by particular cytoplasmic localizations, and responsible in turn for the stabilization of differentiation of individual cells.

The idea that nuclear changes such as we see in endoderm cells might be accidentally induced cannot be ignored. The hazard of nuclear damage is always present in this kind of experimentation. The arguments against it are as follows:

1) The technical problems of making nuclear transfers from endoderm cells are no greater than they are for blastula cells. Yet, the blastula nuclei promote normal differentiation of recipient eggs while the endoderm nuclei generally do not.

2) Although the original transfers of endoderm nuclei give a variety of types of development, subsequent transfers of descendants of a particular nucleus lead to fairly uniform development of the recipient eggs. If the variation were accidentally induced one would expect to find it in the clones as well as in the recipients of the original nuclei. (Unless, of course, endoderm nuclei are somehow much more sensitive to damage in their own cytoplasm than they are in egg cytoplasm.)

3) While the original endoderm transfers usually lead to a variety of types of development, this is not always so. In one experiment (Figure 6) we observed only two classes of embryos, which would be hard to account for on the basis of chance injury to the nuclei.

4) In the majority of clones there was no evidence of chromosome changes such as might be expected to result from nuclear damage.

On the basis of this evidence we may assume that the restrictions in the capacity of endoderm nuclei to promote differentiation are real and not artificially induced. Other points about which definite statements can be made are: 1) that the nuclear changes are highly stabilized, as shown by the serial transplantation experiments, and 2) that they do not occur in all cells at once. Rather it appears that in the late gastrula the endoderm nuclei fall into three general classes: 1) undifferentiated nuclei, 2) nuclei restricted to varying degrees in their capacity to promote normal post-gastrula development, particularly of ectodermal derivatives, and 3) nuclei incapable of participating in the formation of chorda mesoderm, resulting in arrest at gastrulation. In later stages of development the number of nuclei in class 1) (undifferentiated) decreases while those showing restrictions of differentiation-promoting capacity increase. This indicates that a progressive and "irreversible" nuclear change occurs during differentiation. Whether in any given cell this restriction in differentiating-promoting ability occurs slowly or rapidly, continuously or in distinct steps, we do not know, although a study of nuclear changes during the post-blastula development of the clones might eventually give answers to some of these questions. Also, it is unknown which of the nuclear or perinuclear structures are involved. Control experiments have shown that the endoderm cytoplasm by itself is incapable of modifying the differentiation of normally nucleated eggs. However, we cannot yet determine whether it is the nucleus itself or some replicating perinuclear organelle which is responsible for the restricted developmental potencies.

Finally, we should consider briefly the question of the specificity of the nuclear changes in endoderm cells. We have seen that these changes result first in a loss of the capacity to promote normal differentiation of ectodermal derivatives, and presumably later the ability to promote differentiation of chorda mesoderm is also lost. Thus, the nuclear changes are consistent with the fact that the nuclei are derived from endoderm. But whether they are specific for endoderm is uncertain. In order to settle this point it would be necessary to explore the capacity for various types of differentiation by appropriate grafting experiments with parts of the arrested endoderm embryos, and the same sort of analysis would have to be done on embryos containing other types of nuclei. Now that the nuclear changes in endoderm cells are known to be highly stabilized and to give a fairly uniform type of development in the clones, this central problem of specificity may be attacked.

SUMMARY

Nuclei of late gastrula endoderm, transplanted to enucleated eggs (*Rana pipiens*) promote the following general types of development: 1) arrest at gastrula stages, 2) normal gastrulation followed by deficient development in later stages, especially in the ectodermal derivatives, 3) normal development throughout.

In order to determine if the nuclear changes responsible for the deficient development are stable, serial transfers of endoderm nuclei were carried out. Individual nuclei were transplanted to enucleated eggs, which cleaved and produced blastulae. In a given test, one of these blastulae was sacrificed to provide nuclei for transfer to a new group of eggs. Such a group represents a clone, all members of which are nucleated by descendants of one original endoderm nucleus. One member of such a clone may be sacrificed at the blastula stage to provide nuclei for transfer to a new group of enucleated eggs, giving in effect a second blastula generation of the clone. The same process may be repeated to provide several generations.

Analysis of the development of 18 clones revealed the following: Whereas test eggs containing different endoderm nuclei developed in the different ways mentioned above, eggs within one clone developed much more uniformly. In some clones all embryos were arrested at gastrula stage, in others they displayed a fairly uniform set of deficiencies in post-gastrula development, and in a few clones almost all embryos developed normally throughout. Furthermore, within any given clone the development in the second and later generations were generally of the same type as that observed in the first generation. In a few clones the deficiencies became more severe in the later generations, but no case of reversal to a more normal type of development was noted.

Chromosome studies on donor embryos in the clonal experiments showed that chromosome number generally remained unchanged at the diploid value (26). In three clones, all consisting of embryos arresting at early gastrula stage, a few small ring chromosomes were present. Otherwise, no chromosome changes were detected even though the clones exhibited quite different types of development.

These experiments show that descendants of individual endoderm nuclei have a fairly uniform expression with respect to differentiation, which does not reverse to a more normal expression in the course of the serial transfers. In other words, compared with nuclei of undifferentiated cells, the endoderm nuclei show stabilized changes in capacity to promote differentiation. How these changes arise, whether they are specific, and which of the nuclear or peri-nuclear structures are involved, are problems remaining to be worked out.

ACKNOWLEDGEMENTS

We wish to thank Dr. Jack Schultz for the benefit derived from many discussions we have had with him on problems of diffentiation. We also wish to acknowledge the assistance of Miss Marie DiBerardino, who carried out the chromosome studies described in this paper and provided valuable assistance in many other ways as well.

REFERENCES

Beermann, W., 1956, Nuclear differentiation and functional morphology of chromosomes. Cold Spr. Harb. Symp. Quant. Biol. **21**, 217-232.

Briggs, R., Green, E. U., and King, T. J., 1951, An investigation of the capacity for cleavage and differentiation in *Rana pipiens* eggs lacking "functional" chromosomes, J. Exp. Zool., **116**, 455-500.

Briggs, R., and King, T. J., 1952, Transportation of living nuclei from blastula cells into enucleated frogs' eggs. Proc. Nat. Acad. Sci. Wash., **38**, 455-463.

————, 1953, Factors affecting the transplantability of nuclei of frog embryonic cells. J. Exp. Zool., **122**, 485-506.

Comandon, J. and De Fonbrune, P., 1939, Greffe nucleaire totale, simple ou multiple, chez une *Amibe*. Compt. rend. soc. biol.,**130**, 744-748.

Danielli, J. F., Lorch, I. J., Ord, M. J., and Wilson, E. C., 1955, Nucleus and cytoplasm in cellular inheritance. Nature, Lond., **176**, 1114-1115.

Ephrussi, B., 1951, Remarks on cell heredity. In: Genetics in the 20th Century. New York, Macmillan Company, pp. 241-262.

————, 1953, Nucleo-cytoplasmic relations in microorganisms. Oxford, Clarendon Press.

Fankhauser, G., 1934a, Cytological studies on egg fragments of the salamander *Triton*, IV. The cleavage of egg fragments without the egg nucleus. J. Exp. Zool., **67**, 349-394.

————, 1934b, Cytological studies on egg fragments of the salamander *Triton*. V. Chromosome number and chromosome individuality in the cleavage mitoses of merogonic fragments. J. Exp. Zool., **68**, 1-57.

Gluecksohn-Waelsch, S., 1954, Some genetic aspects of development. Cold Spr. Harb. Symp. Quant. Biol., **19**, 41-49.

Grobstein, C., 1952, Effects of fragmentation of mouse embryonic shields on their differentiative behavior after culturing. J. Exp. Zool.,**120**, 437-456.

Grobstein, C., and Zwilling, E., 1953, Modification of growth and differentiation of chorio-allantoic grafts of chick blastoderm pieces after cultivation at a glass-clot interface. J. Exp. Zool., **122**, 259-284.

Hadorn, E., 1948, Gene action in growth and differentiation of lethal mutants of *Drosophila*. Symposia Soc. Exp. Biol., **2**, 177-195.

————, 1956, Patterns of biochemical and developmental pleiotropy. Cold Spr. Harb. Symp. Quant. Biol., **21**, 255-382.

*The experimental work reported in this paper was aided by a research grant from the National Cancer Institute of the National Institutes of Health, United States Public Health Service, and in part by an institutional grant from the American Cancer Society.

Hämmerling, J., 1934, Uber genomwirkungen und Formbildungsfähigkeit bei *Acetabularia*. Arch. Entwickmech. Org., **132**, 424-462.
————, 1953, Nucleo-cytoplasmic relationships in the development of *Acetabularia*. Intern. Rev. Cytol., **2**, 475-498.
Holtfreter, J., 1933, Die totale Exogastrulation, eine Selbstablösung des Ektoderms vom Entomesoderm. Entwicklung und funktionelles Verhalten nervenloser Organe. Arch. Entwick-mech. Org., **129**, 669-793.
————, 1938, Differenzierungspotenzen isolierter Teile der Anurengastrula. Arch. Entwick-mech. Org., **138**, 657-738.
Hungerford, D. A., 1955, Chromosome numbers of ten-day fetal mouse cells. J. Morph., **97**, 497-510.
King, T. J., and Briggs, R., 1954, Transplantation of living nuclei of late gastrulae into enucleated eggs of *Rana pipiens*. J. Embryol. Exp. Morph. **2**, 73-80.
————, 1955, Changes in the nuclei of differentiating gastrula cells, as demonstrated by nuclear transplantation. Proc. Nat. Acad. Sci. Wash., **41**, 321-325.
Lederberg, J., 1956, Infection and heredity. Growth Symp., **13**, 101-124. Princeton Univ. Press.
Lehman, H. E., 1955, On the development of enucleated *Triton* eggs with an injected blastula nucleus. Biol. Bull., **108**, 138-150.
————, 1956, Nuclear transplantation, a tool for the study of nuclear differentiation. AAAS Symp. (In press).
Loeb, J., 1894, Über eine einfache Methode, zwei oder mehr zusammengewachsene Embryonen aus einem Ei hervorzubringen. Pflüger's Arch., **55**, 525-530.
Lorch, I. J., and Danielli, J. F., 1950, Transplantation of nuclei from cell to cell. Nature, Lond., **166**, 329-333.
Moore, J. A., 1955, Abnormal combinations of nuclear and cytoplasmic systems in frogs and toads. Adv. Genet., **7**, 139-182.
Niu, M. C., and Twitty, V. C., 1953, The differentiation of gastrula ectoderm in medium conditioned by axial mesoderm. Proc. Nat. Acad. Sci. Wash., **39**, 985-989.
Porter, K. R., 1939, Androgenetic development of the egg of *Rana pipiens*. Biol. Bull., **77**, 233-257.
Poulson, D. F., 1945, Chromosomal control of embryogenesis in *Drosophila*, Amer. Nat., **79**, 340-363.
Rostand, J., 1943, Essai d'inoculation de noyaux embryonnaires dans l'oeuf vierge de grenouille. Rev. sci., **81**, 454-456.
Schultz, J., 1952, Interrelations between nucleus and cytoplasm: problems at the biological level. Exp. Cell Res. Suppl., **2**, 17-43.
Sonneborn, T. M., 1954, Patterns of nucleocytoplasmic integration in *Paramecium*. Proc. 9th Intern. Congress Genetics. Caryologia, suppl.1954: 307-325.
Spemann, H., 1914, Uber verzögerte Kernversorgung von Keimteilen. Vergandl. deut. zool. Ges., 1914: 16-221.
————, 1938, Embryonic Development and Induction. New Haven, Yale Univ. Press, pp. 211.
Stauffer, E., 1945, Versuche zur experimentallen Herstellung haploider Axolotl-Merogone. Rev. suisse zool., **52**, 231-327.
Subtelny, S. S., 1956, Personal communication.
Sze, L. C., 1953, Changes in the amount of desoxyribonucleic acid in the development of *Rana pipiens*. J. Exp. Zool., **122**, 577- 601.
Tartar, V., 1953, Chimeras and nuclear transplantations in ciliates, *Stentor coeruleus* × S. *polymorphus*. J. Exp. Zool., **124**, 63-103.
Waddington, C. H., and Pantelouris, E. M., 1953, Transplantation of nuclei in newt's eggs. Nature, Lond., **172**, 1050.

Weisz, Paul B., 1951, A general mechanism of differentiation based on morpho-
    genetic studies in ciliates. Amer. Nat., **85**, 293-311.
Wilson, E. B., 1925, The Cell in Development and Heredity. 3rd ed. New York,
    Macmillan Company.

DISCUSSION

BALINSKY: The persistence of the same types of development in
each of the different clones makes it plausible that there are differences
in the nuclei propagating in each clone. Do you have any suggestion
as to why the initial nuclei used to start each clone could have been
different, seeing that they were all taken originally from the same part
of the embryo, the floor of the archenteron of a late gastrula stage?

KING: The embryological evidence for the determination of late
gastrula endoderm is based on explantation and transplantation experiments which involved large groups of cells. We cannot distinguish
whether this determination depends upon differentiation of the individual cells or is to be regarded as a property of the mass as a whole.
Grobstein (1952) and Grobstein and Zwilling (1953), working with
cultured explants of mouse embryonic shield and chick blastoderm, find
that the extent of differentiation depends upon the degree to which
the explant cells are dispersed. Large explants will differentiate into
neural tissue, but if these explants are divided into eighths or sixteenths
the differentiation fails to occur or is poorly expressed. Thus it appears
that in chick and mouse embryos organ determination occurs while
the individual cells are still undifferentiated or in various states of
differentiation. The same situation may exist in the amphibian gastrula.

Another source of heterogeneity is suggested by Holtfreter's (1933)
observation that the midgut contains "lethal" cells, as well as cells which
later form the gut epithelium. In urodeles the lethal cells can be seen
to degenerate in the gut lumen during late embryonic life. However,
we could find no evidence of cell lethality in the developing gut of
the anuran (*R. pipiens*) used in our experiments.

STERN: It has been suggested that if embryonic nuclei from prospective germ cells were transplanted they would demonstrate unrestricted
potentialities in development. This expectation implies the belief that
the genetic totipotency of the nuclei of germ cells at the time of their
presence in mature germ cells is equivalent to developmental totipotency of these nuclei at other stages. However, it may well be that
nuclei of immature germ cells are just as restricted developmentally
as those of somatic cells, while on the other hand, developmentally restricted nuclei of somatic cells may be totipotent genetically.

KING: We would agree with Dr. Stern's comment, especially since we do not yet know what part of the nuclear complex is involved in the changes reported in this paper, and whether these changes might not be reversible under different conditions than those existing in our experiments.

MARKERT: The range of variation in developmental capacity shown by nuclei taken from a restricted area would seem to support the concept that the state of differentiation of a tissue reflects the average state of differentiation of its constituent cells. These cells apparently do not undergo synchronous transformations but gradually differentiate as variable members of a complex population. Such a process of tissue differentiation based on the additive individual contributions of diverse, although related, cells should be relatively "well-buffered" against transitory abnormal influences to which the embryo might be exposed during development. Only those influences which persisted long enough to transform a substantial number of cells with initially different degrees of sensitivity could effectively alter the course of tissue differentiation. Over any short period of time that fraction of the tissue cells in any particular phase of development would be dispensable so far as the development of the entire tissue was concerned.

7

the developmental capacity of nuclei taken from intestinal epithelium cells of feeding tadpoles

J. B. GURDON
*From the Embryology Laboratory,
Department of Zoology, Oxford*

INTRODUCTION

An important problem in embryology is whether the differentiation of cells depends upon a stable restriction of the genetic information contained in their nuclei. The technique of nuclear transplantation has shown to what extent the nuclei of differentiating cells can promote the formation of different cell types (e.g. King & Briggs, 1956; Gurdon, 1960c). Yet no experiments have so far been published on the transplantation of nuclei from fully differentiated normal cells. This is partly because it is difficult to obtain meaningful results from such experiments. The small amount of cytoplasm in differentiated cells renders their nuclei susceptible to damage through exposure to the saline medium, and this makes it difficult to assess the significance of the abnormalities resulting from their transplantation. It is, however, very desirable to know the developmental capacity of such nuclei, since any nuclear changes which are necessarily involved in cellular differentiation must have already taken place in cells of this kind.

The experiments described below are some attempts to transplant nuclei from fully differentiated cells. Many of these nuclei gave abnormal results after transplantation, and several different kinds of experiments have been carried out to determine the cause and significance of these abnormalities.

J. Embryol. exp. Morph.
Vol. 10, Part 4, pp. 622-40 December, 1962

The donor cells used for these experiments were intestinal epithelium cells of feeding tadpoles. This is the final stage of differentiation of many of the endoderm cells whose nuclei have already been studied by means of nuclear transplantation experiments in *Xenopus*. The results to be described here may therefore be regarded as an extension of those previously obtained from differentiating endoderm cells (Gurdon, 1960*c*).

MATERIAL AND METHODS

The animals used for these experiments belong to the subspecies *Xenopus laevis laevis*. The transplantation technique has been carried out as described previously (Elsdale *et al.*, 1960), except that the donor tissue was exposed to the dissociating Versene solution (5×10^{-4} M) for 30-40 minutes. The *Xenopus* nuclear marker was used (Elsdale *et al.*, 1960), and marked donor nuclei were transplanted into unmarked recipient eggs. Among the transplant-embryos described below, all those which developed beyond the blastula stage contained marked nuclei, thus proving that they were derived from the transplanted nucleus and not from the egg nucleus. The nuclear marker can only be seen in embryos which have passed the blastula stage.

Donor cells

The differentiated cells used to provide donor nuclei were intestinal epithelium cells from the mid-intestine of feeding tadpoles (stages 46-48 of Nieuwkoop & Faber, 1956). These cells (plate) have the following features characteristic of their differentiated state: a tall columnar shape with basally situated nuclei; pigment granules inside the surface exposed to the gut lumen; and, most important, the striated border typical of cells having an absorptive function. Some of these cells still contain a few yolk platelets, but these are rapidly absorbed at about this stage. All the epithelium cells in the part of the intestine used for these experiments are of this kind except for less than 1 percent which are typical gland cells; there are no undifferentiated cells in the epithelium at this stage. The epithelium cells are larger than the other cell types present in the mid-intestine, and so can be easily recognized in the dissociated cell preparations.

Controls

Owing to the variable quality of the *Xenopus* recipient eggs laid in the laboratory (Gurdon, 1960*b*), the transplantation of intestinal epithelium cell nuclei has been accompanied by control transplantations of blastula or gastrula nuclei. Since no change in developmental capacity has been detected in Xenopus nuclei until after the late gastrula stage, either blastula or gastrula nuclei have been used as controls according to convenience.

RESULTS

Six experiments involving the trasnplantation of intestinal epithelium cell nuclei (referred to as intestin nuclei) gave similar results, and these have been combined in Table 1. In each experiment control transfers from blastulae or gastrulae (referred to as embryonic nuclei) were interspersed with transfers of intestine nuclei.

Normal tadpoles

Altogether 10 normal feeding tadpoles have been obtained from the transplantation of intestinal epithelium cell nuclei. These tadpoles have diploid nuclei carrying the nuclear marker referred to above. They therefore provide a clear demonstration that at least a few differentiated intestine cells contain nuclei which are capable of giving rise to all the cell types necessary for the formation of a feeding tadpole.

These normal tadpoles constitute only 1½ percent of the 726 transplanted intestine nuclei, and all the remaining transfers resulted in various degrees of abnormality ranging from a complete lack of cleavage to nearly normal tadpoles (Table 1). Some experiments have been carried out in order to determine the significance of these abnormalities and, in particular, whether the abnormalities are due to a limited developmental capacity of the transplanted nuclei or to other factors such as variation in technique. The two methods used were first, the cytological analysis of eggs fixed soon after they had been injected with nuclei, and secondly, the serial transplantation of nuclei from abnormal transplant-embryos.

The cytological analysis of eggs fixed soon after receiving transplanted nuclei

The procedure followed in this analysis was to transplant nuclei from one donor embryo into eggs laid by one frog. Soon after transplantation some of the eggs were taken at random and fixed while the remainder were allowed to develop as far as they were able. The fixed eggs were then serially sectioned and stained. Subsequent microscopic examination of the sections often revealed abnormalities of the transplanted nucleus and achromatic apparatus. The eggs which were not fixed served as exact controls since they were laid by the same frog as the fixed eggs and contained transplanted nuclei from the same donor

TABLE 1

The development resulting from the transplantation of nuclei from differentiated and embryonic cells of *Xenopus laevis*

Donor stage (Nieuw-koop & Faber, 1956)	Total transfers	No cleavage	Total transfers resulting in cleavage	Development resulting from transplanted nuclei									
				Abortive cleavage	Partial cleavage	Complete blastulae	Arrested blastulae	Abnormal gastrulae	Abnormal post-neurulae	Stunted tadpoles	Died as swimming tadpoles	Normal feeding tadpoles
Intestinal epithelium cell nuclei (stage 46-48)	726	347	379	175	156	48	18	8	5	6	1	10
	100%	48%	52%	24%	21.5%	6.5%	—	—	—	—	—	1.5%
Blastula or gastrula endoderm nuclei (stage 8-12)	279	66	213	8	32	173	4	17	19	27	6	100
	100%	24%	76%	3%	11%	62%	—	—	—	—	—	36%

embryo. These showed how the sectioned eggs would have developed if they had not been fixed. In this way a certain cytological abnormality could be associated with a particular developmental abnormality, thus indicating the cause of the latter. This analysis was carried out on eggs with transplanted intestine nuclei as well as on those with transplanted embryonic nuclei.

THE TOTAL LACK OF CLEAVAGE FOLLOWING NUCLEAR TRANSFER

Forty-eight percent of the intestine nuclei and 24 percent of the embryonic nuclei failed to promote cleavage of any kind after transplantation (Table 1). The following results show that this can be attributed to a failure in the technique such that the transplanted nucleus was not effectively exposed to the recipient egg cytoplasm. The eggs fixed about 40 minutes after receiving transplanted nuclei fell into two distinct categories. First there were those with distinct regions of cytoplasm; these had an almost yolk-free area in the animal half of the egg, containing the developing transplanted nucleus, and close to it the dying irradiated egg nucleus (Gurdon, 1960a, Fig. 1). This is the typical condition of irradiated recipient eggs which have been fertilized or in which a successful nuclear transfer has been made. The other fixed eggs revealed an entirely different situation. These had a relatively homogeneous cytoplasm just as in newly laid unfertilized eggs, and the irradiated egg nucleus was found in the vegetal half. There was no yolk-free area in the animal half of the egg and the transplanted nucleus was either entirely absent or else could be seen inside an intact donor cell.

The total absence of the transplanted nucleus from a recipient egg is probably due to the donor cell sticking to the injection pipette and so being withdrawn from the egg with the pipette. This would not be observed in the course of an experiment unless looked for carefully. The presence of a whole donor cell in the egg clearly results from a failure to break the wall of the donor cell when it is sucked into the injection pipette. The successful breaking of the cell wall depends upon the extent to which the cell is distorted in the pipette. A very close correlation has been found between the degree of donor cell distortion and the proportion of transfers which result in normal cleavage (Gurdon, 1960b). It was found that if the cell wall is very little distorted, the great majority of transfers fail to cleave, while strong distortion results in many developmental abnormalities probably through exposure of the nucleus to the saline medium. It is very difficult to distort intestine cells to an ideal degree, and in order to avoid damage to the nuclei these cells were distorted rather little. Transplanted intestine nuclei would therefore be expected to result in a total lack of cleavage much more often than the nuclei of the larger embryonic cells.

TABLE 2

The cytological analysis of eggs
fixed 60-80 minutes after transplantation

	Number of eggs fixed	Eggs with no developing nucleus	Chromosomes clumped at first mitosis	3-4 polar spindle at first mitosis	Normal at first mitosis
(a) Tadpole nuclei from intestinal epithelium cells	70	22 out of 70 31.5%	3 out of 11* 27%	4 out of 11* 36%	—
(b) Nuclei from blastulae and gastrulae	59	8 out of 59 13.5%	0 out of 30* 0%	4 out of 30* 13%	20 out of 30* 67%

The cleavage of control transfers which were allowed to develop as far as they were able

	Numbers of transfers	Uncleaved	Abortive cleavage	Partial blastulae	Complete blastulae
(c) Tadpole nuclei from intestinal epithelium cells	60	18 30%	16 26.5%	21 35%	5 8.5%
(d) Nuclei from blastulae and gastrulae	95	12 12.5%	2 2%	11 14%	67 70.5%

*Only these eggs were fixed at the time of the first nuclear division.

The results of the cytological analysis of fixed eggs are compared with the development of their controls in Table 2. There is a very close correspondence between the proportion of developing eggs which failed to cleave and the proportion of fixed eggs in which the transplanted nucleus was either lacking or was present in an intact donor cell. This applies to the results of transplanting intestine as well as embryonic nuclei, and justifies the conclusion that the total lack of cleavage following nuclear transplantation can be attributed to the technical difficulty described above. The developmental capacity of nuclei which fail to promote any cleavage at all after transplantation has not therefore been tested.

ABORTIVE CLEAVAGE

This term refers to eggs which consist only of abnormal blastomeres and uncleaved regions of cytoplasm. The blastomeres are of irregular size and shape, and contain no normal nuclei though sometimes asters and chromatin can be seen. Such eggs usually die after a few irregular cleavages. Many of the eggs which receive intestine nuclei develop in this way, but very few of those with embryonic nuclei do so (Table 1). Useful information regarding the cause of this abnormality is provided by the cytological examination of eggs fixed during metaphase of the first division of the transplanted nucleus. Only 11 eggs with intestine nuclei were found to have been fixed at exactly this time, and in 3 of these the chromosomes were clumped and pycnotic. In some cases the spindle also seemed abnormal. It is clear that these eggs could not have cleaved normally; the chromosomes would probably have broken up into pycnotic lumps and have been distributed to abnormal blastomers. As shown in Table 2, the percentage of fixed eggs with clumped chromosomes was very close to the percentage of control transfers which resulted in abortive cleavage. It can be concluded that abortive cleavage results from the incapacity of the transplanted nucleus to divide normally at its first division.

It is not known why some nuclei divide abnormally after transplantation, but it is possibly because their chromosomes have not replicated by the time they enter mitosis. The nuclei of intestinal epithelium cells divide infrequently and have a relatively long interphase period between mitoses. Since chromosome replication takes place during interphase, some nuclei would by chance be transplanted when at the beginning of interphase and so would have unreplicated chromosomes. The time at which a transplanted nucleus enters division is determined by the egg cytoplasm, and except in nuclei which become tetraploid, this division takes place at about 80 minutes after transplantation. Thus the situation may arise in which an intestine nucleus is forced to enter mitosis even though its chromosomes are unreplicated. This would be expected to lead to the abnormal chromosome condition described above. Embryonic nuclei, on the other hand, divide at frequent intervals during cleavage. The interphase period in which their chromosomes are unreplicated is short, and embryonic nuclei are therefore generally transplanted with already replicated chromosomes. This would explain why intestine nuclei give abortive cleavage much more often than embryonic nuclei. An hypothesis of this general kind has also been suggested by Briggs, King, & DiBerardino (1960) to account for abnormal cleavage in their experiments.

It can be concluded that transplanted nuclei which promote abortive cleavage do so through their inability to divide normally. This prevents them showing the range of cell types that they are genetically capable of giving rise to.

PARTIAL CLEAVAGE

A blastula is described as partially cleaved when part of it consists of normal blastomeres, and the rest is uncleaved or abortively cleaved. Blastulae of this kind usually die before gastrulation commences, but if the uncleaved portion is very small they may form abnormal gastrulae. Transplanted intestine nuclei result in partial cleavage more commonly than embryonic nuclei (Table 1). Eleven eggs with transplanted intestine nuclei were fixed during the first nuclear division, and 4 of these had apparently normal chromosomes but an abnormal achromatic apparatus with 3- or 4-polar spindles (Table 2). At least some chromosomes were present on each of the three or four metaphase plates. It is possible that a normal set of chromosomes might be distributed to one of the poles of such a spindle, leaving an aneuploid number of chromosomes at the other poles. In this way a partial blastula could be formed with the aneuploid blastomeres giving rise to the abnormally cleaved part of the egg. Whatever the cause of this condition, there is agreement between the proportion of fixed eggs with an abnormal mitotic apparatus but apparently normal chromosomes, and the proportion of the developing controls which became partial blastulae (Table 2). The significance of partial cleavage has been directly determined by the serial transplantation experiments described below.

Development abnormalities following
the transplantation of nuclei from a foreign genus

Experiments involving the transfer of nuclei from different genera to eggs of the same species show that genetically very different nuclei may give rise to the same percentages of abnormal cleavage. These experiments therefore show that the frequency of cleavage abnormalities does not necessarily represent the degree of genetic difference between transplanted nuclei. Blastula nuclei from *Hymenochirus curtipes* and *X. laevis* were transplanted to recipient eggs of *X. laevis,* and the results are given in Table 3. The genetic difference between *Hymenochirus* and *Xenopus* is demonstrated by the early arrest in development of all *Xenopus* eggs which received *Hymenochirus* nuclei in contrast to the normal development of many of the *Xenopus* to *Xenopus* transfers. However, in spite of this, the percentage of transfers which resulted in partial, abortive, or entirely deficient cleavage was the same in both cases. These results show that the post-blastula development of transplant-embryos can indicate a genetic difference between the nuclear and cytoplasmic species, while this is not necessarily so of cleavage. Since genetically very different nuclei give the same frequency and severity of abnormal cleavage, this provides an additional reason for

believing that the abnormal cleavage resulting from transplanted intestine nuclei does not indicate any genetic difference between the nuclei of intestine and embryonic cells.

TABLE 3

The transplantation of nuclei from *Hymenochirus* and *Xenopus*
into recipient eggs of *Xenopus*

Donor nuclei	Total number of trans-plantations	Un-cleaved	Abortive cleavage	Partial blastulae	Com-plete blastu-lae	Neural folds	Normal swimming tadpoles
Hymenochirus cur-tipes early gastrula	169 100%	62 37%	1 1%	22 12%	84 50%	0 —	0 —
Xenopus laevis early gastrula	78 100%	22 28%	3 4%	11 14%	42 54%	35 —	20 —

The transplantation of nuclei from abnormal nuclear transplant-embryos

Information on the cause and significance of partial blastulae and
of abnormal post-blastulae has been obtained by means of serial nuclear
transfers. The basic design of the experiments was as follows. Nuclear
transfers were made using original intestine or embryonic donor cells.
When the resulting 'first-transfer' embryos had differentiated as far
as they were able, some of their endoderm nuclei were used for serial
transfers, giving rise to the 'first serial-transfer' generation. As a result
of experience, the best differentiation that will be achieved by an
abnormal transplant-embryo can be judged to within narrow limits,
before developmental arrest takes place and cell death sets in. For
instance, partial blastulae in which an appreciable part of the surface
area is uncleaved, never develop beyond the late blastula or very early
gastrula stage. Similarly, it has been found that embryos in which
part of the yolk-plug protrudes during gastrulation will never form
normal late gastrulae or neurulae, and that embryos which do not
elongate properly will remain as stunted postneurulae with a belly
oedema. The furthest differentiation to be expected can with practice
be judged to within much narrower limits than these. By this type of
experiment the differentiation of the most normal serial-transfer embryos can be directly compared with that of the first-transfer embryo
from whose nuclei they were derived.

Original donor nuclei were taken from 31 abnormal first-transfer
embryos (11 from original gastrula nuclei and 20 from feeding tad-

pole intestine nuclei). These abnormal embryos were selected arbitrarily and are a random sample of the partial blastulae and abnormal postblastulae included in Table 1. The nuclei from each first-transfer embryo gave rise to a wide range of abnormal embryos, and sometimes to normal tadpoles, as shown in Table 4. The differentiation of each first-transfer embryo is compared with that of the serial-transfer embyros derived from its nuclei in Text-Figs. 1 and 2. In these diagrams the stage of differentiation attained by each first-transfer embryo is shown by a solid line; the dotted continuation of this line represents the most normal differentiation achieved by any of the resulting serial-transfer embryos. It can be seen that in all 31 cases some of the serial-transfer embryos differentiated more normally than the first-transfer embryo from whose nuclei they were derived. It is interesting that the nuclei of partial blastulae can sometimes promote the development of a normal or nearly normal tadpole. This is of some importance since a large proportion of transplanted intestine nuclei result in partial blastulae.

There are two possible explanations for these results. First, the developmental capacity of a nucleus might increase as a result of nuclear transplantation so that serial-transfer embryos are more normal than first-transfer embryos. Second, the abnormality of the first-transfer embryo might be due to some nongenetic cause such as poor egg quality. In the latter case the developmental capacity of the transplanted nucleus would not increase, but would not always be fully expressed owing to the effect of factors such as poor egg quality.

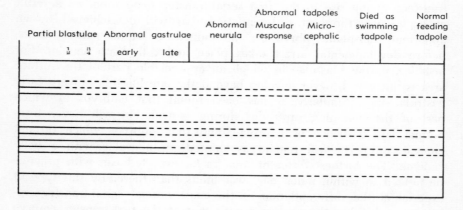

Fig. 1. Serial nuclear transfers from abnormal first-transfer embryos. Original gastrula donor nuclei (embryonic nuclei). Furthest differentiation attained by each first-transfer embryo (solid line) and by the most normal of the serial-transfer embryos derived from its nuclei (dotted line).

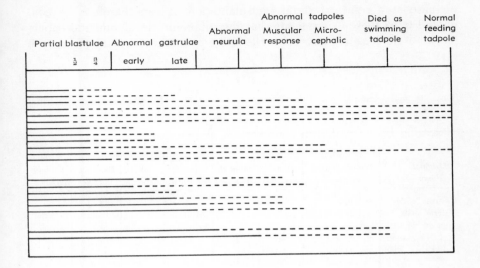

Fig. 2. Serial nuclear transfers from abnormal first-transfer embryos. Original tadpole intestine nuclei. Furthest differentiation attained by each first-transfer embryo (solid line) and by the most normal of the serial-transfer embryos derived embryos derived from its nuclei (dotted line).

Evidence has already been obtained from different kinds of experiments that the developmental capacity of a nucleus does not increase as a result of transplantation (Gurdon, 1960c). Confirmation of this has been obtained in the present experiments by making further serial-transfers in the same way as described above. Nuclei from an abnormal first-transfer embryo gave rise to the embryos of the first serial-transfer generation; the most normal of these embryos was then used to provide nuclei for a further transfer generation. In each case the most normal embryo of one transfer generation was used to provide nuclei for the next. If the development capacity of nuclei increases as a result of transplantation, this kind of selective serial-transfer experiment should lead to more normal development in each successive transfer generation. About ten such experiments have been carried out, and in some of these, four serial-transfer generations were made from the nuclei of one abnormal first-transfer embryo. In every experiment, the development of the embryos in each serial-transfer generation was about the same, and the later transfer generations did not contain more normal embryos than the first serial-transfer generation. These results show that the developmental capacity of a nucleus does not

increase as a result of serial transplantation. It can therefore be concluded from these experiments that the minimum developmental capacity of a nucleus is shown by the most normal transplant-embryo to

TABLE 4

Some typical examples of the development promoted by nuclei from abnormal
nuclear transplant-embryos

Original donor	Abnormal transplant-embryos used as donors	Total transfers	Partial and complete blastulae	Complete blastulae	Post-neurulae	Heartbeat tadpoles	Normal feeding tadpoles
Gastrula endo-derm cells; stages 11-13 of Nieuwkoop & Faber, 1956	½ cleaved blastula	36	8	2 (died as gastrulae)	—	—	—
	½ cleaved blastula	36	13	11	7	4	—
	¾ cleaved blastula	36	13	6	5	4	4
	Total exo-gastrula	35	—	9 (3 de-veloped further than the donor)	—	—	—
	Abnormal mid gastrula	26	—	24	18	8	4
	Abnormal late gastrula	32	—	12	8	3	3
	Control: Normal gastrula	57	—	14	4	3	3
Intestinal cells of feeding tadpoles; stages 46-48 of Nieuwkoop & Faber, 1946	½ cleaved blastula	36	4	4	3	3	—
	½ cleaved blastula	36	10	10	4	4	2
	¾ cleaved blastula	36	15	6 (died as gastrulae)	—	—	—
	Abnormal mid gastrula	48	—	17	4	—	—
	Abnormal late gastrula	54	—	17	4	1	—
	Abnormal early neurula	72	—	20	12	9	4
	Control: Normal neurula	58	—	14	4	4	3

which it gives rise. Thus the presence of a feeding tadpole among any of the transplant-embryos derived from a nucleus shows that the nucleus had the genetic information required for this before transplantation, even though the first-transfer embryo as well as most of the serial-transfer embryos may have been abnormal.

The more normal development of the first serial-tranfers embryos compared to the first transfer embryos can be satisfactorily explained by attributing the abnormalities of the first-transfer embryos to a non-genetic cause. It is known that the quality of eggs laid by *Xenopus* in the laboratory is variable, and that poor egg quality sometimes causes abnormal development of transplant-embryos (Gurdon, 1960*b*). If the quality of some recipient eggs is variable, only a certain proportion of the transplant-embryos resulting from these eggs will develop as normally as the developmental capacity of their nuclei will allow. The effect of making serial transfers is to transplant the mitotic products of a nucleus into several different recipient eggs, so that at least some of these are of good quality and therefore demonstrate the real developmental capacity of the original somatic nucleus. So long as a sufficient number of transfers are made in the first serial-transfer generation for at least some eggs to be of good quality, the later serial-transfer generations would not be expected to contain more normal embryos than the first-transfer generation. As pointed out above, the most normal embryo that can be obtained from an original donor nucleus is generally contained in the first serial-transfer generation. The effects of poor egg quality therefore account for all the results reported here.

It has now been shown that the developmental capacity of a nucleus and of its mitotic products does not increase from one transfer generation to the next, but that the serial-transfer embryos may differentiate more normally than the first-transfer embryo derived from the same original donor nucleus. These two observations together show that the abnormality of many transplant-embryos must be due to non-genetic factors such as poor egg quality. This is true of all abnormal transplant-embryos which contain some nuclei capable of giving rise to more normal differentiation than they showed themselves, and this includes all 31 first-transfer embryos used in these experiments.

The developmental capacity of original donor nuclei from which abnormal first-transfer embryos were obtained

It has been established above that the developmental capacity of a somatic nucleus is generally shown by the most normal embryos of the first serial-transfer generation. The right-hand end of each dotted line in Text-Figs. 1 and 2 therefore represents the developmental capacity of one original somatic nucleus. The developmental capacity of the original intestine nuclei used in these experiments can now be compared with that of the original embryonic nuclei. The capacity of embryonic and intestine nuclei to give rise to normal feeding tadpoles is shown by the number of dotted lines which reach the right-hand extremity of Text-Figs. 1 and 2. It can be seen that 6 out of 11 (55 percent) of the original embryonic nuclei and 4 out of 20 (20 percent) of the original intestine nuclei were able to promote the differentiation of a normal feeding tadpole.

The following conclusions can be drawn for these results: (i) Of the original intestine nuclei which gave rise to partial blastulae and abnormal post-blastulae after first-transfer, 20 percent contained the genetic information required for the formation of feeding tadpoles. The equivalent figure for original gastrula nuclei was 55 percent. The numbers on which these figures are based are too small to show whether they indicate a significant difference in developmental capacity between intestine and embryonic nuclei. (ii) Of the original intestine nuclei which gave rise to partial blastulae and abnormal gastrulae after first-transfer, 12 out of 18 (67 percent) were capable of giving rise to *muscular-response stage tadpoles* with functional nerve and muscle cells. The comparable figure for original gastrula nuclei was 7 out of 10 (70 percent). Both of these values are obtained from the results given in Text-Figs. 1 and 2.

DISCUSSION

The genetic information contained in the nuclei of differentiated cells

The genetic information contained in a nucleus before transplantation is shown by the range of cell types that its mitotic products can form after its transplantation so long as the genetic information carried by a nucleus does not change as a result of transplantation itself. It will be assumed in this discussion that the developmental capacity of a nucleus and of its daughter nuclei does not increase as a result of transplantation. There is no evidence that any increase does take place, and the evidence that it does not comes from the serial transplantation of nuclei between different species and subspecies (Gurdon, 1926b) and of nuclei from abnormal transplant-embryos within the same subspecies (p. 632). Thus, if a transplanted nucleus supports the development of a feeding tadpole, this is regarded as showing that it possessed the genetic information required for this when it was present in the donor cell, and did not acquire this information only after transplantation. This applies to the results of serial transfers just as much as to the results of first transfers, since apart from variation in donor stage, exactly the same procedure is involved in both kinds of experiment. Thus the genetic information contained in a nucleus is regarded as equal to or greater than that required to form the most normal of the transplant-embryos derived from it, whether by first or serial transfer. This is so even when the first-transfer embryo is abnormal and when only a few of the serial-transfers form feeding tadpoles.

The minimum genetic information contained in the nuclei of intestinal epithelium cells can be determined by combining the results of first transfers and serial transfers. The first transfers showed that 1½ percent of the intestine nuclei can give rise to feeding tadpoles. Serial transfers have shown that a further 5½ percent of the intestine nuclei also have this capacity. This figure of 5½ percent represents the proportion of intestine nuclei which gave partial blastulae and abnormal post-blastulae after first-transfer, but which could give rise to some feeding tadpoles after serial transfer. This figure is calculated as follows. It was found that 27 percent of the original intestine nuclei formed partial blastulae and abnormal embryos after first transfer (Table 1). About 20 percent of these, or 5½ percent of the original intestine nuclei, gave rise to feeding tadpoles after serial transfer (p. 633). Combining the results of first and serial transfers, at least 7 percent of intestinal epithelium cell nuclei contain the genetic information required to form all cell types of a feeding tadpole, except perhaps for the germ cells whose presence has not yet been looked for.

This figure of 7 percent is expressed in terms of the total number of transplanted intestine nuclei. However, the developmental capacity of many of these nuclei was not in effect tested, and the percentage of intestine nuclei capable of promoting the formation of feeding tadpoles is increased if this is taken into account. The cytological examination of fixed eggs showed that the total lack of cleavage after transplantation can be wholly attributed to technical difficulties. The transfers which result in no cleavage are a random sample of the total transfers made and can be discounted from the results. The intestine nuclei capable of promoting the formation of feeding tadpoles then constitute 13 percent of the remaining successful transfers (Table 5).

It can be inferred from the cytological analysis of fixed eggs that abortive cleavage results from nuclei which happen to have been taken for transplantation at an unsuitable stage in their mitotic cycle. If this is so, then the nuclei which give rise to abortive cleavage are a random sample of those transplanted, and can be excluded from the total number of transfers. The remaining nuclei are those which were transplanted successfully as well as at a suitable stage in their mitotic cycle for their developmental capacity to be tested; the intestine nuclei capable of supporting the development of feeding tadpoles then constitute 24 percent of these (Table 5).

TABLE 5

Summary of conclusions reached regarding the developmental capacity of nuclei taken from differentiated and embryonic cells of *Xenopus laevis*

Donor nuclei	Developmental capacity of nuclei. Stages of Nieuwkoop & Faber, 1956	Results of first-transfers only as percentage of total transfers	Combined results of first and serial transfers*		
			As percentage of total transfers	As percentage of total transfers, less those resulting in no cleavage	As percentage of total transfers, less those resulting in no cleavage or abortive cleavage
Intestinal epithelium cell nuclei	Capable of forming feeding tadpoles; stage 50	1.5% (10)	7% (49)	13% (49)	24% (49)
Blastula or gastrula cell nuclei		36% (100)	57% (158)	74% (158)	77% (158)
Intestinal epithelium cell nuclei	Capable of forming muscular response tadpoles; stage 26	2.3% (17)	20% (142)	37% (142)	70% (142)
Blastula or gastrula cell nuclei		48% (133)	65% (181)	85% (181)	88% (181)

The figures in brackets represent the number of individuals.
*The figures for serial transfers were calculated as described on p. 141.

The main conclusions from these results are the following, though the evidence for each is not equally strong.

(i) It has been clearly shown that about 7 percent of the total number of transplanted intestine nuclei have the genetic information required to form normal feeding tadpoles. This figure represents the combined results of first and serial transfers expressed as a percentage of total transfers.

(ii) Thirteen percent of the eggs receiving *successfully* transplanted intestine nuclei can give rise to feeding tadpoles. This figure represents the combined results of first and serial transfers expressed as a percentage of those transfers which resulted in some kind of cleavage. There is good evidence that the transfers which result in no cleavage do so for technical reasons and are a random sample of the total transfers.

(iii) The formation of normal feeding tadpoles can be promoted by 24 percent of the intestine nuclei which were transplanted successfully as well as at a suitable stage in their mitotic cycle. This figure is the combined results of first and serial transfers expressed as a percentage of the total transfers excluding those which resulted in no cleavage or abortive cleavage.

If the capacity of a transplanted nucleus to give rise to muscular response tadpoles with functional nerve- and muscle-cells is considered, then a greater percentage of intestine nuclei fall into the three categories above. These percentages as well as the equivalent figures for embryonic nuclei are given in Table 5.

The differentiation of cells and the developmental capacity of their nuclei

The results so far obtained from nuclear transplantation experiments in Amphibia have contributed in two ways to the question of whether stable nuclear changes are causally connected with cellular differentiation. Some experiments have shown that different kinds of cells may have unchanged nuclei, while others have demonstrated a stable restriction of developmental capacity in the nuclei of differentiating cells.

The following results have demonstrated the wide range of genetic information contained in the nuclei of cells which are approaching, or which have actually attained, the differentiated state. The experiments described above are of this kind; they show that at least 7 percent of the nuclei of intestinal epithelium cells can promote the formation of normal feeding tadpoles, and that at least 20 percent can promote the formation of muscular response tadpoles with functional muscle- and nerve-cells (Table 5). Evidence of this kind has also been described by King & McKinnell (1960). From 142 eggs of *Rana pipiens* injected with 10-20 adenocarcinoma cell nuclei they obtained one post-neurula embryo showing a certain degree of tissue differentiation.

It can be argued that some cells may become differentiated under the influence of nuclei from neighboring cells, and hence that a few cells in a differentiated tissue may have nuclei capable of forming normal tadpoles while the majority of cells have nuclei which do not possess the capacity to form other cell types. Such an argument seems to be excluded by the experiments with intestine nuclei in *Xenopus*, since it was found that at least 20 percent, and probably 70 percent (Table 5), of these nuclei could give rise to muscle- and nerve-cells after transplantation. These experiments therefore show that a nucleus can be responsible for the formation of an intestinal epithelium cell and at the same time possess the capacity to form other kinds of differentiated cells.

Other experiments have clearly shown that some of the nuclei derived from somatic cells have undergone a stable change restricting their developmental capacity. The clearest evidence for these changes comes from serial nuclear transplantation experiments in *R. pipiens* (King & Briggs, 1956) and in *Xenopus* (Gurdon, 1960*c*). These experiments have not shown that the nuclear changes took place during the normal development of the donor embryos from which the nuclei were taken. If this should prove to be the case, it still remains to be determined whether these nuclear changes are necessary for cellular differentiation to take place, or whether they are only a result of this.

Until the significance of stable nuclear changes is known, the results of nuclear transplantation experiments seem to be consistent with the view that stable changes restricting the developmental capacity of nuclei are not essential for cellular differentiation to take place. This conclusion can now be related to different theories of differentiation.

Cellular differentiation is most probably initiated by the effect of the cytoplasmic environment on a nucleus, so that the nucleus provides specific genetic information which promotes the formation of a particular cell type (recent discussion by Fischberg & Blackler, 1961). Three possible ways in which this could happen are the following. First, nuclei might undergo a progressive loss of genetic material, so that cellular differentiation would result from the genetic material that is retained in different nuclei. Secondly, an inactivation of certain parts of the genetic material might take place, so that specific genetic information would be provided by the non-inactivated parts of a genome. This kind of inactivation would be stable under the normal conditions of cell mitosis. A theory of differentiation along these lines is suggested by various reports of stable nuclear changes in somatic cells (e.g. Brink, 1960). The third possibility is that the genetic information provided by a nucleus is entirely dependent on its cytoplasmic environment at any one time; in this case a nucleus would never undergo any stable changes having a qualitative effect on its function. This kind of system is suggested by the reversible appearance of puffs in the polytene chromosomes of insects (e.g. Breuer & Pavan, 1955) and by cases of metaplasia (e.g. Reyer, 1954). The first of these three possibilities is rendered very improbable by the results of the experiments reported in this article; these have shown that a nucleus may be responsible for the differentiation of one cell type while still possessing the capacity to form all other types of somatic cell in a feeding tadpole. It has previously been found that most of the normal feeding tadpoles resulting from transplanted nuclei of *Xenopus* will eventually form adult frogs (Gurdon, 1962a). However, the possibility still exists that intestine nuclei may have undergone stable changes restricting their capacity to form adult frogs and normal germ cells, since intestine nuclei have not yet been tested in these respects. These results are therefore consistent with any theory of cell differentiation which does not require that the nucleus of a differentiated cell has lost the genetic information required for the formation of other differentiated somatic cell types.

SUMMARY

1. Nuclei from differentiated intestinal epithelium cells of feeding tadpoles and from control blastulae of *Xenopus* have been transplanted into enucleated recipient eggs. The differentiated state of the intestinal epithelium cells was shown by their possession of a striated border.

2. The cleavage and embryonic development resulting from the intestinal epithelium cell nuclei was much more abnormal than that resulting from control blastula transfers.

3. 1½ percent (10 out of 726) of the first transfers of intestine nuclei resulted in normal feeding tadpoles.

4. The serial transplantation of nuclei and of their mitotic products showed that some of the intestine nuclei which promoted abnormal development after first transfer could nevertheless promote the formation of normal feeding tadpoles after serial transfer. The combined results of first transfers and of serial transfers demonstrated that at least 7 percent of the intestine nuclei possessed the genetic information required for the formation of normal feeding tadpoles.

5. The cytological examination of eggs fixed soon after receiving transplanted nuclei indicated that the lack of cleavage and abortive cleavage following transplantation result from nuclei which were not effectively exposed to the recipient egg cytoplasm or which were transplanted at an unsuitable stage in their mitotic cycle. If these cases are excluded from the results, the intestine nuclei capable of pro-

moting the formation of feeding tadpoles then constitute 24 percent of the remaining successful transfers.

6. A similar interpretation of the experimental results shows that 70 percent of the successfully transplanted intestine nuclei have the genetic information required to form muscular response stage tadpoles with functional muscle- and nerve-cells.

7. These results show that a nucleus can promote the formation of a differentiated intestine cell and at the same time contain the genetic information necessary for the formation of all other types of differentiated somatic cell in a normal feeding tadpole. It is concluded that the differentiation of a cell cannot be dependent upon the incapacity of its nucleus to give rise to other types of differentiated cell.

ACKNOWLEDGEMENT

The author wishes to express his gratitude to Professor M. Fischberg for his interest in this work, and for his help in obtaining the animals and facilities required.

REFERENCES

Breuer, M. E., & Pavan, C., 1955, Behaviour of polytene chromosomes of *Rhynchosciara angelae* at different stages of larval development. *Chromosoma*, **7**, 371-86.

Briggs, R., King, T. J., & Di Berardino, M., 1960, Development of nuclear-transplant embryos of known chromosome complement following parabiosis with normal embryos. *Symposium on Germ Cells and Development*, Inst. Int. d'Emb., pp. 441-77.

Brink, R. A., 1960, Paramutation and chromosome organization. *Quart. Rev. Biol.*, **35**, 120-37.

Elsdale, T. R., Gurdon, J. B., & Fischberg, M., 1960, A description of the technique for nuclear transplantation in *Xenopus laevis. J. Embryol. exp. Morph.*, **8**, 437-44.

Fischberg, M., & Blackler, A. W., 1961, How cells specialize. *Sci. Amer.*, **205**, 124-40.

Gurdon, J. B., 1960a, The effects of ultraviolet irradiation on the uncleaved eggs of *Xenopus laevis. Quart. J. micr. Sci.*, **101**, 299-312.

————, 1960b, Factors affecting the abnormal development of transplant-embryos in *Xenopus laevis. J. Embryol, exp. Morph.*, **8**, 327-40.

————, 1960c, The developmental capacity of nuclei taken from differentiating endoderm cells of *Xenopus laevis. J. Embryol, exp. Morph.*, **8**, 505-26.

————, 1962a, Adult frogs derived from the nuclei of single somatic cells. *Devel. Biol.*, **4**, 256-73.

————, 1962b, The transplantation of nuclei between two species of *Xenopus. Devel. Biol.*, **5**, 68-83.

King, T. J., & Briggs, R., 1956, Serial transplantation of embryonic nuclei. *Cold Spr. Harb. Symp. quant. Biol.*, **21**, 271-90.

King, T. J., & McKinnell, R. G., 1960, An attempt to determine the developmental potentialities of the cancer cell nucleus by means of transplantation. *Cell Physiology Neoplasia*, PP. 591-617. University of Texas Press.

Nieuwkoop, P. D., & Faber, J., 1956, *Normal Table of* Xenopus laevis (Daudin). Amsterdam: North Holland Publishing Company.

Reyer, R. W., 1954, Regeneration of the lens in the Amphibian eye. *Quart. Rev. Biol.*, **29**, 1-46.

EXPLANATION OF PLATE

Sections of the mid-intestin of a feeding tadpole of X. *laevis*. Owing to the coiling of the intestine the sections are only transversely cut in some places. By serial sections it could be seen that some part of each cell reaches the gut lumen and constitutes part of the striated border. The striated border and underlying pigment granules can be most clearly seen in Fig. C.

Figs. A and B. Stage 46 of Nieuwkoop & Faber (1956).

Fig C. Stage 47. Most of the donor cells used in these experiments were taken from tadpoles at this stage.

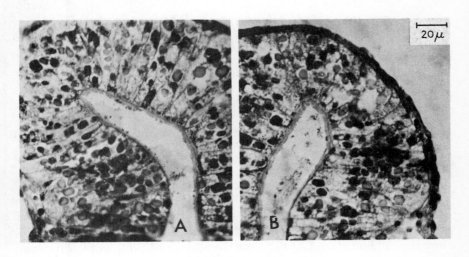

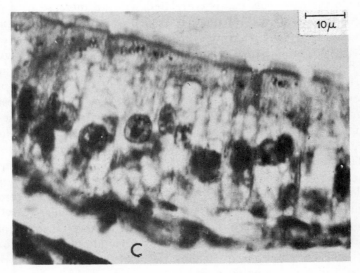

J. B. GURDON

8

absence of ribosomal RNA synthesis in the anucleolate mutant of xenopus laevis

DONALD D. BROWN and J. B. GURDON
Department of Embryology, Carnegie Institution of Washington, Baltimore,
and Department of Zoölogy, Oxford, England

Few new ribosomes appear in the cytoplasm of embryos of *Rana pipiens* or *Xenopus laevis* (the South African "clawed toad") before the tail bud stage.[1] At this time the amount of cytoplasmic ribosomes begins to increase; this rise is correlated with an increase of protein in the high speed supernatant fraction as well as with the first appearance or increase of many enzymes. Soon after these events, the embryos develop a requirement for magnesium ions in the medium. Magnesium-starved embryos characteristically stop growing in length and die at early swimming stages (Shumway[2] stages 21-23 for *Rana pipiens*,[1] or Nieuwkoop-Faber[3] stage 40 for *Xenopus laevis*[4]). The magnesium requirement coincides with the onset of intense ribosome synthesis and presumably is based on the important role of magnesium ions in maintaining the integrity of the functional ribosome particle.

The study of ribosome synthesis during amphibian development has been extended utilizing the lethal anucleolate mutant of *Xenopus laevis* first described by Elsdale *et al.*[5] These workers discovered a heterozygote mutant with only one nucleolus (1-*nu*) in each cell, whereas wild-type *Xenopus laevis* have two nucleoli (2-*nu*) in the majority of their diploid cells. The progeny resulting from the mating of two heterozygotes (1-*nu*) fall into three groups having two, one, or zero nucleoli per cell. The ratio of these genotypes is 1:2:1, respectively,[5,6] as expected of a

Reprinted from the Proceedings of the National Academy of Sciences
Vol. 51, No. 1, pp. 139-146, January, 1964

typical Mendelian factor. The heterozygotes (1-*nu*) lack a secondary constriction ("nucleolar organizer") on one of two homologous chromosomes in diploid cells[7]; the two comparable chromosomes of the anucleolate homozygous mutants (0-*nu*) both lack this secondary constriction. The anucleolate mutant (0-*nu*) has numerous small nucleolar "blobs" instead of typical nucleoli, and both nuclear and cytoplasmic RNA have been shown histochemically to be lower in 0-*nu* embryos after hatching than in controls (1-*nu* and 2-*nu*).[8]

Development of 0-*nu* embryos is first retarded shortly after hatching.[5,9] The mutant embryos become microcephalic and oedematous and die as swimming tadpoles before feeding. It was apparent that magnesium-starved embryos were to some extent phenocopies of the homozygous mutants (0-*nu*) since retardation of embryogenesis and growth occurred in both groups of embryos at about the same developmental stage (Fig. 1). The above data, as well as recent studies relating

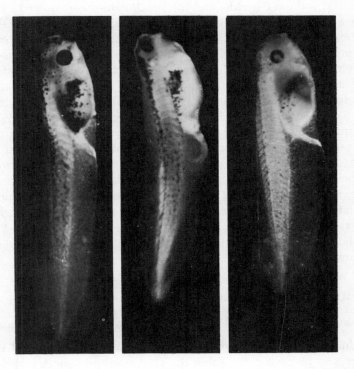

Fig. 1. Comparison of control (left), anucleolate (middle), and magnesium-deficient (right) embryos of *Xenopus laevis*. These embryos are siblings that have developed for the same length of time. Initial symptoms characterizing the anucleolate mutant and magnesium deficiency syndrome are apparent.

nucleolar function to ribosome synthesis, suggested that the anucleolate mutant might be incapable of synthesizing ribosomes and ribosomal RNA.

MATERIAL AND METHODS

Radioactivity was introduced into developing embryos by incubation with $C^{14}O_2$ at pH 6.0[10]. The methods for measuring ribosome and DNA contents have been described previously[1]. Total RNA was isolated from frozen embryos after homogenization in $0.1M$ sodium acetate pH 5.0 containing 4 μg/ml polyvinyl sulfate (a ribonuclease inhibitor prepared synthetically by the method of Bernfeld *et al.*)[11] and 0.5% sodium lauryl sulfate (Mann Research Co.). The homogenate was shaken for 5-10 min at 0°C with an equal vol of phenol. Nucleic acids were precipitated from the aqueous phase with 2 vol of ethanol and 0.1 vol of M sodium chloride, and the precipitate was dissolved in $0.01M$ sodium acetate pH 5.0 containing 1 μg/ml polyvinyl sulfate. DNase I (5 μg/ml) and 10^{-3} M $MgCl_2$ were added and the solutions incubated for 10 min at 20°C. The RNA was further purified by two subsequent precipitations with NaCl-ethanol and the final precipitate drained of alcohol and dissolved in 1 ml of the 0.01 M sodium acetate-polyvinyl sulfate solution. Zonal sucrose gradient centrifugation[12] was performed in the SW-25 rotor of the Spinco Model L centrifuge for 14½ hr at 24,000 rpm. The nucleic acid solutions were layered over linear gradients of sucrose which varied from 20% to 5% and which contained $10^{-4}M$ versene and $0.01M$ sodium acetate pH 5.0. Following centrifugation, the tubes were punctured and fractions collected for optical density measurement at 260 mμ and radioactivity determinations. Nucleic acids precipitated from each fraction by adding trichloroacetic acid to a concentration of 5% were caught on Millipore filters (HA) and dried. After phosphor was added, the filters were counted in a liquid scintillation counter.

RESULTS AND DISCUSSION

Absence of ribosomal RNA synthesis in the anucleolate mutant

Values for the RNA and DNA contents of anucleolate and control embryos are presented in Table 1. The most pronounced difference between the anucleolate *Xenopus* (0-*nu*) and the control mixture of 1-*nu* and 2-*nu* embryos is the reduced quantity of RNA and in particular the small amount of ribosomes in the 0-*nu* mutants.

TABLE 1

Comparison of RNA and DNA Contents of Anucleolate and Control
Xenopus laevis Embryos

| | μg/embryo | |
	Homozygous mutant	Control*
DNA†	0.88	0.97
Total RNA†	5.1	11.8
RNA contents of isolated ribosomes‡	3.2	5.4

*Analyses performed on a mixture of heterozygous (1-*nu*) and wild-type
(2-*nu*) embryos.

†Control and mutant sibling embryos were at stages 40-41[3].

‡Control and mutant sibling embryos were at stages 38-40[3].

The relatively small numbers of ribosomes present in the 0-*nu*
embryos might have been synthesized entirely during oögenesis before meiotic reduction when the growing oöcytes were heterozygous
for nucleolus formation. Alternatively some ribosome synthesis might
have occurred during embryogenesis. To distinguish between these
possibilities, radioactive precursor was presented to the developing
embryos during neurulation, when ribsosomal RNA synthesis is known
to have already begun in wild-type embryos;[4,13] at this stage the 0-*nu*
mutants are still developing normally and are morphologically similar
to the control embryos. RNA was isolated 48 hr after termination of
the radioactive incubation period so that ample time was allowed for
complete utilization of the precursor and its incorporation into RNA. The
density gradient centrifugation patterns of the total RNA isolated
from 90 anucleolate (0-*nu*) mutants and 90 controls (a mixture of
1-*nu* and 2-*nu* embryos) are shown in Figure 2. The mutants contain
about one-half as much total RNA as the controls. This quantity
(5 μg/embryo) is about the same as that found in the unfertilized egg
of *Xenopus laevis*.[4] The control *Xenopus* embryos have synthesized
radioactive 28S and 18S ribosomal RNA as well as 4S RNA. However,
the 0-*nu* mutants have synthesized less than 5 percent as much radioactive ribosomal RNA but about the same amount of 4S material
as the control embryos. The radioactivity in the 4S region was eluted
from the Millipore filters with dilute NH_4OH, made 0.3N with KOH
and incubated overnight at 37°C. About 80 percent of the radioactivity
in both mutant and control samples was presumably RNA since it was
rendered acid-soluble by this treatment. The remaining alkali-resistant
radioactivity was solubilized by hot TCA and probably was partially
degraded radioactive DNA.

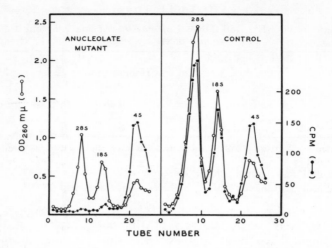

Fig. 2. Sucrose density gradient centrifugation of total RNA isolated from 0-*nu* and control embryos. Two heterozygote (1-*nu*) adult were mated and the embryos allowed to develop to neurulation (Nieuwkoop-Faber[3] stages 14-18). At this time the embryos were incubated in a closed serum bottle at pH 6.0 with about 0.2 μc $C^{14}O_2$ for 20 hr at 18°C with mild shaking. By the end of this incubation period, development had proceeded to stages 26-28 (muscular response), and the mutant embryos were still indistinguishable grossly from the control embryos. The medium was changed, and the embryos continued development in nonradioactive tap water for 48 hr at 20°C (stages 40-41). The anucleolate mustants were recognized by examination of their tail tips with a phase contrast microscope and separated from the two control genotypes (1-*nu* and 2-*nu*). Both groups were then washed with distilled water and frozen at –20°C. The frozen embryos were packed in dry ice and flown from Oxford to Baltimore for chemical analysis. The bulk of the RNA (O—O) is represented by optical density measurements at 260 mμ. The RNA synthesized between neurula and muscular response stage is represented by the radioactive measurements (●—●).

In these 0-*nu* mutants the ribosomal RNA made during oögenesis has persisted, and the embryos are incapable of synthesizing new ribosomal RNA. Since these embryos develop normally to early swimming stages, it can be concluded that *Xenopus* embryos do not *need* new ribosomal NRA until after this stage of development.

Synthesis of rapidly labeled RNA by the anucleolate mutant

To define the classes of rapidly labeled RNA synthesized by the mutant, RNA was isolated immediately after a 2-hr incubation with labeled precursor (Fig. 3). Because of the small number of embryos used in this experiment, purified carrier RNA (unlabeled) was added at the beginning of the isolation procedure, so that the optical density peaks of the carrier RNA serve as reference markers for the three classes of bulk RNA, i.e., 28S, 18S, and 4S RNA.

Experiments by Scherrer *et al.*[14] and Perry[15] indicate that the 28S and 18S ribosomal RNA molecules are both derived from larger precursor molecules. Radioactive label appears first in these rapidly sedimenting precursors and only later in 28S and 18S RNA. The results plotted in Figure 3 demonstrate that 2 hr after addition of radioactivity the control already has synthesized 28S and 18S RNA as well as at least two distinct peaks of heavier RNA (labeled A and B). In contrast, the mutant embryos not only failed to synthesize typical 28S and 18S ribosomal RNA but also lack the heavy precursor RNA that sediments in region B of Figure 3 (about 35S). Yet heavier classes of RNA (type A and even more rapidly sedimenting molecules) have been synthesized by the mutant, as well as heterogeneous RNA that sediments throughout the gradient solution. This latter observation is more evident when the sedimentation pattern of rapidly labeled mutant RNA is compared before and after ribonuclease digestion (Fig. 3).

The rapidly labeled RNA synthesized by the mutant is most probably "messenger" RNA. This conclusion is based on the fact that in

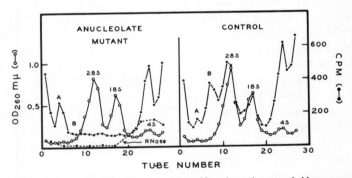

Fig. 3. Rapidly labeled RNA of mutant (0-*nu*) and control *Xenopus* embryos. Previously separated 0-*nu* mutants and control (1-*nu* and 2-*nu*) embryos (32 embryos each) at stage 27-28 were placed in a 2 ml vial with 1 ml of preboiled Holtfreter-M_g++ medium[1] containing 0.3M sodium phosphate pH 6. After gently blowing CO_2-free air over the medium for 5 min, the vials were sealed with rubber injection caps, and 25 μc of $Na_2C^{14}O_3$ dissolved in 0.01M NaOH was injected into each bottle. The vials were gently shaken for 2 hr at 21°C, then cooled, and the embryos washed with cold distilled H_2O. Nonradioactive RNA (0.8 mg) isolated from *Xenopus* oöcytes was added to each group of embryos and the total RNA purified. The purified RNA was dissolved in 1.5 ml, and 1.0 ml (equivalent to RNA from 20 embryos) was centrifuged. The remaining 0.5 ml of the mutant RNA preparation was made 0.1M with tris buffer pH 7.2 and incubated in a total volume of 1 ml with 20 μg of pancreatic RNase for 10 min at 20°C. Values for the RNase-treated preparation have been corrected for volume and tube number so that they are directly comparable with the untreated RNA.

the mutant all the radioactive RNA sedimenting more rapidly than 4S can be recovered associated with the purified ribosomes of the mutant. When isolated by this technique, the rapidly labeled RNA is degraded to molecules having sedimentation constants between 4 and 18S. The base composition of this heterogeneous RNA labeled with P^{32}, which has been isolated in association with purified ribosomes of normal *Xenopus* embryos, is invariably DNA-like.[4]

The nucleolus as the site of ribosomal RNA synthesis

In control *Xenopus* embryos, although other classes of RNA are synthesized at earlier stages, new ribosomal RNA synthesis is not detectable until gastrulation,[4] the same stage that definitive nucleoli first become visible cytologically. (The many small "blobs" seen in blastula nuclei do not seem to be equivalent to "definitive" nucleoli.) Although synthesis of ribosomal RNA begins at gastrulation, the quantity of this newly synthesized RNA remains small when compared to the RNA already present in the unfertilized egg. It is only after hatching that the total RNA content of wild-type *Xenopus* embryos begins to increase significantly.[4] The absence of typical nucleoli at very early stages of development has been reported for other amphibia[16] as well as other developing organisms.[17] Furthermore, Beermann[18] has described developmental arrest in anucleolate recombinants resulting from the mating of two different species of the dipteran, *Chironomus*. The relationship between nucleolar function and ribosome synthesis has been suggested by several observations including electron microscopy,[19,20] base composition analyses,[20] and radioautographic studies.[15] The close correlation of the time of ribosomal RNA synthesis with the appearance of definitive nucleoli in *Xenopus* and particularly the simultaneous absence of both ribosomal RNA synthesis and normal nucleoli in the 0-*nu* mutant support this relationship.

Difference in nucleotide composition between 28S and 18S RNA

This single mutation prevents the formation of both 28S and 18S RNA molecules (Fig. 2); however, evidence has been presented suggesting that the structure of these two molecules is determined by different gene loci. Yankofsky and Spiegelman[21] have shown that 23S and 16S ribosomal RNA of bacteria hybridize independently with homologous bacterial DNA. Thus, the two molecules must have different nucleotide sequences each complementary to a distinct region of the bacterial DNA. In *Xenopus*, the 28S and 18S ribsomal RNA have different base compositions. Table 2 contains analyses for 28S, 18S, and 4S RNA's separated by density gradient centrifugation from RNA purified from

TABLE 2

Nucleotide Composition of 28S and 18S Ribosomal RNA and 4S RNA Purified from
Xenopus laevis Eggs and Embryos

Approximate	Unfertilized Eggs			Stage 45 Embryos		
S Value	28	18	4	28	18	4
AMP	17	22	20	18	22	21
GMP	37	31	28	37	31	31
CMP	30	29	32	28	29	30
UMP	16	18	20	17	18	18
%GC	67	60	60	65	60	61

Following density gradient centrifugation, the RNA was precipitated from the sucrose solutions with cold TCA, washed with ethanol, and hydrolyzed in NHCl at 100°C for 1 hr. Base composition was determined following chromatography in the isopropanol; HCl solvent described by Wyatt.[22]

unfertilized eggs and embryos of *Xenopus laevis*. The 28S RNA has a significantly higher G-C content than the 18S RNA. There is also a difference in base composition between the 23S and 16S ribosomal RNA's of different bacteria[23] as well as the 28S and 18S ribosomal RNA's of chick embryos.[24]

Quantitative regulation of ribosomal RNA gene activity

The rates of ribosomal RNA synthesis in 1-*nu* and 2-*nu* embryos were compared. The results shown in Table 3 demonstrate that all three classes of RNA molecules are synthesized at comparable rates by the heterozygote and homozygous wild-type embryos. Furthermore, the synthesis of 28S and 18S RNA is coordinate since their specific activities are the same. Thus, the haploid complement of ribsomal RNA genes in the heterozygote must produce twice as much ribosomal RNA as do the same genes in the wild-type homozygote. It is of interest to note that the combined volume of the 2 nucleoli in 2-*nu* embryos is the same as that of the single nucleolus in 1-*nu* heterozygotes.[6, 25]

TABLE 3

RNA Synthesis by 1-*nu* and 2-*nu* Xenopus laevis Embryos

	1-nu	2-nu
Total RNA μg/embryo	9.1	10.8
	CPM/μg RNA	
28S	0.45	0.38
18S	0.39	0.37
4S	0.95	0.89

The same protocol that is described in the legend to Fig. 2 was followed. Thus, sibling embryos were made radioactive at the same stage and under the same conditions. The radioactice 1-*nu* and 2-*nu* embryos were separated, and the specific activity of 28S, 18S, and 4S RNA was calculated following density gradient centrifugation of the purified RNA.

Genetic basis of the anucleolate condition

The mutation affecting nucleolar number behaves as a single Mendelian factor and results in a cytologically visible alteration on one chromosome, i.e., in "the nucleolar organizer" region.[7] The defect when homozygous does not alter nucleic acid metabolism generally, but specifically prevents the synthesis of both molecular species of ribosomal RNA. Thus DNA (Table 1), 4S RNA (Fig. 2), and rapidly labeled high molecular weight heterogeneous RNA (Fig. 3) are all synthesized by the mutant 0-*nu* embryos. Furthermore, the relative synthesis of both 28S and 18S RNA is the same (Table 3), even at different developmental stages when ribosomal RNA is formed at widely different rates.[4]

Spiegelman[26] and Scherrer *et al.*[14] have reasoned that closely linked genes (perhaps whole operons[27]) might be transcribed as single large RNA molecules ("polycistronic" RNA[28]) which are subsequently degraded specifically to smaller and, in the case of ribosomal RNA, stable subunits. If adjacent 28S and 18S genes were transcribed together as a single molecule, such a large precursor would be expected to have a molecular weight of about $2\text{-}3 \times 10^6$ with a sedimentation constant of approximately 35S. This is about the sedimentation constant of the ribosomal RNA precursor (Region B, Fig. 3). This hypothesis accounts for the fact that large precursor molecules give rise to smaller ones as well as providing a molecular basis for coordinate expression of the several genes of an operon. Since the 28S and 18S ribosomal RNA molecules function together as components of a single structure, the ribosome, it is reasonable that their synthesis should be controlled together.

Two general mechanisms adequately account for the characteristics of the anucleolate mutant. The anucleolate condition might be considered as a primary defect of nucleolus formation which secondarily results in the absence of ribosomal RNA synthesis. The alternative hypothesis would have the primary defect of preventing ribosomal RNA synthesis. This latter idea suggests that the nucleolus marks the location of ribosomal RNA and ribosome synthesis in the nucleus, and the presence of the nucleolus is secondary to these synthetic processes. The comments to follow do not distinguish between these two general possibilities but serve to analyze pertinent genetic mechanisms in the light of the data presented in this report.

The consequences of the anucleolate mutation cannot be explained by the alteration of a "repressor or activator" substance[27] that might circulate in the nucleoplasm and inhibit or activate the structural genes for ribosomal RNA. If a substance exists in the nucleoplasm which regulates expression of the ribosomal RNA genes, it would be expected to act equally on *both* nucleolar organizers of a diploid cell (unless it only acts in the immediate vicinity of its own synthesis). Thus an altered repressor such as a "superrepressor"[29] would be *dominant* resulting in an *anucleolate heterozygote* since the altered repressor would inhibit expression of both nucleolar organizers in diploid cells. If, on the other hand, expression of nucleolar organizers required the constant presence of an "activator" substance of endogenous origin, the nonproduction of such a substance would have a *recessive* effect, i.e., the heterozygote embryos (1-*nu*) would contain two nucleoli in each cell just as the control embryos. *In fact, the anucleolate mutation has resulted in nonfunctional gene loci which remain nonfunctional even in the presence of their normal alleles.*

It is highly probable that many genes are involved in the synthesis of ribosomal RNA. Both in bacteria[21] and in mice[30] the ribosomal RNA is complementary to 0.3 percent of the DNA (0.6% of the nucleotide pairs). It seems likely that a similar proportion will be present in the *Xenopus laevis* genome since ribosomal RNA can constitute such a large fraction of the gene product. If so, there must be thousands of separate gene loci for each class of ribosomal RNA.

If the DNA for ribosomal RNA is distributed among many chromosomes, it is difficult to imagine how its products can be concentrated into one nucleolus, while still accounting for the biochemical and cytological properties of the 0-*nu* and 1-*nu embryos*. On the other hand, the entire complement of DNA for ribosomal RNA may be adjacent on a single chromosome. Since there are 18 haploid chromosomes in *Xenopus* the ribosomal region would occupy roughly 10 percent of one of them, presumably the one containing the nucleolar organizer.

A single deletion would account for the results but would require the loss of an extremely large piece of DNA. Alternatively, an operator mutation[27] would account for the features of the anucleolate mutation. However, this would imply that a single operator locus could control the expression of thousands of genes.

Any mechanism invoked to explain ribosomal RNA synthesis must account for the fact that the activity of the entire complement of genes determining ribosomal RNA structure can be restricted by a single mutation.

SUMMARY

A mutation in *Xenopus laevis* that prevents the formation of a normal nucleolus at the same time prevents the synthesis of 28S and 18S ribosomal RNA as well as high molecular weight ribosomal RNA precursor molecules. DNA, 4S RNA, and rapidly labeled heterogeneous RNA are synthesized by the anucleolate mutant. Anucleolate mutants survive until the swimming tadpole stage and show normal differentiation of all the main cell types despite their inability to synthesize new ribosomal RNA. Homozygous mutants (0-*nu*) and control embryos conserve the ribosomes made during oögenesis and associate rapidly synthesized RNA with these old ribosomes.

The 28S and 18S ribosomal RNA's differ in base composition and are probably products of different genes; yet their synthesis is co-ordinate. In the heterozygous (1-*nu*) embryos, the wild-type genes regulate to produce twice as much 28S and 18S ribosomal RNA as do the same genes when present in homozygous wild-type individuals. Since the activity of the entire complement of genes determining ribosomal RNA structure can be curtailed by a single mutation, it is suggested that these genes are under common control and located at the "nucleolar organizer" site of a single chromosome.

ACKNOWLEDGEMENTS

The authors are indebted to Miss Elizabeth Littna for her expert technical assistance and to Dr. Igor Dawid for his critical reading of the manuscript.

REFERENCES

[1] Brown, D. D., and J. D. Caston, *Develop. Biol.*, **5**, 412 (1962).
[2] Shumway, W., *Anat. Record*, **78**, 139 (1940).
[3] Nieuwkoop, P. D., and J. Faber, *Normal Table of Xenopus laevis (Daudin)* (Amsterdam: North-Holland Publishing Company, 1956).
[4] Brown, D. D., manuscript in preparation.
[5] Elsdale, T. R., M. Fischberg, and S. Smith, *Exptl. Cell Res.*, **14**, 642 (1958).
[6] Fischberg, M., and H. Wallace, in *The Cell Nucleus* (London: Butterworth, 1960), p. 30.
[7] Kahn, J., *Quart. J. Microscop. Sci.*, **103**, 407 (1962).
[8] Wallace, H., *Quart. J. Microscop. Sci.*, **103**, 25 (1962).
[9] Wallace, H., *J. Embryol. Exptl. Morphol.*, **8**, 405 (1960).
[10] Cohen, S., *J. Biol. Chem.*, **211**, 337 (1954).
[11] Bernfeld, P., J. Nisselbaum, B. Berkeley, and R. Hanson, *J. Biol. Chem.*, **235**, 2852 (1960).
[12] Britten, R. J., and R. B. Roberts, *Science*, **131**, 32 (1960).
[13] Brown, D. D., and J. D. Caston, *Develop. Biol.*, **5**, 435 (1962).
[14] Scherrer, K., H. Latham, and J. E. Darnell, these *Proceedings*, **49**, 240 (1963).
[15] Perry, R. P., these *Proceedings*, **48**, 2179 (1962).
[16] Karasaki, S., *Embryologia*, **4**, 273 (1959).
[17] Cowden, R. R., and C. L. Markert, *Acta Embryol. Morphol. Exptl.*, **4**, 142 (1961).

[18]Beermann, W., *Chromosoma*, **11**, 263 (1960).

[19]Birnstiel, M. L., and B. B. Hyde, *J. Cell. Biol.*, **18**, 41 (1963). Dr. Elizabeth Hay has found the same particulate structure resembling ribosomes in nucleoli of *Xenopus laevis* embryos (personal communication).

[20]Gall, J. G., in *Cytodifferentiation and Macromolecular Synthesis* (Academic Press, 1963), p. 119.

[21]Yankofsky, S. A., and S. Spiegelman, these *Proceedings*, **49**, 538 (1963).

[22]Wyatt, G. R., *Biochem. J.*, **48**, 584 (1951).

[23]Midgley, J. E. M., *Biochim. Biophys. Acta*, **61**, 513 (1962).

[24]Lerner, A. M., E. Bell, and J. E. Darnell, Jr., *Science*, **141**, 1187 (1963).

[25]Barr, H. J., and H. Esper, *Exptl. Cell Res.*, **31**, 211 (1963).

[26]Spiegelman, S., in *Informational Macromolecules* (New York: Academic Press, 1963), p. 27.

[27]Jacob, F., and J. Monod, in *Cellular Regulatory Mechanisms*, Cold Spring Harbor Symposia in Quantitative Biology, Vol. 26 (1961), p| 193.

[28]Ohtaka, Y., and S. Spiegelman, *Science*, **142**, 493 (1963).

[29]Willson, C., D. Perrin, F. Jacob, and J. Monod, unpublished observations cited in ref. 27.

[30]Hoyer, B. H., personal communication.

9

templates for the first proteins of embryonic development*

PAUL R. GROSS, LEONARD I. MALKIN†,
and WAYNE A. MOYER‡
*Department of Biology, Brown University,
and Marine Biological Laboratory, Woods Hole*

The gathering strength of the messenger hypothesis,[1] and accumulating evidence in favor of polyribosomes as the sites of protein synthesis,[2] are exerting strong influence on current research in chemical embryology. The scheme now generally accepted for microorganisms and certain mammalian cells[1,2] provides a number of specific mechanisms by which cellular differentiation could be initiated and controlled. Their essential feature is a direct genomic regulation of the spectrum of proteins made in different cells of the developing organism.

Sea urchin eggs, with a long history of use in experimental embryology,[3] are a particularly favorable material, because they can be obtained in quantity, develop with excellent synchrony, and are reasonably permeable to labeled precursors. During the past two years, a conflict has arisen from experiments on macromolecule synthesis during early development in these forms. Some of the data were available earlier, but the conflict itself stems from the requirements of the current scheme of protein synthesis, according to which the sequence information is carried by more-or-less unstable messenger RNA's. Protein synthesis is either greatly stimulated or actually switched on at fertilization. RNA synthesis is negligible or absent before fertilization, and even after fertilization, is either very slow[4-6] or absent.[7] Brachet *et al.*[7] and

Reprinted from the Proceedings of the National Academy of Sciences
Vol. 51, No. 3, pp. 407-414, March, 1964

Gross and Cousineau[8] have expressed doubt that the postfertilization synthesis of messenger RNA could be sufficient to account for the observed stimulation of protein synthesis. Nemer[5] and Wilt,[6] among others, consider that postfertilization RNA synthesis does supply missing templates, and that this gives competence to previously inactive ribosomes and may therefore switch on protein synthesis. The inactivity of ribosome preparations from unfertilized eggs, their activation upon fertilization, and their responsiveness to poly-U[9, 10, 12, 24] have been used in support of the second hypothesis. Consideration of the behavior of parthenogenetic merogones and experiments with actinomycin D[4, 11] have, however, led Gross and Cousineau[8] to support the idea that templates for the early proteins may pre-exist in the unfertilized egg. Tyler[12] has reported experiments on egg fragments and homogenates thereof whose results are consistent with such an idea.

The experiments reported here do not prove that templates pre-exist in the unfertilized egg; but if templates are a requirement for all protein synthesis, they make such a conclusion reasonable. They suggest strongly that the early acceleration of protein synthesis following fertilization cannot depend upon new messenger RNA.

The strategy is based upon the following considerations. Failure to label RNA with exogenous precursors after fertilization is necessary but *not* sufficient evidence that no RNA is being synthesized. For various reasons, the pools of immediate precursors might be inaccessible to exogenous label. More useful would be a system in which messenger RNA synthesis *is* demonstrated, or in which some heavy, non-ribosomal RNA can be labeled. If the synthesis of these RNA's were then turned off without an accompanying depression of protein synthesis, and if the block to RNA synthesis were imposed at fertilization, then it could be concluded that some, at least, of the first proteins made in development are assembled independently of genomic readout (cf. Gross *et al.*[13]).

MATERIALS AND METHODS

Two species of sea urchins were used. *Arbacia punctulata* was obtained at Woods Hole, and *Lytechinus pictus* was supplied from the California coast through the kindness of Professor Albert Tyler. The gametes were obtained by routine methods for each species: excision of ovaries and testes for Arbacia, and isotonic KCl injection for Lytechinus. In all experiments, the eggs were used only if they gave 90% or better fertilization *after* any pretreatment.

Protein synthesis

Eggs were suspended at a density of about 10^4 ml^{-1} in MBL artificial sea water.[14] They were fertilized by the addition of 1 ml of 1% sperm suspension per 100 ml of egg suspension. At various intervals thereafter, 1-ml aliquots were removed to test tubes containing: 0.05 ml C^{14}-L-valine, 10 μc/ml and 5.8 μg/ml (from New England Nuclear Corp.); 0.025 ml unlabeled valine (200 μg/ml); and 0.075 ml double-strength artificial sea water.[14] The embryos were agitated in this medium by very gentle bubbling with air; after 20 min, incorporation was stopped by adding trichloroacetic acid (TCA) to a final concentration of 5%, plus 0.5 mg/ml unlabeled valine. After centrifugation, the pellets were resuspended in cold TCA and stored in the cold. They were then brought to 90°C in 5% TCA and held there for 20 min, washed again in cold TCA, and dissolved in N NaOH. Proteins were reprecipitated with acid and then washed with water, ethanol-ether-chloroform (2,2:1), and ether, and finally air-dried. The dry protein was dissolved in 1 ml of N hyamine hydroxide in methanol,[15] and mixed for liquid scintillation counting with Bray's solution.[16] Triplicate samples of the embryo suspensions were collected and treated as described, except that the final precipitate was dissolved in 0.5 N NaOH and analyzed for protein by the method of Lowry *et al.*[17]

RNA extraction

RNA was extracted from embryos (which had been centrifuged and frozen at –40°C) by the hot phenol method, essentially as employed by Scherrer and Darnell.[18] Pellets were resuspended in 3 ml of homogenization medium (sodium acetate buffer, 0.01M, pH 5; NaCl, 0.1M; MgCl$_2$, 10^{-3}M; sodium dodecyl sulfate, 0.5%, bentonite, 1 mg/ml; unlabeled uridine, 1 mg/ml). Bentonite was purified according to Fraenkel-Conrat *et al.*[19] The pellets were homogenized by hand for 1 min in a Potter-Elvejhem homogenizer with a Teflon pestle and immediately brought to 60°C and combined with hot water-saturated phenol. Three extractions were performed, and then the aqueous phase was incubated for 15 min with 0.25 mg of 2× crystallized DNAase (Nutritional Biochemicals Corp.), followed by a fourth phenol etraction. The RNA was precipitated from the final chilled aqueous layer with addition of two volumes of cold ethanol. Phenol was removed by washing the precipitate with ether. The RNA was stored as a precipitate under 75% ethanol; for sedimentation analysis it was dissolved in sodium acetate buffer (0.01M), pH 5, containing NaCl (0.1M) and MgCl$_2$ (10^{-3}M).

Sedimentation analysis

0.2 ml of the RNA solution were layered atop 4.5 ml of a sucrose gradient (5-20% w/w, linear, in acetate-NaCl-MgCl$_2$). The sucrose had been stirred overnight in the cold with 1 mg/ml bentonite, then cleared by high-speed centrifugation. Gradients were centrifuged for the times indicated in the figure legends at 37,000 rpm in a Spinco Model L centrifuge, swinging-bucket head type SW-39L. Fractions were collected dropwise from the tubes. These were diluted to 1 ml for measurement of the optical density at 260 mμ and for scintillation counting in Bray's solution. Sample gradients were checked for linearity in a sugar refractometer. *E. coli* 4S RNA and hemoglobin were used as sedimentation velocity markers. H^3- and C^{14}-uridine were used to label RNA in these experiments and were obtained from the New England Nuclear Corporation or Schwarz BioResearch, Inc. Activity data are given in the appropriate figure legends.

Actinomycin D was generously supplied by Dr. H. B. Woodruff of Merck, Sharp and Dohme.

RESULTS

Rates of protein synthesis during continued exposure to actinomycin

It has been established that actinomycin, in concentrations at 20 μg/ml or above, depresses RNA turnover to a small fraction of the normal rates after the first 4 hr of development, and that the rate of protein synthesis continues as high as that in controls for considerably longer.[8] To eliminate possible ambiguities in the design of the earlier experiments, and to obtain better estimates of the actual rates, a pulse experiment was done with C^{14}-valine, during the first 26 hr of development (i.e., to the gastrula stage).

Results are shown in Figure 1. In controls, protein synthesis began at fertilization, and the rate rose steadily for about 3 hr. It remained high and constant until 8 hr postfertilization, then rose rapidly again for the next 7 hr, attaining a level twice that of the initial plateau. From the fifteenth to the twenty-sixth hour, there was no change. In embryos which had been exposed to 20 μg/ml of actinomycin D for 3 hr before fertilization, the post-fertilization release of protein synthesis took place just as in the controls. By 5 hr, the rate was somewhat higher than in the controls. This condition persisted until the controls began to enter the second acceleration. Actinomycin-treated embryos showed

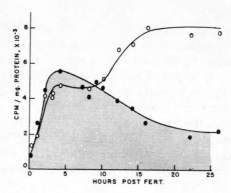

Fig. 1. Rates of incorporation of C^{14}-L-valine into fertilized eggs of Arbacia, with and without actinomycin D (20 μg/ml). Filled circles: 20-min pulse incorporations for embryos in actinomycin, pretreated with actinomycin for 3 hr before fertilization. Open circles: controls in normal artificial sea water. Activity and preparation data in the text.

no sign of this second rate increase; the rate of protein synthesis now began a slow decline. At the end of the experiment, actinomycin embryos were still incorporating labeled amino acid at about the same rate as had been attained 2 hr after fertilization.

Effect of actinomycin on the synthesis of heavy RNA

ARBACIA

Eggs were suspended in MBL artificial sea water alone or with 20 μg/ml actinomycin D at a density of 2×10^4 cells (0.58 mg protein) per ml. Following a 3-hr preincubation at 23°C, the eggs were fertilized and placed in contact with tritiated uridine. Further details are given in the legend to Figures 2 and 3. The time of exposure to labeled precursor was 20 min. Figure 2 shows the sedimentation behavior of the control RNA, and Figure 3 that of the RNA from actinomycin-treated embryos. Centrifugation was sufficiently prolonged to spread the 18–4S region over the gradient, since it was anticipated, on the basis of Wilt's[6] observations and others, that much of the label would be found there. Labeled RNA in controls was found, however, throughout the gradient, significant amounts of it heavier than 18S. The O.D. readings represent ribosomal and transfer RNA. There was a large incorporation into the 4S region as well. The nature of the peak of radioactivity in the 10S region is unknown, but it is not due to DNA.

Figure 3, which represents the actinomycin-RNA, explains why the drug does not reduce RNA synthesis to zero in these cells: incorporation

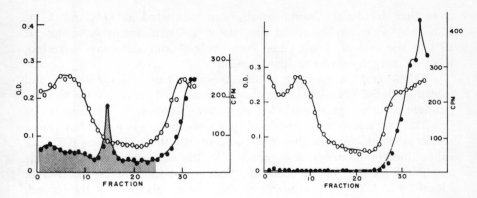

Figs. 2 and 3. Distribution of radioactivity in RNA of Arbacia eggs. Fig. 2, controls; Fig. 3, eggs pretreated for 3 hr with actinomycin D (20 μg/ml) and remaining in the presence of the drug during the pulse incubation. Eggs were fertilized and then placed in contact with H³-uridine, 0.2 mc, and 20 μg/ml. After 20 min, eggs were sedimented and frozen at 40°C. RNA was extracted with hot phenol-SLS-bentonite, as described in the text. 0.2 ml of the RNA dissolved in buffer (acetate, 0.01M, NaCl 0.1M, MgCl₂ 10⁻³M, pH 5) was layered onto 4.5 ml of a sucrose gradient (5-20%, linear) in the same buffer, and the gradients were spun in a Spinco SW-39L rotor at 37,000 rpm for 8 hr. Two-drop fractions were collected for measurement of O.D. at 260mμ and for liquid scintillation counting with Bray's solution. A minimum of 1,000 counts were recorded for each point. Open circles: optical density. Filled circles: counts/min. On the basis of previous experience and marker location, we assign sedimentation constants (approximate) of 18S and 4S to the first and second O.D. peaks, respectively. The small red pellet in each tube had negligible radioactivity. The shaded area in Fig. 2 represents non-4S RNA labeled in the controls.

of label into species sedimenting at 4S and less is very rapid. Much of it may reflect end-labeling of the terminal CCA sequence of transfer RNA, via conversion of the uridine to cytidine. The important point, however, is that there is no detectable incorporation of label into heavier species of RNA. On the assumption that messenger RNA's, coding for polypeptides of normal length, would sediment at rates faster than 4S,[23] we may conclude that actinomycin had at least severely depressed messenger RNA synthesis.

LYTECHINUS RNA AND PROTEIN SYNTHESIS

This result seemed worth confirming in another species. Eggs of *Lytechinus pictus* were accordingly preincubated with or without actinomycin (20 μg/ml) for 200 min. The suspensions were each then divided; an aliquot was placed in contact with C¹⁴-valine (0.20 μc and 5 μg/ml) for measurement of amino acid incorporation into protein, and another was given C¹⁴-uridine to label the RNA. All suspensions were then fertilized simultaneously, and incubated at 17°C for 1 hr. This interval is equivalent to the 20-min pulse given Arbacia eggs at 23°; at the end of it, all eggs, both controls and actinomycin-treated, were in metaphase of the first division.

At the end of the hour, the suspensions were quickly chilled and centrifuged; the RNA-labeled eggs were frozen and processed for sucrose-gradient analysis; protein-labeled eggs were fixed with 5 percent TCA.

The actinomycin-treated embryos incorporated somewhat more amino acid into protein than did the controls: the rates were 0.032 μg valine incorporated/mg cell protein for the actinomycin-treated eggs and 0.025 μg/mg for the controls. Sedimentation data are plotted in Figures 4 and 5, with pertinent experimental details given in the legend. The result of this experiment duplicates that obtained with Arbacia: there was a small but significant synthesis of heavy RNA in the controls, RNA whose sedimentation is noncoincident with that of the ribosomal RNA represented by the first two optical density peaks (at 28S and 18S, approximately[5]), as well as a relatively heavy incorporation into material sedimenting at 4S and less. In the presence of actinomycin, the 4S material is labeled as in the control, but there is no measurable incorporation into heavy molecules.

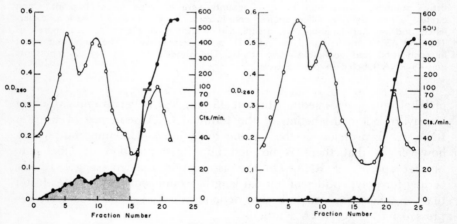

Figs. 4 and 5. *Lytechinus pictus*. Same experimental design as in Figs. 2 and 3. Preincubation with actinomycin for 200 min. Pulse duration: 0-60 min postfertilization. RNA label: C^{14}-uridine, 0.5 μc and 4.0 μg/ml, in artificial sea water. For protein synthesis and development data, see text. Centrifugation time at 37,000 rpm: 5 hr. Fig. 4, controls; Fig. 5, actinomycin-treated eggs. O.D. peaks (open circles) correspond, on the basis of previous experience, to (approx.) 28S, 18S, and 4S, with sedimentation toward lower fraction numbers. The filled circles give counts/min of each fraction in 15-ml Bray's solution. At least 3,000 counts were accumulated per sample. Shaded area in Fig. 4 represents newly synthesized non-4S RNA. Each fraction comprised 3 drops from a 4.7 – ml gradient.

Developmental effects

While we are not here primarily concerned with developmental implications, it is worth documenting the characteristic effects of actinomycin on mitosis and differentiation for the same experiment in which both early protein and early RNA synthesis data are available. Aliquots of the two suspensions of Lytechinus eggs used in the sedimentation analysis were permitted to remain in the waterbath. After 18 hr, controls were rapidly swimming mesenchyme-blastulae, as exemplified by Figure 6a. The embryos in actinomycin had divided at about the same rate as the controls, and had produced a blastocoel, but none had altered beyond an early blastula morphology, except that continued cell division had caused numbers of cells to loosen from the blastula wall. Half of the embryos had formed cilia and were rotating sluggishly; the others had not. One third had hatched. Figure 6b shows one of the actinomycin embryos at this time, with its fertilization membrane still intact. Figure 6c is a phase-contrast surface view of the actinomycin embryo, provided to show that mitotic division, and not fragmentation, was taking place: the phase contrast optics reveal normal cell-contact planes and the fact that every cell has a nucleus. One of the cells in the optical plane is at metaphase.

DISCUSSION AND CONCLUSIONS

Biological and chemical implications of a complete but inhibited system of protein synthesis (including templates) in the unfertilized egg are discussed at length elsewhere.[8] It is, however, worthwhile to state what is, in our opinion, demonstrated by these experiments. First, we find (in agreement with Nemer[5] and Wilt[6]) that synthesis of non-ribosomal, non-4S RNA begins very soon after fertilization. To what extent the heavy, new RNA is messenger and to what extent it is a ribosomal precursor or other RNA is not certain, but in view of the enormous supply of ribosomes packaged into the egg, and in view of Nemer's pulse-chase results,[5] it seems likely that an important fraction of the new RNA is messenger.

Actinomycin, at 20 μg/ml, inhibits the synthesis of RNA heavier than *ca.* 25,000 mol wt. The failure to suppress incorporation *in toto*, as is accomplished with suitable concentrations of this drug in bacteria,[22] results from the rapid synthesis of 4S material, or possibly from rapid end-labeling of the CCA sequence of transfer RNA, or both. Perhaps there are long GC-free regions of sea urchin DNA, which are used as templates by the RNA polymerase even in the presence of actinomycin:

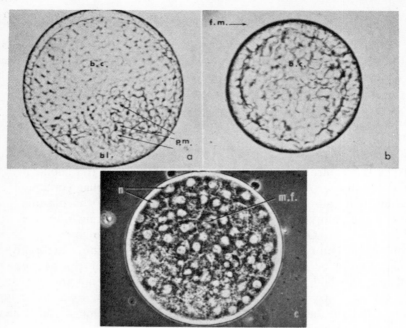

Fig. 6. Development of Lytechinus embryos from RNA-labeling experiment described in text and in Figs. 4 and 5. (a) Mesenchyme blastula from control suspension, showing thin body wall, blastocoel (b.c.), primary mesenchyme cells (p.m.) migrating away from presumptive region of gastrula invagination (bl.). These embryos were swimming vigorously. (b) Embryo from actinomycin-suspension, with blastocoel, body wall 1-3 cells thick, and fertilization membrane (f.m.), showing that hatching had not occurred in this specimen. The actinomycin-treated embryos died in this condition. (c) Phase-contrast surface view of an actinomycin-treated embryo, showing cell contact planes in the body wall, and a nucleus (n) in each cell. One cell in the optical plane is in metaphase (m.f.). This provides evidence that divison continued in actinomycin, but that no differentiation occurred beyond a stage resembling the early blastula.

the specificity of actinomycin for dGMP residues in DNA has been well established.[21] Possibly the low molecular weight RNA is made in an RNA-dependent system.

The effect on RNA synthesis contrasts with the protein synthesis rates, which are equal to or higher than in the controls. The condition persists for many hours; the very slow decay of protein synthesis in actinomycin-treated embryos suggest that the templates for the early proteins are very stable in this system.

Failure of the second rise in protein synthesis rate suggests that an important class of new messenger RNA's has not been elaborated;

the timing of this rise in controls suggests a relation to the differentiation of primary mesenchyme, skeleton formation, and gastrulation.

We conclude that the release of protein synthesis from whatever inhibits it in the unfertilized egg does not require messenger RNA synthesis. Since defective ribosomes,[10] absence of transfer RNA,[24] and deficiency in amino acid-activating enzymes[25] have been eliminated as possible causes of the inhibition, its nature remains a problem.

The low molecular weight RNA that does become labeled in the presence of actinomycin D might represent incomplete messenger fragments, capable of stimulating the synthesis of some abnormal polypeptides. It is known, however, that the sea urchin egg must make some proteins for each division,[26] and presumably serious changes in the character of proteins made after fertilization would lead to inhibition of mitosis. But the actinomycin-treated embryos divide at normal or near-normal rates, indicating that some of the proteins being assembled are also normal.

We now consider it, therefore, a good working hypothesis that the first proteins are made by the embryo independently of direct genomic control; that their templates (if all protein synthesis requires templates) are present in the unfertilized egg. It is perhaps of interest that many or all of these templates bear information about the proteins needed for cell division,[27] but not about differentiation beyond the early blastula.

SUMMARY

In the presence of actinomycin D, two species of sea urchin egg fail to incorporate isotopically labeled uridine into RNA of high molecular weight, while controls do so. Both actinomycin-treated and control eggs do begin to synthesize new proteins immediately after fertilization. It is concluded that the release of protein synthesis from its prefertilization inhibition is not a result of the synthesis of new messenger RNA. Such synthesis is required for normal development beyond the early blastula.

We are grateful to Drs. Albert Tyler, Alberto Monroy, Cyrus Levinthal, and David A. Shemin for discussions of various problems associated with this work and for the opportunity to examine unpublished data. Drs. Arya K. Bal, Gilles H. Cousineau, and Miss Meredith Stevens have been of material assistance.

*Supported by grants from the National Science Foundation (GB-156) and the American Cancer Society.

†National Institutes of Health postdoctoral fellow.

‡Some of the data reported are taken from a thesis submitted by W. A. Moyer to the Graduate School of Brown University in partial fulfillment of the requirements for the degree of Master of Science.

REFERENCES

[1]Monod, J., and F. Jacob, in *Cellular Regulatory Mechanisms*, Cold Spring Harbor Symposia on Quantitative Biology, vol. 26 (1961), p. 389.

[2]Goodman, H. M., and A. Rich, *Nature*, **199**, 318 (1963).

[3]Harvey, E. B., *The American Arbacia and Other Sea Urchins* (Princeton University Press, 1956).

[4]Gross, P. R., and G. H. Cousineau, *Biochem. Biophys. Res. Commun.*, **10**, 321 (1963).

[5]Nemer, M., these *Proceedings*, **50**, 230 (1963).

[6]Wilt, F. H., *Biochem. Biophys. Res. Commun.*, **11**, 447 (1963).

[7]Brachet, J., *et al.*, *Biochim. Biophys. Acta*, **72**, 662 (1963).

[8]Gross, P. R., and G. H. Cousineau, *Exptl. Cell Res.*, in press.

[9]Hultin, T., *Exptl. Cell Res.*, **25**, 405 (1961).

[10]Wilt, F. H., and T. Hultin, *Biochem. Biophys. Res. Commun.*, **9**, 313 (1962).

[11]Melton, C. R., *Genetics*, **48**, 901 (1963).

[12]Tyler, A., *Am. Zoologist*, **3**, 109 (1963).

[13]Gross, P. R., W. Spindel, and G. H. Cousineau, *Biochem. Biophys. Res. Commun.*, **13**, 405 (1963).

[14]Cavanaugh, G., ed., *Formulae and Methods of the Marine Biological Laboratory*, IV (Woods Hole, 1956).

[15]Herberg, R., *Science*, **128**, 199 (1958).

[16]Bray, G., *Anal. Biochem.*, **1**, 279 (1960).

[17]Lowry, O., *et al.*, *J. Biol. Chem.*,**193**, 265 (1951).

[18]Scherrer, K., and J. Darnell, *Biochem. Biophys. Res. Commun.*, **7**, 486 (1962).

[19]Fraenkel-Conrat, H., B. Singer, and A. Tsugita, *Virology*, **14**, 54 (1961).

[20]Hurwitz, J., *et al.*, these *Proceedings*, **48**, 1222 (1962).

[21]Reich, E., I. H. Goldberg, and M. Rabinowitz, *Nature*, **196**, 743 (1962).

[22]Levinthal, C., A. Keynan, and A. Higa, these *Proceedings*, **48**, 1631 (1962).

[23]Monier, R., *et al.*, *J. Mol. Biol.*, **5**, 311 (1962).

[24]Nemer, M., and S. G. Bard, *Science*, **140**, 664 (1963).

[25]Maggio, R., and C. Catalano, in preparation.

[26]Hultin, T., *Experientia*, **7**, 410 (1961).

[27]Gross, P.R., and G. H. Cousineau, *J. Cell Biol.*, **19**, 260 (1963).

10

activation of protein biosynthesis in non-nucleate fragments of sea urchin eggs*

PAUL C. DENNY AND ALBERT TYLER
*Division of Biology, California Institute of Technology,
Pasadena, California*

Among various mechanisms that can be formulated (cf. Brachet, 1962; Tyler, 1963) to account for the initiation of active protein synthesis upon fertilization two favored possibilities are (1) the neutralization of an inhibitor of the ribosome-messenger RNA (mRNA) system assuming adequate mRNA to be present in the unfertilized egg, and (2) the production of mRNA, presumably by the nucleus. The former, with reference to the ribosomes, is supported particularly by Hultin's (1961) experiments showing that the microsomal fraction of unfertilized egg remains relatively inactive with fertilized egg supernatants whereas the reciprocal combination is active; also, that "unfertilized" microsomes could be activated by butyric acid treatment of homogenates. With reference to mRNA it is favored by experiments of Gross and Cousineau (1963) showing activation of protein synthesis upon fertilization in presence of actinomycin D.

The second possibility is supported mainly by the findings (Tyler, 1962, 1963; Nemer, 1962; Nemer and Bard, 1963; Wilt and Hultin, 1962) that ribosomal preparations from unfertilized eggs can be stimulated by polyuridylic acid (poly U) to incorporate phenylalanine into protein and that the stimulation is of the same order of magnitude as obtained with preparations from fertilized eggs.

Reprinted from Biochemical and Biophysical Research Communications
Vol. 14, No. 3, 1964

The present experiments with artificially activated non-nucleate egg-fragments, to which reference has been made earlier (Tyler, 1962, 1963), oppose the proposition that nuclear production of messenger RNA is responsible for the increased protein synthesis upon fertilization. In an article in press, a preprint of which we recently received, Brachet, Ficq and Tencer (1963) report similar experiments, independently performed, with similar results.

MATERIALS AND METHODS

The sea urchins *Lytechinus pictus* and *Strongylocentrotus purpuratus* were used. An artificial sea water (Tyler, 1953) was used for culturing the eggs and for maintaining the animals.

Separation of the eggs into non-nucleate and nucleate fragments was done by a modification of E. B. Harvey's (1936) method. Eggs, deprived of their gelatinous coats by slight acidification (Tyler, 1949) or preliminary centrifugation, were centrifuged in the cold at 10,000 rpm for 15 minutes in a Spinco Model L centrifuge (SW 25.1 rotor) in tubes containing two layers of sucrose-sea water of graded density and a top layer of sea water. For *L. pictus* the lowest layer was 2 ml of a 3:1 solution of 1.1 molar sucrose and sea water, the latter containing a dense suspension of the eggs. The second layer was 6 ml of a 3:2 solution of 1.1 molar sucrose and sea water. For *S. purpuratus* the second layer was a 6.3:3.7 solution of 1.1 molar sucrose and sea water. Upon centrifugation the nucleated parts of the whole eggs banded just below the sea water layer and the non-nucleate parts banded at the boundary of the two sucrose solutions. The top band was generally removed first. Contamination of the non-nucleate with nucleate fragments was less than 0.2% in the present experiments.

The fragments were washed with ice cold sea water, allowed to warm to 20°C, and aliquots activated by ½ to 1½ minute treatment with 0.004 or 0.005M butyric acid in sea water. Incorporation of C^{14}-amino acids into protein, *in vivo* and *in vitro*, was determined by a modification of the filter paper method of Mans and Novelli (1961) as previously described (Tyler, 1963).

EXPERIMENTS

The effect of butyric acid treatment on incorporation of amino acid into protein by homogenates prepared from non-nucleate egg-fragments was examined in three sets of experiments (Table 1) and by the intact fragments in eight others (Table 2). In the three homogenate experiments the increases in activity were 4.6-, 3.0- and 5.3-fold. Estimates of the percentage of eggs that are visibly parthenogentically activated (membrane elevation) are more readily made with S. *purpuratus,* used in experiment 3. It approximated 50% in this experiment. In parallel tests (not listed) the untreated nucleate fragments, in this experiment gave incorporation values (19, 14 cpm per 0.075 ml) similar to the non-nucleate, as did also the butyric acid treated samples (94, 91 cpm). The latter, however, showed 100% membrane elevation. In experiment no. 1 incorporation values (not listed) for the untreated nucleate egg-fragments are much lower (3.6, 5.0 cpm) than for the non-nucleate.

TABLE 1

Effect of treatment with butyric acid (0.005M) on incorporation of C^{14}-valine by homogenates from non-nucleate fragments of eggs of L. *pictus* (Exper. 1 and 2) and S. *purpuratus* (Exper. 3)

Experiment	Treatment time	Counts per minute		Ratio T/U
		Untreated (U)	Treated (T)	
1	½ min.	16.3, 14.3	68.4, 72.8	4.6
2	1½ min.	2.6, 1.4	6.6, 5.6	3.0
3	1 min.	19 , 17	98 , 92	5.3

The amounts of egg material are the same for treated and untreated samples in each experiment; in no. 1 and no. 2 values are per mg protein; in no. 3 values are per 0.075 ml of packed egg-fragments. Incubation mixture: 9 volumes homogenate: 1 volume reaction mixture (0.8 ml M/8 PEP; 0.1 ml 0.0038M C^{14}-L-valine at 4.8 curies/mole; 0.1 ml M/10 ATP).

A similar difference was noted in the experiments with the intact egg-fragments when the values were calculated on the basis of the same amount of egg-protein. Thus for experiment no. 1 (Table 2) the corresponding values for the untreated nucleate fragments are less than half (10,450; 9,745 cpm) of those for the non-nucleate. Treated nucleate fragments in this experiment also gave values less than half (26,835; 22,390 cpm) of those for the non-nucleate.

The effect of fertilization on amino acid incorporation by non-nucleate fragments was also determined in four of the experiments listed in Table 2. In these the values are of the same order as obtained by butyric acid treatment, except for one (no. 8) in which fertilization gave distinctly higher values. The data show, then, that artificial activation of non-nucleate fragments can result in as much increase in protein-synthesis as is obtained upon fertilization.

TABLE 2

Effect of treatment with butyric acid (0.004M, 1 min.) on incorporation of C^{14}-amino acids by intact non-nucleate fragments of eggs of *L. pictus*

Experi-ment	Counts per minute			Ratios	
	Untreated (U)	Treated (T)	Fertilized (F)	T/U	F/U
1	25,650; 25,230	72,750; 72,300		2.8	
2	1,040; 920	3,340; 2,663		3.1	
3	5,861; 5,584	8,877; 8,669		1.5	
4	1,475; 1,281	3,384; 3,017		2.3	
5	9,540; 6,700	20,753; 17,467	19,348; 18,451	2.3	2.3
6	247; 220	788; 769	665; 663	3.3	2.8
7	1,005; 833	8,885; 7,526	8,969; 8,122	8.9	9.3
8	999; 879	4,627; 4,307	7,645; 7,404	4.8	8.0

Values for exper. 1 are per mg protein; for the other experiments quantities of egg-fragments were not determined but amounts were the same for treated as for untreated samples in each experiment. Incubations were for ¼ to 2 hours at 20°C in 50 mm³ of a 2.5 μc/ml sea water solution of C^{14}-valine per ml of egg-fragment suspension, except for exper. 5 in which C^{14}-phenylalanine was used.

DISCUSSION

The ability of non-nucleate sea urchin egg-fragments to syn-thesize protein has been demonstrated earlier (Malkin, 1954). The present experiments, and those by Brachet et al. (1963), show that the great increase in protein synthesis that normally occurs upon fertiliza-tion can take place in absence of a nucleus, and is thus not due to production or release of new mRNA by the nucleus. Brachet et al. (1963) point out that a change in permeability to amino acid is not excluded as a basis for their results. The present homogenate-experi-ments rule out this possibility.

Among the possibilities previously considered (cf. Brachet, 1962; Tyler, 1963) an "unmasking" of blocked cytoplasmic mRNA is favored by these results in addition to the "chemical enucleation" experiments of Gross and Cousineau (1963). Since there is evidence (Monroy and Tyler, 1963) that polysomes form following fertilization it would ap-pear that the blocked mRNA is not attached to the ribosomes. One reservation that applies to these conclusions is the possibility of produc-tion of mRNA from a cytoplasmic DNA. However, there is considerable uncertainty (cf. Brachet, 1962) about the amount, nature and activity of the so-called cytoplasmic DNA of unfertilized eggs.

SUMMARY

Incorporation of amino acid into protein by non-nucleate fragments of sea urchin eggs can be stimulated by artificial activation to the same extent as by fertilization.

REFERENCES

Brachet, J., 1962, *J. Cell. Comp. Physiol.*, **60**, (Suppl. 1), 1-18.
Brachet, J., Ficq, A. and Tencer, R., 1963, *Exptl. Cell Res.* (in press).
Gross, P. R. and Cousineau, G. H., 1963, *Biochem. Biophys. Res. Comm*, **10**, 321-326.
Harvey, E. G., 1936, *Biol. Bull.*, **71**, 101-121.
Hultin, T., 1961, *Exptl. Cell Res.*, **25**, 405-417.
Malkin, H. M., 1954, *J. Cell. Comp. Physiol.*, **44**, 105-112.
Mans, R. J. and Novelli, D. G., 1961, *Arch. Biochem. Biophys.*, **94**, 48-53.
Monroy, A. and Tyler, A., 1963, *Arch. Biochem. Biophys.* (in press).
Nemer, M., 1962, *Biochem. Biophys. Res. Comm.* **8**, 511-515.
Nemer, M. and Bard, S. G., 1963, *Science*, **140**, 664-666.
Tyler, A., 1949, *Am. Naturalist*, **83**, 195-219.
Tyler, A., 1953, *Biol. Bull.*, **104**, 224-239.
Tyler, A., 1962, *Proc. Conf. Immuno-Reproduction*, The Population Council, N.Y., p. 13-15.
Tyler, A., 1963, *Am. Zoologist*, **3**, 109-126.
Wilt, F. H. and Hultin, T., 1962, *Biochem. Biophys. Res. Comm.*, **9**, 313-317.

*Supported by grants from the National Institutes of Health (GM-06965, HE-03103) and the National Science Foundation (GB-28).

11

DNA synthesis and myogenesis*

F. E. STOCKDALE† AND H. HOLTZER‡
Department of Anatomy, School of Medicine,
University of Pennsylvania, Philadelphia, Pa., U.S.A.

This paper is concerned with two related aspects of myogenesis. The first is whether nuclei within myotubes synthesize DNA. The second is whether embryonic muscle cells which are synthesizing myosin, the meromyosins, and actin are also synthesizing DNA.

Three theories emerge from the older literature [12, 16, 19, 20, 45] to explain the formation of multinucleated myotubes during embryogenesis and regeneration: (1) mitotic divisions of myoblast and myotube nuclei without cytoplasmic divisions; (2) amitotic divisions of myoblast and myotube nuclei without cytoplasmic divisions; (3) fusion of mononucleated myoblasts with one another and with myotubes. Many recent reports favor amitosis as being largely responsible for the multinucleated myotube [1, 2, 3, 5, 7, 9, 10, 15, 17, 18, 21, 37, 38, 40]. Evidence for fusion of cells may be found in Lash, Holtzer and Swift [30], Holtzer, Marshall and Finck [28], Holtzer, Abbot, and Lash [27], Holtzer [22], Capers [8], and Konigsberg *et al.* [32].

In conventionally embedded and stained material embryonic cell membranes are often difficult to see; consequently it is often difficult to determine whether a dividing nucleus lies within a myotube or within a mononucleated cell adhering to the surface of a myotube. To avoid these difficulties, monolayers of myotubes in tissue culture or glycerinated squashes of developing muscle from embryos were examined. DNA

Reprinted from Experimental Cell Research 24,
508-520, 1961

synthesis was followed by tracing the incorporation of tritiated thymidine by means of radioautographs and by a study of mitotic figures.

It was found that myotubes form by fusion of cells. Nuclei within myotubes do not synthesize DNA, hence they cannot divide mitotically or amitotically. In addition, evidence will be presented suggesting that when embryonic muscle cells begin to synthesize contractile proteins they do not replicate their DNA.

MATERIAL AND METHODS

Thigh muscle from 10 day and somites from 3 day chick embryos were used for tissue culture. Ten day thigh muscle consists of long, multinucleated myotubes, connective tissue cells and presumptive myoblasts; the somites consist of a small number of mononucleated myoblasts, connective tissue cells, presumptive cartilage cells and presumptive myoblasts. The muscle was removed, cut into small pieces (1 mm³), and incubated for 1 hr at 37°C in a 0.5 percent trypsin (Difco 250) solution (Ca-, Mg-free Simms' solution) after the procedure of Moscona [36]. The tissue was washed in Simms' balanced salt solution (BSS) and nutrient medium (2 parts horse serum: 2 parts BSS: 1 part 11 day embryo extract) and dissociated into a suspension of mononucleated cells by repeated pipetting [41]. The suspension was filtered through a Swinny Filter (Millipore Co.) containing lens paper, and diluted with nutrient medium. The suspension was then plated in Leighton tubes on coverslips covered with thin chicken plasma clots, or on Gey slides, at concentrations of 5×10^5 to 2×10^6 cells per milliliter. They were incubated at 37° for periods up to three weeks. Leighton tube cultures were fed every third or fourth day. After two to five days, depending upon the concentration of the original suspension, a monolayer of multinucleated myotubes interspersed with mononucleated cells was obtained.

Living cells on Gey slides were inspected under the phase microscope. For studies of mitotic figures Leighton tube cultures were fixed in Bouin's solution or acetic alcohol and stained with hematoxylin. Other cultures were fixed with 1 percent neutral formalin or extracted in 50 percent glycerol at 0°C for 2 days and then treated with fluorescein-labelled antibodies to myosin, the meromyosins or actin as described in Holtzer, Marshall and Finck [28] and Holtzer [23].

To detect DNA synthesis Leighton tube cultures were exposed to tritiated thymidine (Schwarz BioResearch, Inc., Mt. Vernon, N.Y., 1.9 C/mM) at various times during the formation of the myotubes. Individual experiments will be described in context. Radioautographs were

178

made by covering the tissue on the coverslips with Kodak NTB-3 emulsion [29] or stripping film [13].[1] After exposures of 2 to 7 days the radioautographs were developed, followed by staining with Delafields's hematoxylin. When radioautographs were to be studied in conjunction with the binding of labelled antibodies, the cells on coverslips were first stained with the antisera and then radioautographed. Gelatin was used to bind the coverslips to the slides, since it was found that HSR mounting medium was autofluorescent and albumin absorbed too much of the exciting UV light. The grains produced by the tritium were readily observed under the fluorescence microscope with antibody-stained material.

In this paper a "myotube" is a bi-, tri- or higher multinucleated cell containing myofibrils; a "myoblast" is a mononucleated cell containing a single myofibril; and a "presumptive myoblast" refers to a theoretical mononucleated cell which will differentiate into a myoblast but which currently cannot be chemically or histochemically distinguished from any other embryonic mesenchymal cell.

RESULTS

Mitotic activity in cultures of 10 day thigh muscle and myotubes in vivo

Within 3 hr many of the suspended cells settle on and attach to the coverslips. Mitotic figures are rare before the 16th hour (Table 1). With concentrated cell suspensions bi- and trinucleated cells appear at the end of the first day and increase thereafter. Multinucleated myotubes become abundant by the 4th day. Myotubes may exceed 3 mm in length and may contain over 200 nuclei by the 3rd day. The distance between nuclei within a myotube may be over 100 μ, whereas in other regions of the same myotube the nuclei may be so packed as to deform one another's surface (Fig. 1).

Nuclei within the myotubes move longitudinally. Shifts of nuclei over a distance of 80 μ in one hour have been observed. Nuclear profiles change due to the appearance and disappearance of deep clefts in the nuclear membranes. Where living nuclei have been observed over several hours, we have never seen these invaginations result in nuclear division. It is believed these transitory invaginations of the nuclear membranes and the deformation of the nuclei due to crowding are responsible for claims of amitosis in fixed and stanied myotubes.

---

[1]We are indebted to Dr. L. Goldstein and Dr. M. Mendelsohn of the University of Pennsylvania for advice on radioautographic procedures.

TABLE 1

Cultures of suspended 11 day thigh muscle fixed at different times and stained *in toto with iron hematoxylin.*

Only metaphase plates were scored as dividing cells: the mitotic activity is given in terms of numbers of metaphase plates/1000 cells. The increase in numbers of myotubes and the increase in numbers of nuclei/myotube with time is shown in the second part of the table.

	16 hr	25 hr	40 hr	66 hr
Mitotic Figures				
Metaphase figures in mononucleated cells	10/1000	54/1000	28/1000	11/1000
Metaphase figures in multinucleated myotubes	0	0	0	0
Formation of Myotubes				
Number of multinucleated myotubes per 10 fields	5	8	18	23
Median number of nuclei per myotube (range)	2.19 (2-10)	2.65 (2-10)	3.33 (2-19)	8.25 (2-198)
Total number of nuclei in 100 myotubes	322	376	519	1620

TABLE 2

See text for explanation

Labelled nuclei present in:	Cultures exposed to tritiated thymidine as:		
	Mononucleated cells (Series I)	Mononucleated cells followed by 4 day culture (Series II)	Myotubes (Series III)
Mononucleated cells	+	+	+
Myotubes	0	+	0

Table 1 summarizes observations on metaphase plate figures and nuclear counts of stained cultures from a typical experiment. Inspection of living and stained cultures from time cells adhere to the coverslips, until a week or more following myotube formation reveals mitotic figures only in mononucleated cells.

To determine whether nuclei within myotubes *in vivo* divide mitotically, squashes of 7 day trunk muscle were prepared. These myotubes were stained with the fluorescein-labelled antibodies and inspected under the phase and fluorescence microscopes.

Fig. 2 is a phase photomicrograph of a single myotube treated with fluorescein-labelled antibodies against myosin. Fig. 3 is a photomicrograph of the same myotube as observed under the fluorescence microscope. Of the several thousand nuclei examined not a single mitotic figure has been observed in myotubes obtained directly from embryos.

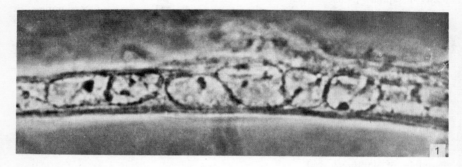

Fig. 1. A phase photomicrograph of a living unstained myotube from a 5 day old Gey slide culture. The irregular shape of the individual nuclei is due to their being crowded together. Several hours after this photograph was taken the nuclei separated and they exhibited their more common oval configuration. In the past photographs of this type have been cited as evidence of amitosis.

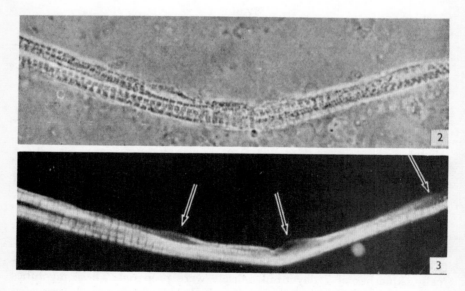

Figs. 2 and 3. Fluorescence and phase photomicrographs of an isolated myotube from a 7 day chick embryo treated with fluorescein-labelled antimyosin. The arrows indicate individual nuclei. Many thousands of such myotubes have been inspected under the phase and fluorescence microscopes and in not a single case has a mitotic figure been observed.

These findings clearly eliminate the possibility that conventional mitotic divisions of myotube nuclei lead to the multinucleated condition.

Thymidine uptake in cultures of 10 day thigh muscle

It is possible that either mitosis or amitosis was occurring but in a fashion not readily observed under the microscope. If myotube nuclei divide mitotically or amitotically, they must synthesize DNA at some stage in the division cycle, for muscle nuclei contain the normal 2 *n* complement of DNA. Therefore a study of DNA synthesis *in vitro* using tritiated thymidine was undertaken. Three types of experiments were performed. *Series I*: Labelled thymidine (0.25 μC/ml of nutrient medium) was added to cultures of mononucleated cells for 30 min 18 hr after the cultures were established, and the cultures were immediately fixed and radioautographed. *Series II*: The same as in series I, but instead of fixing immediately, the cultures were rinsed 3 times in BSS, placed in fresh nutrient medium, cultured until myotubes formed 3 to 5 days later and then fixed and radioautographed. *Series III*: After myotubes had formed (in cultures 3 to 5 days old) the labelled thymidine was added for 30 minutes and the cultures immediately fixed

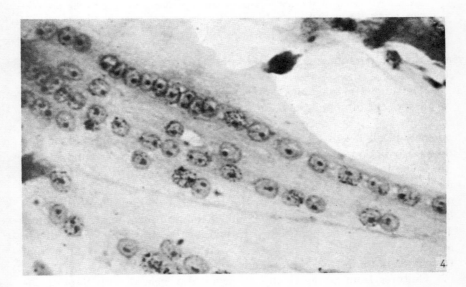

Fig. 4. A radioautograph of fixed and stained myotubes from a 4 day old culture. The tritiated thymidine was added for 30 min when the culture was 18 hr old. At the time the culture was exposed to the thymidine only mononucleated cells were present. This photomicrograph, which was taken through the emulsion, is focused on the nuclei within the myotubes.

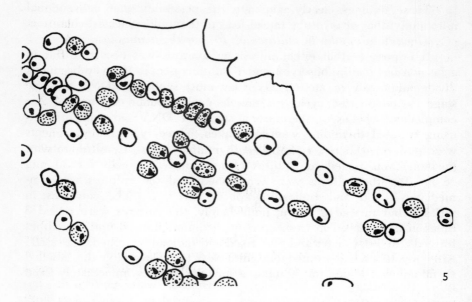

Fig. 5. A tracing of the above section showing diagrammatically the presence of grains above the individual nuclei. The stippled nuclei were labelled.

and radioautographed. The results of these experiments are shown in Table 2.

The nuclei of mononucleated cells take up the labelled thymidine in all series, but there is no incorporation of the thymidine by nuclei inside the myotubes in Series III. In Series II, where the labelled mononucleated cells were allowed to form multinucleated myotubes, a random distribution of labelled and unlabelled nuclei are found within the myotubes. Figs 4 and 5 illustrate myotubes from Series II; Fig. 6 illustrates a myotube from Series III. Clearly nuclei labelled in mononucleated cells can contribute to the formation of multinucleated myotubes, but once within a myotube, nuclei cease to incorporate thymidine. These results are incompatible with theories that myotube nuclei divide mitotically or amitotically, but are consistent with the theory that fusion leads to the multinucleated units.

Cultures from Series II and III were also treated with fluorescein-labelled antibodies. The developing process and the presence of emulsion obscured fine cytological detail under the fluorescence microscope; nevertheless the following observations were made. Grains were found over myotube nuclei in Series II, but not over those from Series III.

In both series grains were found only over mononucleated cells. Mononucleated cells were not fluorescent. Only the longitudinal filaments of the myotubes of both series bound the different antisera. A more detailed description of the fluorescent patterns produced by the different antibodies in developing myotubes has been presented elsewhere [23]. The number of cross-striated myofibrils in myotubes from 5 day cultures was considerably greater than that found in myotubes from 3 day cultures. From these experiments it is concluded that multinucleated myotubes are synthesizing contractile proteins and that the intracellular irradiation due to the tritiated thymidine does not greatly interfere with these synthetic activities.

Mixed cultures of 3 day somites and 10 day thigh muscle

If marked cells which by themselves do not form myotubes are incorporated into myotubes when mixed with cells capable of forming myotubes, fusion would be demonstrated in still another manner. In addition, such experiments could yield information as to what kinds of cells are capable of fusing to f orm a myotube. Accordingly the following experiments were performed. Somites from 3 day chick embryos were cultured on plasma clots until

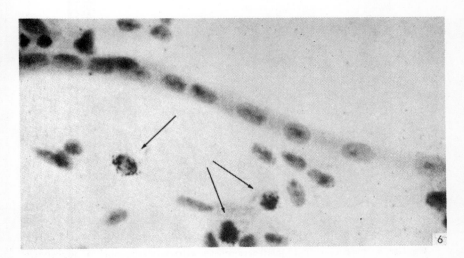

Fig. 6. A radioautograph of a fixed and stained myotube from a 4 day old culture. The tritiated thymidine was added for 30 min when the culture was 4 days old and the material was immediately fixed. Nuclei within the myotube do not incorporate the labelled thymidine, though many mononucleated cells (arrows) outside the myotube do.

they formed a sheet of cells. These cells were exposed for 24 hr to tritiated thymidine (0.05 μC/ml of nutrient medium), suspended by means of trypsin, and mixed with freshly suspended 10 day thigh muscle in proportions of 10 or 20 percent somite cells to 90 or 80 percent thigh muscle cells. Control cultures consisting of labelled somite cells alone at the same initial cell concentration (5×10^5 cells/ml) as that of the mixtures, did not form myotubes. In the mixed cultures of labelled somite cells and unlabelled thigh muscle cells, long myotubes developed containing a random distribution of labelled and unlabelled nuclei. The presence of labelled nuclei within myotubes from such mixtures can only be explained by fusion. These results suggest that fusion may occur between mononucleated and "initiating" or "seeding" cells, in that somite cells which do not form myotubes by themselves can fuse with other cells undergoing myotube formation. It is of interest that 3 day somite cells can fuse with 11 day thigh muscle cells.

Mitotic divisions and the synthesis of contractile proteins

The experiments in which radioautography was combined with fluorescein-labelled antibody staining demonstrate that myotubes formed

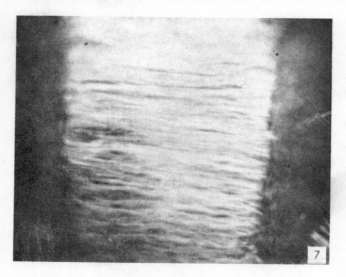

Fig. 7. A low-power fluorescence photomicrograph of a single 4 day somite. This photograph was taken through the skin and dermis. In the photographic field there are large numbers of non-fluorescing mesenchyme cells, nerve cells, and notochord cells. Only the cross-striated myofibrils (see Fig. 8) within the elongated, mononucleated myoblasts bind the antibody. The fluorescent haze is due to the over-lay of individual myofibrils in different myoblasts.

Fig. 8. A fluorescence photomicrograph of a portion of a squashed 4 day somite taken directly from the embryo and treated with fluorescein-labelled antimyosin. The individual, mononucleated myoblasts are remarkably uniform in length. Only the A bands of the myofibrils bind the antimyosin. The thousands of mononucleated cells in the photographic field not committed to myogenesis cannot be observed for they do not react with the antimyosin. This preparation is over 200 μ in thickness, hence all of the A bands are not in the same plane of focus. This is why in some areas the fluorescence appears diffuse.

in vitro do not synthesize DNA but do synthesize myosin, the meromyosins and actin. These findings suggest that the synthesis of DNA and the synthesis of contractile proteins may be mutually exclusive events, that is, a cell synthesizing DNA does not synthesize myosin, the meromyosins and actin and vice versa.

There are some uncertainties as to the meaning of the staining patterns obtained with fluorescein-labelled antibodies immediately after cells are trypsinized and cultured [25,26]. Therefore *in vivo* material was analyzed to test whether an embryonic muscle cell which is just beginning to produce contractile proteins does indeed undergo mitosis. Particularly favorable for this study are the myotomal plates of 3 or 4 day embryos. In this area there are large numbers of dividing cells, and the individual myoblasts can be readily identified.

Somites were removed from 3 to 4 day embryos and treated with labelled antisera to myosin, actin, and H- and L-meromyosin. Fig. 7 is a low-power fluorescence photomicrograph of a single somite and its myotomal plate. At this stage the myotomal plate consists of hundreds of elongated myoblasts aligned in parallel. As reported previously [23, 33, 43], the myofibrils in these mononucleated cells bind the different antisera in the same pattern as myofibrils found in mature muscle (Fig. 8). To facilitate observation of cytological detail the myotomal plate can be teased and observed under the phase and fluorescence microscopes. The following observations were made with such teased material. (1) Mitotic figures were found in many hundreds of rounded, mononucleated cells, particularly in the myoseptal area. (2) Fluorescein-labelled antisera against myosin, actin and the meromyosins were never bound by rounded, mononucleated cells. (3) Mitotic figures were never found in elongated mononucleated myoblasts which bound the antibodies. From these results it is concluded that myoblasts, like myotubes, which are synthesizing contractile proteins, do not synthesize DNA for mitotic division.

DISCUSSION

These experiments demonstrate that during myogenesis cells fuse to form multinucleated myotubes and that once nuclei are within myotubes they neither divide mitotically nor do they synthesize DNA.

The absence of mitotic figures in myotubes from *in vitro* and *in vivo* material rules out mitotic divisions as being responsible for myotube formation (see also ref. [31]). If amitosis were responsible for multinucleated myotubes, it should be detected by an increase in the DNA of myotube nuclei before [6, 39, 42, 44] or after the amitotic division—otherwise muscle nuclei could not retain their constant diploid value. Our findings can be reconciled with amitosis if it is assumed that only nuclei with a $4n$ complement of DNA fuse and that such nuclei undergo direct division forming two nuclei with the normal amount of DNA. But if this occurred it must be a rare event or a large number of paired labelled nuclei would have been found. The random distribution of labelled and unlabelled nuclei within the myotubes makes even this assumption unlikely.

The failure of embryonic myotube nuclei to synthesize DNA are in agreement with the observations reported by Bintliff and Walker [4], who followed thymidine uptake in rat muscle during regeneration. They are also in harmony with the finding that of all tissues studied thymidine phosphorylase is lowest in skeletal muscle [46].

With respect to fusion, many challenging problems remain. What types of cells fuse? It is a selective process occurring only between presumptive myoblasts, myoblasts and myotubes? Can cells not normally associated with myogenesis be swept into myotubes? If fusion is a specialized kind of phagocytosis, what are the mechanisms which selectively destroy the cell membranes at the area of junction, but which leave the rest of the sarcolemma intact?

It is an old observation that cell differentiation and cell division are antagonistic processes. In many tissues differentiation only occurs in cells which have ceased dividing (e.g. nerve cells, keratinizing cells, reproductive cells and others). The finding that myoblasts and myotubes containing myofibrils fail to incorporate thymidine or fail to exhibit mitotic figures may indicate that these cells cannot synthesize DNA and contractile proteins concurrently. Recent work on virus systems also indicates a possible mutual exclusiveness between the synthesis of DNA and of specialized proteins [11, 35]. It should be stressed that it is the production of specialized proteins like myosin and actin which may be linked to the cessation of DNA synthesis and it does not preclude the resumption of DNA synthesis and the inhibition of contractile protein synthesis under other conditions such as regeneration [24, 30]. It is still another problem whether proteins required for cell division—proteins associated with DNA synthesis [14], the mitotic spindle [34], or energy-yielding systems [47]—can be synthesized concurrently with DNA. It would be of great interest to know if the synthesis of DNA in other embryonic cells is incompatible with the synthesis of specialized macromolecules.

SUMMARY

Differentiating muscle cells synthesizing myosin, the meromyosins, and actin do not concurrently synthesize DNA. Presumptive myoblasts which synthesize DNA do not concurrently synthesize myosin, the meromyosins or actin. The multinucleated skeletal muscle fiber is the product of cell fusion.

---

*This investigation was supported in part by Research Grants B-493 and B-1629 from the National Institute of Neurological Diseases and Blindness of the National Institutes of Health, United States Public Health Service, and NSF G-14123 from the National Science Foundation.

An abstract of these experiments appeared in *Anat. Record*, **138**, 384 (1960).

†Post Sophomore Medical Student Research Fellow of the Public Health Service.

‡Scholar in Cancer Research of the American Cancer Society.

REFERENCES

[1]Adams, R. D., Denny-Brown, D. and Pearson, C. M., Diseases of Muscle. Paul B. Hoeber, Inc., New York, 1954.

[2]Altschul, R., *Science*, **103**, 566 (1946).

[3]————————, *Anat. Record*, **136**, 153 (1960).

[4]Bintliff, S. and Walker, B. E., *Am. J. Anat.*, **106**, 233 (1960).

[5]Boyd, J. D., *In Muscle*, Vol. I. Ed. G. Bourne, Academic Press, New York, 1960.

[6]Brachet, J., Biochemical Cytology. Academic Press, New York, 1957.

[7]Bucher, O., *Protoplasmologia*, **6**, 1 (1959).

[8]Capers, C. R., *J. Biophys. Biochem. Cytol.* **7**, 559 (1960).

[9]Chévremont, M., *Arch. Biol.* **51**, 313 (1940).

[10]Clark, W. E. and LeGros, *J. Anat.* **80**, 24 (1946).

[11]Cohen, S., *Cancer Research*, **20**, 698 (1960).

[12]D'Ancona, U. and Fosi, V., *Arch. Ital. Anat. Embriol.*, **39**, 377 (1937).

[13]Doniach, I. and Pelc, S. R., *Brit. J. Radiol.*, **23**, 184 (1958).

[14]Flaks. J. G. and Cohen, S., *Biochim. et Biophys. Acta*, **25**, 667 (1957).

[15]Frédéric, J., *Compt. Rend. Soc. Biol.*, **148**, 621, (1948).

[16]Godlewski, E., *Arch. Mikroskop. Anat.*, **60**, 111 (1902).

[17]Godman, G. C., *In* Frontiers of Cytology. Ed. S. L. Palay, Yale University Press, New Haven, 1958.

[18]————————, *J. Morphol.*, **100**, 27 (1957).

[19]Häggquist, G., Handbuch der mikroskopischen Anatomie des Menschen, Vol. **3**. J. Springer, Berlin, 1931.

[20]Heidenhain, M., Handbuch der Anatomie des Menschen. Plasma und Zelle, L. 2. Verlag von G. Fischer, Jena, 1911.

[21]Herrmann, H., *In* Cytodifferentiation. Ed. D. Rudnick, University of Chicago Press, Chicago, 1958.

[22]Holtzer, H., *In* Cytodifferentiation. Ed. D. Rudnick, University of Chicago Press, Chicago, 1958.

[23]————————, XIX Growth Symposium. Ed. D. Rudnick, Randall Co., 1961.

[24]————————, *In* Regeneration. Ed. C. Thornton, University of Chicago Press, Chicago, 1959.

[25]————————, *Exptl. Cell Research Suppl.*, **7**, 234 (1959).

[26]Holtzer, H., Abbot, J. and Cavanaugh, M., *Exptl. Cell Research*, **16**, 595 (1959).

[27]Holtzer, H., Abbot, J. and Lash, J., *Anat. Record*, **131**, 567 (1958).

[28]Holtzer, H., Marshall, J. and Finck, H., *J. Biophys. Biochem. Cytol.*, **3**, 705 (1957).

[29]Joftes, D. L., *Lab, Investigations*, **8**, 131 (1959).

[30]Lash, J., Holtzer, H., and Swift, H., *Anat. Record*, **128**, 679 (1957).

[31]Lewis, W. R. and Lewis, M. R., *Am. J. Anat.*, **22**, 169 (1917).

[32]Konigsberg, I. R., McElvain, N., Tootle, M. and Herrmann, H., *J. Biophys. Biochem. Cytol.*, **8**, 333 (1960).

[33]Marshall, J., Holtzer, H., Finck, H. and Pepe, F., *Exptl. Cell Research Suppl.*, **7**, 219 (1959).

[34]Mazia, D., *In* Harvey Lectures, Series 53, 1959.

[35]Mellors, R. C., *Cancer Research*, **20**, 744 (1960).

[36]Moscona, A., *Exptl. Cell Research*, **3**, 535 (1952).

37————, *In* Cytodifferentiation. Ed. D. Rudnick, University of Chicago Press, Chicago, 1958.

38Murray, M., Muscle, Vol. I. Ed. G. Bourne, Academic Press, New York, 1960.

39Painter, R. B. and Drew, R. M., *Lab. Investigations,* **8,** 278 (1959).

40Pogogeff, I. A. and Murray, M. R., *Anat. Record,* **95,** 321 (1946).

41Stockdale, F., Holtzer, H. and Lash, J., *Acta Embryol. Morphol. Exptl.,* **4,** 40 (1961).

42Swift, H., *Int. Rev. Cytol.,* **2,** 1 (1953).

43Szent-Györgyi, A. G. and Holtzer, H., *Biochim. et Biophys. Acta,* **41,** 14 (1960).

44Walker, P. M. B. and Mitchison, J. M., *Exptl. Cell Research,* **13,** 167 (1957).

45Weed, I., *Z. Zellforsch. u. Mikroskop. Anat.,* **25,** 516 (1936).

46Weissman, J., Paul, J., Thomson, R., Smellie, B. and Davidson, J., *Biochem. J.,* **76,** 1 (1960).

47Zeuthen, E., *Arch. neerl. Zool.,* **10,** *Suppl.,* **1,** 31 (1953).

12

the differentiation of gastrula ectoderm in medium conditioned by axial mesoderm

M. C. NIU AND V. C. TWITTY
Stanford University

The widely accepted conclusion that embryonic "inductors" can transmit their stimuli only when in direct physical contact with the reacting cells has seemed to rest on the best of evidence. Separation of the two tissues by the smallest gap, or interposition of the thinnest cellular or artificial barriers, have invariably proved to block inductive action. In fact, so consistent have been the findings in this respect that it has not been warranted, in spite of the great amount of work on the chemistry of inductors, to assert positively that diffusible substances are involved in the inductive control of differentiation. The results of Holtfreter[1] and others on the neuralization of young gastrula ectoderm in solutions of various substances do not constitute true exceptions, since according to Holtfreter the action of these agents was probably indirect, through toxic damage which activates strictly endogenous mechanisms.

The present study was originally undertaken with the object of investigating inductive relationships in very small cell populations. Encouraged by earlier success in the cultivation of propigment cells isolated singly or in groups of two or more[2], it was hoped that it might be possible to work on a similar scale with dissociated chordamesoderm and gastrula ectoderm cells, perhaps bringing together representatives of each in

Reprinted from the Proceedings of the National Academy of Sciences
Vol. 39, No. 9, pp. 985-989, September, 1953

small groups or even single pairs to test for any demonstrable effects upon their differentiation. At first technical difficulties, and later other considerations, led to the gradual modification of this approach, and the procedure eventually adopted was to isolate minute pieces of young gastrula ectoderm, the smallest that can readily be excised by ordinary microsurgical methods, together with pieces of axial mesoderm of more substantial size. The mesodermal explants consisted variously of: dorsal blastoporal lip; posterior medullary plate (the portion which invaginates during late gastrulation and forms the mesodermal structures of the tail and posterior part of the trunk); and blocks of mesodermal somites taken from embryos in young tailbud stages of development. In preliminary trials the mesodermal and ectodermal explants were placed in close apposition and often underwent intimate fusion, but it is important to emphasize that in this paper we are concerned only with experiments in which the two tissues were separately situated and had no physical contact with one another.

The species employed were *Triturus torosus, T. rivularis,* and *T. granulosus*; and *Amblystoma tigrinum* and *A. mexicanum.* The culture medium was a modified physiological salt solution devised by us some years ago. Its formula, first published by Flickinger[3], is repeated here:

Solution A (500cm³)		Solution B (250cm³)		Solution C (250cm³)	
NACl	3400 mg.	Na_2HPO_4	110 mg.	$NaHCO_3$	200 mg.
KCl	50	KH_2PO_4	20		
$Ca(NO_3) \cdot 4H_2O$	80				
$MgSO_4$	100				

Solutions A, B, and C are brought to a boil separately, and mixed after cooling.

When small pieces of young gastrula ectoderm are isolated alone in drops of this medium, they attach temporarily to the glass substratum and spread into very thin epithelial sheets which commonly release a few migrating ameboid cells. Later these scattered cells round up and lose their attachment to the glass, and the intact sheet also eventually retracts and falls free from the cover slip. Except for the development of ciliation, in no case have the explant or the emigrating cells shown any evidence of histological or cytological differentiation.

The ectodermal explant likewise fails to differentiate if a piece of mesoderm has been introduced simultaneously into the same drop. There is active outgrowth from the mesodermal explant, notably of myoblasts, but the behavior of the ectodermal isolate is essentially indistinguishable from that when it is cultivated alone.

The results are very different, however, when the ectodermal piece is introduced into a drop in which a mesodermal explant has already been developing for a period of approximately one week. In the complete absence of physical contact between the two explants, and independently of the distance separating them, the ectodermal piece undergoes striking histological differentiation in well over half the cases tested.

In the most representative cases the behavior is remarkably similar to that of neural crest explants. The ectodermal pieces attach intimately to the cover slip, but spread somewhat less extensively than in "unconditioned" medium, and after a few days begin to give outgrowths of ameboid cells. A variable number of these may later round up and fall free from the glass, but the majority remain attached and eventually differentiate into highly branched chromatophores (Figs. 1 and 2). Meanwhile nerve fibers usually grow out, often in profusion, from the residual explant mass. Occasionally the explant may disperse completely into chromatophores, and at the other extreme are rare cases in which the explant remains compact and forms only nervous tissue. When ectoderm is placed in even older (about 14-18 days) cultures of mesoderm, particularly cultures of embryonic somites, there is a noticeable change in the quality of its differentiation. In general, fewer pigment cells and more nervous tissue are formed, and frequently clearly identifiable myoblasts emerge.

It appears highly improbable that the differentiation of the explants it attributable merely to nonspecific toxic effects of the medium. The explants appear to be completely healthy, and cell dissociation or other evidences of injury are definitely rarer than in unconditioned medium, in which no differentiation occurs. It is also significant that no differentiation ensues when ectoderm pieces are introduced into cul-

Fig. 1. *Below,* explant of *T. torosus* posterior medullary plate, with outgrowth of differentiating myoblasts. *Above,* scattered chromatophores which have originated from a small piece of torosus gastrula ectoderm (Harrison, stage 10) introduced into the culture 10 days after isolation of the posterior medullary plate. Nerve fibers have grown out of the residual portion of the ectodermal isolate. Photographed 23 days after isolation of the ectoderm.

Fig. 2. Chromatophores formed from a piece of black axolotl gastrula ectoderm (stage 10) after introduction into a 10-day old culture of *T. torosus* posterior medullary plate. The two explants were situated remotely from one another in the drop. Photographed 12 days after introduction of the ectodermal isolate.

Fig. 3. Chromatophores and neural tissue (note nerve fibers) formed from a piece of young *T. torosus* gastrula ectoderm isolated in cell-free medium withdrawn from a 6-day-old culture of torosus posterior medullary plate. Photographed 20 days after isolation.

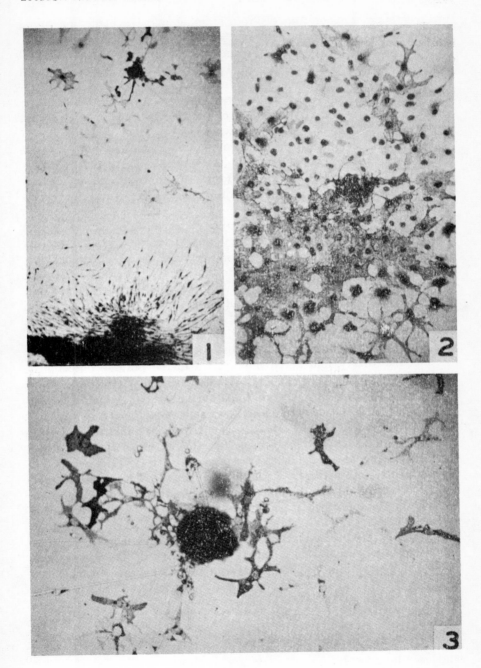

194   ZOOLOGY: NIU AND TWITTY

tures of endoderm, or into drops containing massive pieces of young epidermis.

The physical presence of the mesodermal explant is not essential to the differentiation of the ectodermal pieces. This has been demonstrated repeatedly by cases in which explants have differentiated into chromatophores and nervous tissue after isolation in cell-free medium drawn from established mesodermal cultures (Fig. 3). In a few series, after the medium had been withdrawn from the latter cultures, it was replaced by fresh physiological salt solution and the mesoderm allowed to continue its differentiation for another week or ten days. When this medium was in turn withdrawn and tested, it often induced ectodermal pieces to give rise to myoblasts in addition to nervous tissue and chromatophores.

The results of the investigation thus seem to indicate clearly that inductor tissues indeed contain, and under the conditions of these experiments can release, diffusible substances capable of effecting "at a distance" the inductive control of ectodermal differentiation; they suggest further that the inductive specificity of the substances released changes with the age or degree of differentiation of the inductor.

The modified physiological salt solution employed for this study has the incidental property of causing ectoderm to attach intimately and spread extensively upon a glass substratum, and it is believed that this fact may have contributed importantly to the positive outcome of the tests. Pieces of ectoderm isolated in Holtfreter's standard salt solution characteristically round up into unattached vesicles, which by virtue of the intact "surface coat" investing them are undoubtedly impervious to larger molecules. This insulating coat is probably torn and disrupted, under the conditions of the present experiments. by the tensions and cellular rearrangements incidental to spreading of the explants into thin sheets, with the result that the constituent cells are partly denuded and thus more accessible to diffusible substances in the medium.

Samples of conditioned medium examined by Dr. Hubert S. Loring of the Department of Chemistry show appreciable light absorption in the ultraviolet with maxima and minima at 265 and 245 respectively, suggestive of nucleic acid or certain of its components. Various experiments are in progress to determine the nature of the substance or substances present.

REFERENCES

[1] Holtfreter, J., *J. Exp. Zool.*, **98**, 161-209 (1945).
[2] Twitty, V. C., *Science*, **113**, 476 (1951).
[3] Flickinger, R. A. Jr., *J. Exp. Zool.*, **112**, 465-484 (1949).

13

analysis of the development of the eye-lens in chicken and frog embryos by means of the precipitin reaction

G. TEN CATE AND W. J. VAN DOORENMAALEN
*Anatomical Embryological Laboratory, University of Amsterdam,
Director Prof. M. W. Woerdeman, M.D.*

INTRODUCTION

The developmental physiology of the eye-lens appears to be a very suitable subject for a biochemical analysis of some aspects of the general problem of organ-differentiation, because this part of the eye has a relative simple structure and a remarkable chemical specificity.

This organ-specificity, probably due to its protein components, has been detected by Uhlenhuth (1903) by means of the precipitin reaction, and several authors since then have substantiated his result (e.g. Kraus, c.s., 1908, Krusius, 1910, Wollman, a.o. 1938 *a, b*.). The precipitin test enables us to differentiate simple aqueous extracts of the lens from similar preparations from any other organ of the body, even other parts of the eye itself. Moreover, especially when carried out on a micro scale, this test is an extremely sensitive reaction, so that a hundredth of a microgram of protein substance can be detected. Eventually it seems to become possible to combine this test with the biochemical technique of isolating and concentrating lens proteins, in order to find the slightest traces of these substances in very young embryos.

This possibility opens perspectives for an analysis of lens induction and regeneration but, although these may be very attractive objects to direct the course of investigations, biochemical work on lens pro-

Reprinted from Proceedings of
Koninkijke Nederlandse Akademie Van Wetenschappen, Vol. LIII, No. 6, 1950

teins in our laboratory has only been started this year and results cannot be awaited within short time.

Meanwhile, applying the precipitin reaction on simple extracts, we carried out an investigation about the presence of adult lens antigens in embryonic lens vesicles before the beginning of the morphological differentiation. The reason for this study has been the question, discussed among embryologists, whether the substances, constituting the adult organism, are present already in the youngest stages of ontogenetic development or whether these materials originate only in the course of the differentiation of the embryo.

The old controversy between preformationists and epigeneticists seems to be continued on this chemical level.

Recognizing the important role of the genes, the preformationist standpoint supposes that, at least qualitatively, all of the building substances of the adult organism will be present at the onset of embryonic

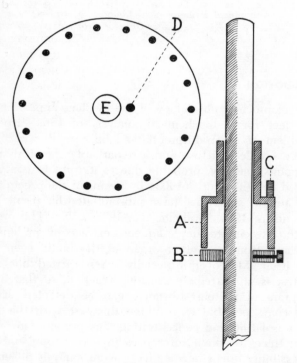

Fig. 1.

development, either bound in the genes of the nucleus, in plasmagenes, or free in the cytoplasm. Perhaps the great mass of yolk may conceal the minute amounts of these specialised substances, so that only in the course of development will they become detectable because of their increasing quantity by assimilation of the food from yolk; nevertheless these materials will be present already at the beginning.

The epigenetic view supposes that, may it be under the influence of the genes, most of the adult materials will become newly created qualitatively in different stages of development. Perhaps under the impression of the developing complicated form out of a simple egg, many embryologists adhere to the epigenetic viewpoint, which in a biochemical sense has been expressed by Needham (1942) in the following words: "Antigens come into being at successive points in time" (l.c., p. 349). Such opinion, however, based upon negative evidence, has to be changed as soon as positive experimental results are favoring an opposite view. A short survey of the literature concerning the antigenetic properties of the embryonic organism will demonstrate this.

In 1906, Braus arrived to the conclusion that embryos are devoid of any antigenetic action. This was a result of experiments in which he tried to immunize rabbits by three intraperitoneal injections of a small quantity of an extract, made from Bombinator larvae.

In the same decade, however, other investigators were able to immunise rabbits by eggs or fishes and amphibia; they found a difference between embryos and adult tissues (Dunbar 1910, Uhlenhuth and Haendel 1910). Also Kritchevski (1914) showed that amphibian larvae have antigenetic capacities, using larvae of Rana esculenta. For his conclusion that, corresponding with Haeckel's biogenetic law, there is a difference between the chemical structure of embryos and that of adult frogs, the results of the complement fixation tests were not giving very strong evidence; in two out of seven tests the larval antigen reacted with the heterologous (adult) antiserum almost as strongly as with the homologous one and with heterologous antiserum a very great number of plus minus reactions was noted (in 33 out of 40 dilutions).

In 1923, Kritchevski studied the same problem in chick embryos and from his results inferred the following statement: "The facts presented in this article suggest the conclusion that the biochemical properties of animal cells are subject to transformations during the ontogenetic development" (l.c. p. 194). The author presented the following

facts: he had been able to demonstrate the existence of Forssman antigen in embryos of four days and older by the results of immunisation
experiments in rabbits, whereas he failed to obtain the same result,
using two days old embryos and unincubated eggs. Having indicated
that this antigen is contained in the cell nucleaus (1916), Kritchevski
also stated that the chemical structure of the nucleus changes during
ontogenesis, an opinion that probably will be refuted by most embryologists.

Iwae (1915), using the same method as Kritchevski, however had
demonstrated the presence of the Forssman antigen in yolk of chicken
eggs and Idzumi (1924), Guggenheim (1929), Witebsky and Szepsenwol
(1934) confirmed this. The antigen has also been detected in one day
old chick embryos by the last authors, who found its concentration in
young embryos to be about the same as in adult tissues.

Idzumi (1924), injecting the whole content of chicken eggs in the
peritoneal cavity of rabbits for immunisation, found an increase in
quantity of both Forssman and serum antigen during the incubation
period and a decrease in that of the egg-white, determined after the
titer of the antisera he could obtain. Although it may be very comprehensible that these quantitative changes are occurring during development, the results do not indicate any alteration in quality. The method
of determining the amount of an antigen by the effect of immunisation
is not very quantitative, because great differences exist in reaction of
the injected rabbits. Therefore, exceptions in the rather regular quantitative changes, noted by Idzumi, might be expected; so the serum
antigenicity in chickens, four days after hatching, was found to be six
times weaker than in unincubated eggs.

The results of Abe (1931) led this author to believe that the
species specificity of organ lipoids is stronger in human adults than in
fetuses and new-borns, but this belief is based upon rather subtile and
only quantitative differences in the results of complement fixation tests.

Perlman and Gustafson (1948) demonstrated the presence of certain antigens in plutei of Paracentrotus lividus and found them missing
in young embryos, from which result the authors concluding that these
antigens "are not present at all, or perhaps in only undetectable quantities" in the younger stages. Certainly this careful statement is likely
to express the true situation; it corresponds with the opinion, expressed
by Cooper (1948): "the failure so far to demonstrate the presence
of some complex molecules in early embryos does not necessarily indicate that they are all absent" (l.c., p. 430).

The article of Avrech and Heronimus (1937) has not been available. Results of recent biochemical investigations about the blood proteins are indicating that some differences do exist between embryonic proteins and those of adults. It has been found that the amino-acid composition of the fetal hemoglobin in mammals differs from that of the adult type, but still the possibility remains that both types of the globin molecules may be present in both life periods but that one type is predominating quantitatively.

The different composition of the blood serum too may be caused by differences in quantity of the constituent proteins. Even the special embryonic protein fetuin, discovered by Pedersen in fetuses of the cow perhaps may be present in minor quantities in adults. However, it is questionable if such functionally inactive proteins will continue their existence in the cytoplasm, but perhaps they remain preserved in the genome.

Besides these differences, some similarity between the embryonic and adult organism has been noted, e.g. by Rössle (1905) and Wilkoewitz a.o. (1928), who could not find any seizable difference in antigenicity, but like many authors in their time, both used a rather obsolete technique, causing denaturation of the antigens, so that their results cannot be useful in the present discussion.

Furthermore, evidence has been given that in the yolk several substances, found in the blood of the mothers may be present, e.g. serum proteins and antigens. (Schechtman 1947, 1948 and Cooper 1946, 1948). The article of Cooper (1948) contains an extensive review of literature on this subject to which may be referred.

Finally, the presence of many non-antigenetic enzymes in the unfertilized egg may be taken as an evidence of similarity.

The problem about the presence of more specialized materials, building up the organs, is more interesting however, and has been attracting our attention in connection with the development of the eye-lens. There is one report already, given by Burke, and collaborators (1944), describing the presence of organ specific lens substances in chick and frog embryos. In embryos of the chicken, however, younger than 146 hours, the adult antigens could not be found by means of the complement fixation test, and using the precipitin reaction only embryos of 250 hours of age and older reacted positively.

Although they used these reactions ". . . to determine the age at which adult lens antigen appears in sufficient amount to be detected by these methods" (l.c., p. 229), the authors, in accordance with the epigenetic theory of changing chemical structure during morphological development, arrive at the conclusion that: "Adult organ specificity does not arise in the chick and frog until the organs are well differentiated morphologically" (l.c., p. 232). This conclusion is very interesting because it may be related to the problem of the organ-forming substances.

According to a theory which has been accepted by many embryologists, morphological differentiation is preceded by a chemo-differentiation (Huxley, 1924), by which the fate of organ-forming regions is determined. There is a common opinion that the determination of the organ-development is due to the presence of certain organ-forming or perhaps organ-determining substances. It has, however, not yet been possible to demonstrate irrefutably the existence of such an organ-determining or organ-forming substance. Histochemical evidence for the action of certain enzymes in this respect could not become substantiated by the results of microchemical investigations, and the enzymes which have been indicated by the histochemical pictures can be found in several organs.

Now there seems to exist the possibility that the organ specific substances may be responsible for the determination of organ-differentiation and especially in the development of the eye-lens it might be feasible to try and analyse this problem of the relation between organ-specific, organ-forming and organ-determining substances.

Two questions may be asked:

First, are organ specific substances present before morphological differentiation or do they arise only after or during this differentiation? And second:

If the organ specific substances might be detected before the stage of morphological differentiation, may they be indicated as organ-forming (organ-building) substances or do they determine the fate of the presumptive lens-region in still younger stages where no indication of a beginning lens-formation can be found?

The former question has already been answered by Burke c.s., who only found the specific adult lens antigen present after morphological differentiation, but, using a very careful technique and isolating a greater number of young lens vesicles by means of a micro surgical method we made an attempt to improve the sensitivity of the reaction. Indeed this has been successful, so that by demonstrating the presence of adult antigens in the embryonic lens before its morphological differentiation, our answer to the first question has become contrary to that, given by Burke c.s.

METHODS

Immunisation

The adult antigen was prepared from fresh lenses, carefully dissected out and weighed. Then the material was thoroughly ground in a mortar and a suspension prepared, adding nine volumes of saline ($p_H = 7$). After centrifuging at 4000 r.p.m., the supernatant opalescent solution was used for immunisation. Strong rabbits, about three kilograms of body weight, were immunised by seven to eight injections of 2 to 3 ml of the 10% antigen solution in the marginal vein of the ear, once in two or three days. Beginning with the fourth injection the rabbits received a subcutaneous injection of the same dose one hour before the intravenous injection in order to prevent shock. (In the last year this injection was given on the night before). One week after the last injection the antiserum was tested and if it had a sufficient high titer (1 : 20000 to 1 : 50000), the animal was bled to death from the carotid artery or the blood was obtained by puncture of the heart. After clotting, the serum was removed, sterilized by filtration through a Seitz filter, distributed over a series of ampullae and stored in the refrigerator.

Serological test.

In 1948 we used the complement fixation test, as it is a most sensitive reaction. The results, however, were unsatisfactory for several reasons. First, specificity was low, probably caused by the presence of nonspecific lipoids in the eye-lens; Krause (1935) estimated the lipoid content to be 1% of dry weight. We tried to improve specificity by absorbing the antisera with other antigens or by eliminating the lipoids with ether in the cold, but these methods reduced the strength of the sera too much. Furthermore, especially in extracts from whole parts of frog larvae, a sensitizing action was met with, so that more embryonic material had to be used for control titrations of complement, and finally these extracts sometimes caused a spontaneous hemolysis.

Therefore, several experiments were made for comparing the specificity of the complement fixation test with that of the precipitin reaction. The results of these experiments demonstrated a very great difference between the two reactions, the precipitin test being almost completely specific. This phenomenon perhaps may be explained by the possibility that the precipitin test in our experiments reacted with the proteins more than with lipoids or lipoid complexes (cf. Witebsky, 1928). In our definitive experiments we thus made use of the precipitin reaction.

Some details of the micro-technique we have been using may be described here:

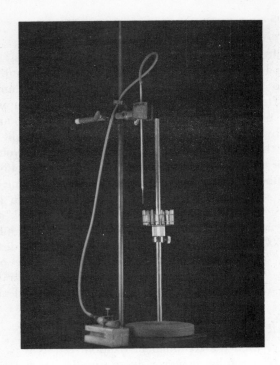

Fig. 2.

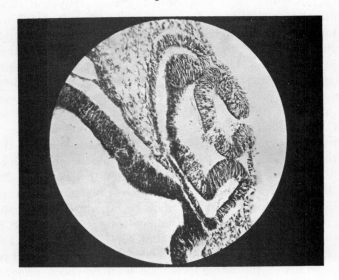

Fig. 3.

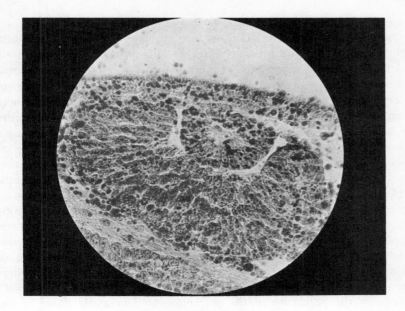

Fig. 4.

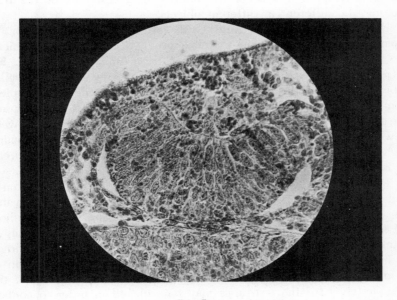

Fig. 5.

BOYD'S MICRO-METHOD

A series of antigen dilutions was prepared in micro test-tubes
(25×2.5 mm). Each tube received 20 microliters of antigen solution
and then an equal amount of antiserum was layered carefully beneath
the antigen. After a 20 minute period of incubation at 37°C the presence of a ring at the interface between the two layers could be noted
in case of a positive reaction. The result was expressed by recording
the last positive dilution. This maximum dilution could be taken as an
index for the strength of the antiserum as well as for estimating the
amount of antigen present in a solution of unknown concentration.

It must be remarked that in mixtures of several antigens it is rather
difficult to find the exact concentration of one antigen because one
protein may change the reactivity of another, so that, if the concentration of the separate components is not known, any quantitative determination will be impossible. This could be demonstrated by the reaction between antisera prepared to a complete extract of the lens and
different lens proteins. The α-cristallin fraction reacts more intensively
than the other components and after mixing this fraction with the
β-cristallin the reactivity of the α-fraction is decreased. This phenomenon must be taken into account if a comparison has to be made
between antigens from different species or different stages of embryonic development, because the relative concentrations of the fractions may be different in different objects.

For filling the micro test-tubes with antigen and serum and for the
preparation of dilutions, microburettes are used, calibrated in microliters, in which the fluid can be moved by air-pressure changes. For
this purpose the microburette, by means of a narrow and thick-walled
rubber tube, is connected with a small reservoir, made from a piece
of rubber tubing (internal diameter about 10 mm). This reservoir and
a great part of the narrow tube are filled with water, so that between
the water and the fluid in the burette only a small air volume remains.
By changing the volume of the reservoir with a screw-clamp the burette
can be filled or emptied (Fig. 2).

The tubes are placed in a circular rack (Fig. 1) which fits on a
stand (hole E) and rests upon a ring (A); this ring is freely movable
along the rod and is resting itself on a second ring (B). The hole
(D) in the bottom plate of the rack is fitted for a pin (C) on ring A.
By taking ring A between thumb and fingers the rack may be turned
and lifted and so each of the tubes can be brought around the tip of
the microburette. For filling the burette, eventually one or two of the
holes, designed for the test-tubes may be widened in order to contain
a larger tube, supplying the saline or serum.

This design (Fig. 2) has been found to be very practicable for more rapid work. The rack was placed in the incubator, after the incubating period the tubes taken out and the result read against a dark background.

CAPILLARY METHOD

In experiments where only small amounts of antigen are present, it is useless to prepare a series of dilutions, and the initial concentration has to be taken as high as possible. Therefore, a method was developed, using narrow, thin-walled glass capillaries, so that for each test only one microliter was needed. From the extract this quantity was sucked up in the narrow capillary tube and then about the same volume of antiserum (or control fluid) followed. Both were blown out on a glass slide, mixed by stirring with the tube and the mixture again sucked up into the capillary. By repeating this a suitable mixing could be achieved and finally the mixture was brought in the middle of the tube, the ends of which were sealed by melting the glass in a micro flame. The tubes were put with their lower ends into plasticene and incubated during one hour, whereafter they were left standing over night at room temperature. Next day the result was read under a dissection microscope in dark-field illumination. Of course there were several control tubes, corresponding with the ordinary method.

The mixing of the reacting fluids is known to decrease the sensitivity as compared with the ring test. We found, by comparing both methods, the mean difference, expressed by the quotient of the last positive dilutions, to be about 5.

The increase in sensitivity by using the capillary method thus became about fourfold, using one microliter in stead of twenty in the ring test. (Of course, in both methods still smaller volumes may be used).

In some experiments only, a third method was used. The antigen extract was distributed over three watch-glasses and then frozen in dry ice and dried. For the reaction the antigen was dissolved directly in the antiserum or control fluid and with use of the capillary method sensitivity again was increased.

Preparation of antigen from embryos

The young lens-vesicle was cut out from the embryo by means of the ordinary glass-needle technique. In this way as little yolk or other materials as possible have been taken together with the lens antigen itself.

For focussing the microscope during dissection we used a modification of the device, published by La Rue (1932).

To the focussing wheel a lever of variable length was attached which could be moved by means of a flexible cable (choke cable from an automobile). Instead of moving the pedal, to which this cable was connected, up and down with the foot, the displacement of the cable was obtained by moving the foot in a horizontal direction. The cable was attached at the fore-end of the pedal and the axis of motion placed near to the heel, so that by rotating the leg in the knee the microscope could be focussed. This modification of the original design, invented by our instrument maker de Vries, has become very useful, being less tiresome because in every position the foot is resting on the floor.

The material was assembled on the top of a small cylindrical glass pestle, cooled in ice. The extract was prepared by grinding the material in a small glass-mortar, made from a thick-walled glass capillary (pyrex) of 2 mm internal diameter, about 25 mm long, and widened at the upper end. After grinding and adding a few microliters of saline the "mortar" was centrifuged and the supernatant fluid used.

RESULTS

Control experiments

COMPARATIVE EXPERIMENTS WITH BOYD'S TECHNIQUE
AND CAPILLARY TECHNIQUE

The well-known fact that the precipitin reaction in a mixture is somewhat less sensitive than the ring test was also demonstrated by the results of our experiments (Table 1). From each of the tubes, in which an antigen dilution had been prepared for the ring test, one microliter had been taken out into a capillary tube, mixed with the same volume of antiserum and the results of both tests compared.

TABLE 1

Relation (Q) between last dilution of antigen, reacting positive in Boyd's test (B) and in the capillary method (C)

	B	C	Q
Chicken lens (embryo) + frog lens antiserum	1600	400	4
Chicken lens (adult) + chicken lens antiserum	25600	3200	8
Frog lens + frog lens antiserum	51200	12800	4
Frog lens + frog lens antiserum	25600	12800	2
Frog lens + frog lens antiserum ($p_H = 9$)	6400	3200	2
		Mean $Q = 5$	

The difference in sensitivity has been expressed in the table by the quotient between the factors of the last positive dilutions. It may be concluded that the ring test is about five times more sensitive than the capillary test.

ORGAN SPECIFICITY OF THE ANTISERUM

In Table 2 the results have been given of precipitation reactions of lens-antiserum and extracts of other organs.

The number of experiments and of the negative and positive reactions as well as the last dilution index in case of positive tests has been presented. One of the antisera had to be rejected because of its weak specificity, but in all other sera this quality has been satisfactory, as may be seen from the facts in the table. Only the vitreous body has been reacting positively in three out of six experiments. Probably this can be explained by the possible presence of small parts of the lens, remaining adhered to the vitreous after this had been dissected out.

TABLE 2

Reactions between eye-lens antiserum and 5% extracts (in saline) from other organs

Organ (part)	adult frog		adult chicken		chick embryo	
Results:	neg.	pos.	neg.	pos.	neg.	pos.
muscle (leg of embryo)	3	—	1	—	15	—
liver	1	—	1	—	3	—
skin	5	—	3	—	4	—
brain	3	—	3	—	4	—
retina	5	—	1	—	4	—
iris	4	—	1	—		
vitreous corpse	—	1 (160)	1	1 (80)	3	1 (40)
eye cup (complete)					12	—

(The number of experiments has been given. In case of a positive reaction the last positive dilution has been indicated in parentheses).

SPECIES SPECIFICITY

By combining several portions of one antigen solution with different antisera and by combinations between one antiserum and different antigens an impression could be obtained about this quality. The results of the first method are presented in Table 3a and those of the second in Table 3b, the last positive dilution having been indicated.

TABLE 3

Species specificity

a. Reactions between one solution of antigen, combined with homologous and heterologous antisera.

Antigen from lens of:	Chicken lens antiserum	Frog lens antiserum
adult chicken	51200	25600
chick embryo (15 days)	25600	3200
chick embryo (9 days)	1600	800
adult frog	12800	51200

(indication of last positive dilution)

b. Reactions between one (adult frog lens) antiserum and lens antigens from different species.

antiserum no. 2		antiserum no. 7	
antigen	last dilution	antigen	last dilution
frog	32000	frog	16000
chicken	16000	chicken	8000

Certainly a small difference is present, caused by species specificity, although it is possible that in the second combination the exact concentration of the active antigen is varying with the species. Such a variation also may be present in the first experiments, if the antisera are gained by injections of quantitatively differently constituted antigens, but the effect may be less intense.

Obviously the lens antigen only is weakly species specific and strongly organ specific.

The presence of adult lens antigen in embryos

CHICK EMBRYOS

By means of the Boyd technique the presence of adult lens antigen in embryos 74 hours of age and older clearly could be demonstrated. Probably this result was due to the careful dissection and assembling of the lens material.

In a 72-hour embryo the reaction still was positive when 11 lens vesicles were dissolved in 10 microliters of saline, and in the 66 hours stage a positive result could be got by preparing an extract from 40 lens vesicles in 20 microliters saline. In the 60-hour embryo this method failed, however, and henceforth the capillary method was used, extract-

TABLE 4

Adult lens antigen in chick embryos

Age of embryo (hours)	Number of expts.	Number of lenses	Last. dil. Boyd's method.
192	1		6400
168	1		3200
144	1		3200
120	1		1600
96	1		800
84	1		400
74	1		400
72	1	11	+
66	1	40	+
60	1	40	—
capillary method:			
60	3	40	+; +; ++.
58	1	60	+
54	3	50; 30; 30.	±; ±; —.
51	1	50	—
48	1	50	—

ing the material, assembled from 20 to 30 embryos with about 4 microliters of saline.

By this procedure positive results were obtained in embryos of 60 and 58 hours (four experiments) and weakly positive reactions in material from 54-hour embryos. In 51- and 48-hour embryos only negative results could be noted.

Taking into account the possible individual variations, we thus safely may draw the conclusion that the 60-hour embryo already possesses the adult antigen (or one of the less antigens) and in a sufficient amount to be detectable by this method.

The change in quantity of the antigen is apparent from the fact that in younger stages the detection of it is becoming increasingly difficult. Also the results of our quantitative tests in older embryos demonstrate this phenomenon. The series of decreasing values of the last positive dilutions from 1/6400 in 8-day embryos to approximately 1/400 in 3-day embryos makes this clear.

In nearly all experiments the results have been checked by comparing the lens material with extracts from other parts of the same embryos. In all these controls the reaction gave negative results, even in extracts, prepared from eye-cups. Other control experiments, using normal serum, muscle antiserum as well as saline have been negative.

Because the time, required for operating so great a number of embryos became rather long, extending to about 6 hours, it was possible that, if the embryos were stored in this period at room temperature, they were changing too much. We, therefore, carried out some experiments in which the total number of eggs was divided into portions of ten and these were incubated one after another with intevals of one hour. So, during the dissection period, at each hour a portion of ten embryos became available.

The individual variation in rate of development remained, but the few exceptional cases were excluded from the experiments. Ordinarily, about 30 embryos out of 50 incubated eggs could be used, because of mortality or of low fertilisation percentage.

The results of these experiments in chick embryos have been presented in Table 4.

FROG EMBRYOS

In these experiments, material from embryos of Rana esculenta has been investigated. In most cases the embryos were reared before the experiment at 12°C for retarding the development. There was no opportunity to compare these results with the properties of embryos, reared at higher temperatures.

In the eldest stages the antigen material was assembled from about 50 to 100 embryos, in the younger stages some 200 embryos have been used for each experiment.

The results have been reported in Table 5 in which also the control experiments have been presented, because of the small number of these experiments.

In stage 18-19 (according to Shumway, 1940, 1942) one experiment was a failure, because of interference by a vast amount of yolk, resulting in a cloudiness in the extract that could not be removed by centrifuging at 4000 r.p.m. during a long period. In stage 19 two experiments gave negative results, whereas at the same stage a positive reaction could be obtained by drying the extract and dissolving the antigen directly in the sera, as has been described.

In stage 19-20 the result was positive, but no control experiments could be done.

From these facts it may be concluded that the appearance of the first positive reaction has been found at about stage 19 to 20.

MORPHOLOGY

According to the normal tables of development of the *chick embryo* (Keibel a.o. 1900) the formation of the lens-plate and its invagination

TABLE 5

Adult lens antigen in frog embryos

Stage (Shumway)	Antigen	Lens antiserum	Muscle antiserum	Normal serum
25	lens + eye-cup	+		
23	lens + eye-cup	+	—	
23	rest of embryo	—	—	
21—22	lens + eye-cup	+		
21—22	ventral epidermis	—	± (adhering mesoderm?)	
19—20	lens + eye-cup	+		
19	lens	—		
19	lens	—		

Antigen material dried and dissolved in the sera:

19	lens	+	—	—
17—18	lens ectoderm	—	—	—

takes place at the age of 42 to 50 hours. The separation of the lens vesicle from the epidermis can be found at the 60 to 63 hours' stage and thickening of its wall as a beginning of fiber differentiation takes place at about 70-hours stages. The microphotograph (Fig. 3) shows a section through the lens vesicle of a 60-hour embryo, where it is still opening to the surface.

According to our experience, at the 60-hour stage this connection between ectoderm and lens vesicle is constantly present.

In embryos of *Rana esculenta*, stage 19, according to Shumway, is characterized by the presence of a lens bud only, no vesicle having been formed yet (Fig. 4). In stage 20 the formation of a lens vesicle has taken place, but the vesicle is still very primitive (Fig. 5). Because of the presence of abundant yolk, the structure of the lens bud in Fig. 4 seems to be more irregular than it is.

Consequently the conclusion may be drawn, that the adult lens antigen in both species could be detected in stages before the complete formation of the lens-vesicle in which no specific morphological differentiation could be found.

DISCUSSION

The experimental results have demonstrated that organ-specific antigen(s) is(are) present in developmental stages where no specific differentiation of the lens-vesicle is visible, and even practically no difference can be found between the morphology of this primitive lens and the rudiments of nose and ear.

It therefore seems justifiable to draw the conclusion that chemical differentiation is preceding morphological differentiation. This answer to the question about the priority of these two modes of differentiation is contradicting the conclusion of Burke c.s. (1944), but the conclusion of these authors has not been based upon positive results.

The early appearance of chemical differentiation is substantiating the theory of chemo-differentiation which, since Huxley, has been discussed in embryological literature. It seems very unlikely that these important constituents of the adult lens would not have any significance in the period of construction of this organ-part. At least it may be supposed that the adult antigens, being organ-specific substances, also may represent organ-forming materials, enabling the embryo to build up its eye-lens. Whether these antigens also may be representing organ-determining substances cannot yet be stated, because they have not yet been detected in the period before the first beginning of the morphogenesis of the lens.

It is clear that preformationists have strong trumps in hand, if they state that qualitatively all specialised materials of the adult organism will be present at the onset of ontogenesis, because a theory of epigenetic creation of such substances during embryonic development only can get its evidence from negative results of experiments and these always may be explained by deficiency of technique.

Another question is that of the presence of other than adult antigens in the lens. Burke and collaborators are of the opinion that embryonic lens antigen, differing from that of the adult lens, may be present in young stages of development. These authors immunised rabbits by the 300-hour embryonic lens antigen and the immune sera reacted with younger stages than the adult antiserum. The explanation for this phenomenon seems to be at hand: there must be another antigen common to the 120-hour and 300-hour lens but not present in the adult lens. But now that we demonstrated the presence of adult antigen in still younger embryonic lenses the possibility remains that the different antisera, used by Burke, have been reacting with different intensity; as no control experiments have been reported, solution of this problem is difficult. It also may be remarked that these results only have been obtained by the complement fixation test, and we were necessitated to leave this test for the precipitin reaction. The fact, that Burke did not mention any difficulty when using this technique whereas we found a very weak specificity, is difficult to explain. Perhaps the mode of preparation of the antigen for immunization has been different. Burke reports the use of formalin in some cases for preserving this antigen, while in our experiments only fresh preparations were used. Denaturation may be expected by the treatment with formalin, and perhaps the antigen preparation of Burke contained less lipoids than ours, because they centrifuged it during 20 to 30 minutes at high speed; no data about the centrifugal force have been given, however.

In the experiments with 160-hour lens antiserum the authors themselves remarked that these sera were rather unspecific. They have based their opinion on the general damage, inflicted to embryos, and no control experiments have been reported. It seems possible that the presence of yolk in the material, used for immunising the rabbits has resulted in the production of antiserum against yolk, more than against the very small quantity of lens antigen that has been present. The reactions with yolk also may have disturbed some of the precipitin or complement fixation tests. Whether the embryonic antigen, met in the 300-hour lens, also may be a yolk antigen cannot be excluded nor can it be proved.

The possibility remains that a special embryonic lens antigen may be present. Moreover, it is possible that the ratio between the concentration of the different protein fractions of the lens will be changing during ontogeny. Such changes have been reported to occur in the lens during post-natal life, where a shift is found in the relative concentration of α- and β-cristallin. Such a change in quantitative relation between the different protein components of the lens would correspond with the differences in protein composition of the blood that have been found.

The increasing indexes of the last positive dilutions during the development from the 3-day to the 8-day embryo suggest a gradual increase during this period of development. Whether periods of more rapid increase do occur cannot yet be stated. Perhaps the period of lens induction is characterised by a large increase in quantity of the lens antigen, caused by the stimulus.

SUMMARY

It has been possible to demonstrate the presence of adult lens antigen in young embryonic lenses by means of the precipitin technique. In the chick embryo the youngest stages where the adult antigen could be detected were about 60 hours old and in the embryo of Rana esculenta the adult antigen was present from stage 19 to 20 (Shumway) on.

In the 60-hour chick embryo the young lens-vesicle still opens to the surface and no specific morphological differentiation can be observed. In the frog embryo the lens vesicle is absent in stage 19 and just has been formed in stage 20; in stage 19 only a lens bud is found.

Therefore it can be concluded that the chemical differentiation of the lens is preceding the morphological differentiation. This conclusion is contradictory to the results of Burke and collaborators (1944), but their opinion, like that of many others, has been based upon negative experimental results.

Our results thus do not permit the conclusion that in still younger stages the characteristic adult substances may be lacking. Improving the technique probably will result in positive reactions in these stages.

The suggestion has been made that the organ-specific lens substances really may be called organ-forming substances, whereas it still remains more doubtful whether they also can be ranged among the organ-determining substances.

The complement fixation test in our experiments has failed to give reliable and specific results. Some additional notes about the technique and the organ- and species-specificity of the antisera, used in these experiments, have been presented.

The authors are much indebted to the State Organization for pure scientific Research (Z.W.O.) for granting a subsidy, covering the greater part of the expenses of this work. The first series of experiments have been carried out in the State Laboratory for Veterinary Research at Amsterdam, director Dr. Frenkel. We want to express our gratitude to Dr. Frenkel for his hospitality and advice.

REFERENCES

Abe, M., Jap. journ. of Obst. a. Gynecol., **14**, 2 (1931).

Braus, H., Arch. Entw. mech. Org. **22**, 564 (1906).

Burke, V., N. P. Sullivan, H. Petersen and R. Weed, Journ. infect. Dis. **74**, 225 (1944).

Cooper, R. S., Journ. exp. Zool. **101**, 143 (1946).

——————————, Journ. exp. Zool., **107**, 397 (1948).

Dunbar, W. P., Zeitschr. f. Immun. forsch., **7**, 454 (1910). In the same article there is a communication from Uhlenhuth and Haendel.

Guggenheim, A., Zeitschr. f. Immun. forsch., **61**, 361 (1929).

Huxley, J. S., Nature **113**, 349 (1924).

Idzumi, S., Mitt. a. d. Med. Fak. Univ. Tokyo, **32**, 197 (1924).

Iwae, S., Mitt. d. med. Ges. zu Fukuoka (in japanese), **9**, 1 (1915). (cf. J. Needham, Chemical Embryology (1931), p. 1445).

Keibel, F. and K. Abraham, Normentafel zur Entwicklungsgeschichte des Huhnes, Jena (1900).

Kraus, R., R. Doerr and Sohma, Wien. Klin. Wochenschr., **30**, 1084 (1908).

Krause, A. C., Arch. of Ophthalmol., **13**, 187 (1935).

Kritchevski, I. L., Centralbl. Bakteriol. u. Parasitenk., **72** (Orig.), **81** (1914).

——————————, Journ. exp. Med., **24**, 233 (1916).

——————————, Journ. infect. Dis., **32**, 192 (1923).

Krusius, F. F., Zeitschr. f. Immun. forsch., **5**, 699 (1910).

La Rue, C., Science, **76**, 104 (1932).

Needham, J., Biochemistry and Morphogenesis, 1942.

Perlman, P. and T. Gustafson, Experientia, **4**, 481 (1948).

Rössle, J., Münch. Med. Woch., **52**, 1276 (1905).

Schechtman, A. M., Journ. of exp. Zool., **105**, 329 (1947).

——————————, Proc. Soc. exp. Biol. a. Med., **68**, 263 (1948).

Shumway, W., Anat. Rec., **78**, 139 (1940) and Anat. Rec.,**83**, 309 (1942).

Uhlenhuth, P., Festschrift Robert Koch (1903), 49.

Wilkoewitz, K. and H. Ziegenspeck, Botan. Arch. **22**, 229 (1928).

Witebsky, E., Zeitschr. f. Immun. forsch., **58**, 297 (1928).

—————————— and J. Szepsenwol, C. R. Soc. de Biol., **115**, 921 (1934).

Wollman, E., Ph. Gonzalez and P. Ducrest, C. R. Soc. Biol., **127** 1188 (1938a).

——————————, —————————— and ——————————, C. R. Soc. Biol., **127**, 668 (1938).

14

the development in vitro of chimeric aggregates of dissociated embryonic chick and mouse cells*

A. MOSCONA
Laboratory of Developmental Biology,
Rockefeller Institute for Medical Research, New York, New York

Various embryonic tissues and organ rudiments can be dissociated into suspensions of discrete, viable cells following treatment with Ca- and Mg-free saline and trypsin.[1-3] When cultivated in vitro under appropriate conditions, such cells reaggregate into compact clusters (Figs. 1-6), which subsequently re-establish tissue-like relationships and differentiate histotypically.[2, 3] These findings, originally established for chondrogenic, nephrogenic, and myogenic cells, have recently been extended to other embryonic tissues.[3-8]

If two different types of embryonic chick cells are intermingled in the same suspension, the resulting aggregates incorporate both types of cells; however, in the course of the further development of such heterotypic aggregates,† the diverse types of cells form distinct, histogenetically uniform groupings.[2] The problem of grouping of animal cells in its relation to morphogenesis was discussed in detail by Weiss[9] in reference to the concepts of "affinities"[10] and "coaptation";[11] its experimental implications were explored in the chick embryo[12] and in amphibian embryos[13-14] and larvae[15, 17] and also under conditions of tissue culture.[3, 18-20] Several of these studies strongly suggested that cells of diverse lineages manifested characteristic preferences in establishing intercellular contacts and tissue contiguity. This view was further

Reprinted from the Proceedings of the National Academy of Sciences,
Vol. 43, No. 1, pp. 184-194, January, 1957

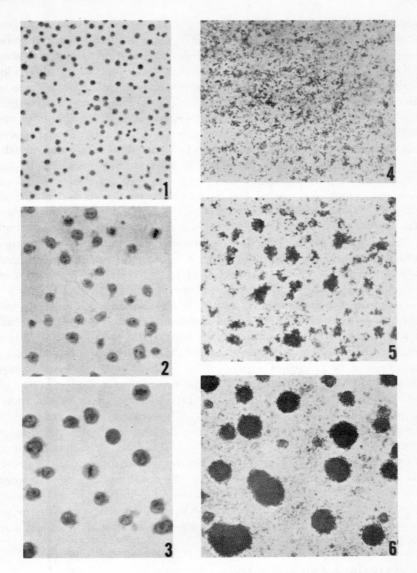

Fig. 1. Suspension of chondrogenic cells from limb-buds of chick (4-day) and mouse (12-day) embryos. Ehrlich's hematoxylin-Biebrich's. ×160.

Fig. 2. Suspension of chick chondrogenic cells. ×460.

Fig. 3. Suspension of mouse chondrogenic cells. ×460.

Fig. 4. Dissociated chondrogenic cells beginning to aggregate. 2-hour culture; living. ×50.

Fig. 5. A similar culture to that in Fig. 4, after 12 hours.

Fig. 6. A similar culture to that in Fig. 4, after 36 hours.

supported by the results of recent experiments on heterotypic aggregates of chick cells[2] which convincingly demonstrated a type-specific grouping of cells in the formation and development of such aggregates. These observations fell short of proof, however, due to the difficulty of identifying early embryonic chick cells when dissociated into discrete units in suspension; under these conditions, nearly all types of such cells look alike, and their identities in heterotypic mixtures are therefore not readily determined. The obvious solution to this impasse was to have cells marked in a way which would make them individually distinguishable in a mixed population. In searching for suitable "marker cells," an attempt was made to exploit the morphological differences between chick and mouse cells; mouse cell neclei are larger than chick cell nuclei and stain differently with basic stains and hematoxylin. Previous studies have shown that mouse and chick tissue can be successfully cultured in heterologous media[21, 22] and maintained simultaneously in culture without apparent incompatibility;[23-25] it has further been noticed that under such conditions the differences of size and staining properties of the cells and nuclei of the two species are retained.

Accordingly, the feasibility of obtaining composite aggregates, consisting of both chick and mouse cells, was explored. Preliminary experiments[26] demonstrated that aggregates formed in suspensions of intermingled chick and mouse cells incorporated, under appropriate conditions, cells of both species. Upon further cultivation, such heterologous aggregates developed histogenetically in accordance with the origin of their cellular components. Due to the differences in size and the staining properties of chick and mouse nuclei, the two types of cells could be easily distinguished and their precise distribution in the aggregates determined. As a further variation along this line, dissociated mouse tumor cells were introduced into suspensions of embryonic chick cells, and the structure and composition of the resulting aggregates were examined. With the aid of these differential cellular systems, various aspects of tissue reconstruction and development in cell aggregates were studied. Some of the observations bearing on the problem of cellular grouping are reported below.

MATERIALS AND METHODS

The preparation by treatment with trypsin of cell suspensions from embryonic organ rudiments and tumor tissue followed procedures described previously.[1-3] The experiments reported here were made with chondrogenic, mesonephric, and hepatic cells from chick and mouse embryos. Different age combinations of these tissues were tried, as it turned out that embryonic chick and mouse cells of diverse ages and types migrated and aggregated at different rates. This communication reports on tissues from 3- to 5-day chick embryos and from 11- to 13-day mouse embryos. The tumor tissue used was pigmented melanoma S91, maintained in a DBA/2JN strain of mice. Suspensions of cells were mixed in the desired proportions, and aliquots of the heterologous mixtures were distributed into hollow-ground (Maximow) slides with 1.0 cc liquid culture medium in each. The medium consisted of 40 percent chicken serum, 40 percent embryo extract (freshly prepared from 10- to 12-day chick embryos), and 20 percent Earl's balanced salt solution. Horse serum was sometimes added in proportions not exceeding 4 percent of the total quantity of the medium. The culture medium was kept at room temperature for about an hour before being used. The slides with the cell suspensions were sealed and incubated at 38°C for twenty-four hours. The medium was then changed, and the cultures maintained for an additional day or two. The aggregates which had formed by that time were then transferred to a plasma clot for further cultivation in watch glasses. After fixation in Zenker's fixative, the cultures were sectioned at 6 or 8μ, and the sections were stained briefly with Ehrlich's hematoxylin and Biebrich's scarlet, which rendered cell nuclei of the chick a light purple tint, while mouse nuclei stained a deep blue.

ISOTOPIC COMBINATIONS OF CHICK AND MOUSE CELLS

Dissociated chondrogenic cells from the limb-buds of 4-day chick embryos were thoroughly intermingled in suspension with chrondrogenic cells from the limb-buds of 12-day mouse embyos (Figs. 1-3) The amount of mouse cells was about double that of chick cells. At this stage of development, the presumptive chondroblasts of the limb-bud are still in the form of stellate mesenchyme cells. The aggregates that formed in such suspensions were cultured for 6 days. Histological sections showed that they consisted of typical cartilage formed by chick and mouse cells interspersed with each other (Fig. 7). Both types of cells were intimately associated and bound by the common cartilaginous matrix into a uniform tissue fabric: the matrix surrounding a mouse cell merged quite imperceptibly with that around the chick cell next to it (Figs. 8-10). Cultures of such aggregates were maintained for periods up to one month without evidence of deterioration or incompatibility between the chick and mouse cells. Evidently the common histogenetic fabric reconstructed by the cells under these conditions was acceptable to both chick and mouse cells and suitable for their histotypical development.

An additional instance of such formative integration of interspersed chick and mouse cells was observed in combinations of liver cells.

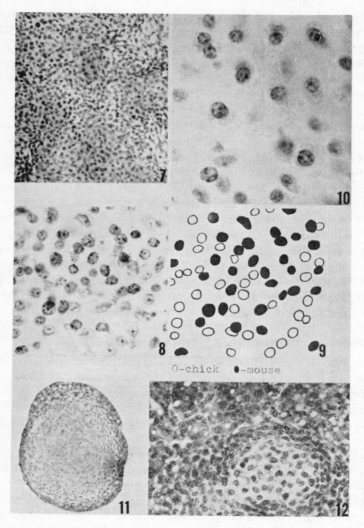

Fig. 7. Cartilage masses composed of interspersed chick and mouse chondrogenic cells. ×120: (Figs. 7-19. Stained with Ehrlich's hematoxylin-Biebrich's scarlet.)

Fig. 8. Same at ×280. Compare with Fig. 9.

Fig. 9. Outlines of nuclei of Fig. 8 to show the distribution of mouse (*circles*) and chick (*dark*) nuclei.

Fig. 10. Full differentiated, composite cartilage, showing chick and mouse chondrocytes in a common matrix. ×980.

Fig. 11. Aggregate of mouse liver and chick chondrogenic cells, showing a "capsule" of hepatic tissue surrounding the globule of cartilage. 4-day culture. ×80.

Fig. 12. A 5-day culture of an aggregate of mouse hepatic and chondrogenic cells, showing the cells separated according to types. ×620.

Liver tissue was obtained from 5-day chick embryos and from 13-day mouse embryos. The dissociated cells from both sources aggregated to form hepatic cords that consisted of interspersed chick and mouse cells producing glycogen or fat. In this case as well, the cells, regardless of their generic origin, reconstructed a common tissue fabric which developed in accordance with their pre-established properties.

HETEROTYPIC COMBINATIONS OF CHICK AND MOUSE CELLS

The cellular architecture of aggregates formed by cells of two diverse histogenetic types was quite different from that of isotypic cell aggregates. Mixtures of dissociated chick chondrogenic cells and mouse liver cells formed aggregates in which, after 4 days in culture, both cartilage and hepatic tissue were present. In this case, however, the two cell types had become regionally separated: the cartilage cells formed one or more central clusters, and the hepatic cells were situated around the periphery of the cartilage. In the present case, contrary to isotypic combinations, the two constituent tissues were not of mixed, chimeric composition, but each contained cells of the species that had furnished the respective cell type; that is, cartilage consisted solely of chick cells, hepatic tissue exclusively of mouse cells (Figs. 11, 12). This spatial arrangement was quite characteristic for the heterologous, as well as the homologous, combinations of these two types of cells (see also Wolf[24]).

Such type-specific grouping of cells was perhaps even more striking in combinations of mesonephric and chondrogenic cells, because of the structural characteristics of nephric tissue. In composite aggregates of 4-day chick mesonephric cells and 12-day mouse chondrogenic cells, cultured for 5 days, both kidney and cartilage cells reconstituted their recognizable tissue patterns (Figs. 13-16). The cells became consistently grouped according to type: chick chondroblasts formed areas of cartilage, mouse nephroblasts built nephric tubules. Careful examination of this material revealed no chick cells that had become chondrocytes or mouse cells that had turned into nephrocytes. Single cells that were occasionally trapped in a nonmatching environment, if they took and multiplied, developed according to their original identities. In the reversed combination of cells, namely, in aggregates of mouse mesonephric with chick chondrogenic cells, similar type-specific, separate groupings of the corresponding tissues were formed. The reconstituted nephric and chondrified showed no regular distribution within the aggregates such as was typical of combinations of hepatic and chondrogenic cells.

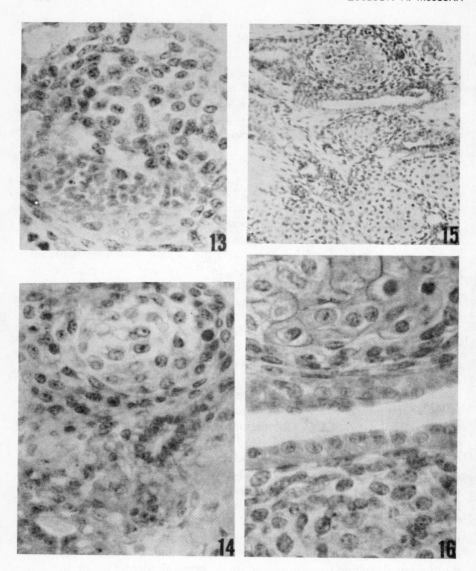

Fig. 13. Aggregate of mouse chondrogenic and chick mesonephric cells, showing groups of cells with beginning differentiation .3-day culture. ×250.

Fig. 14. 4-day culture of a chimeric aggregate as in Fig. 13, showing advanced histodifferentiation. ×250.

Fig. 15. 6-day culture of a chimeric aggregate as in Fig. 13, showing mosaic distribution of the cellular groupings. ×100.

Fig. 16. Enlarged part of Fig. 15 to show the topographical proximity of the reconstituted chick and mouse tissues. ×830.

COMBINATIONS OF EMBRYONIC CHICK CELLS
AND MOUSE MELANOMA CELLS

In another aspect of this study of the grouping properties of embryonic cells, observations were made on their behavior in the presence of tumor cells. Dissociated hepatic or chondrogenic cells of the chick embryo were intermingled in suspension with dissociated cells of pigmented melanoma S91 of mice (Figs. 17, 18). Embryonic and tumor cells became incorporated in common clusters, which were then further cultured for 3-5 days. Aggregates of chondrogenic chick cells and S91 cells were found to consist of a central core of cartilage surrounded by S91 cells. In older cultures, scattered melanoma cells had infiltrated into the cartilage. Aggregates of hepatic chick cells and S91 cells consisted of a central core of melanoma cells surrounded by a compact capsule of hepatic parenchyma (Fig. 19). It appears, then, that also when intermixed with tumor cells of this type, the embryonic cells clearly manifested their tendency for typewise association as well as for type-specific localization—cartilage centrally, liver peripherally.

COMMENT

The experiments reported in the foregoing demonstrated the following facts. (a) Chick and mouse cells, when cultured together in vitro, retained characteristics by which they could be identified as to their origins. (b) When cells from both species, belonging to the *same* histogenetic type, were cultured in random mixtures, they combined to form uniform chimeric tissues. (c) Chick and mouse cells belonging to *different* histogenetic types, however, did not readily combine but gave rise each to its discrete type-specific differentiation. Previous experiments with heterotypic cell combinations from a single species (chick embryo) had already suggested that dissociated cells tended to preserve their original type specificities and to sort out and differentiate accordingly:[2] these observations, together with the results obtained presently with cells marked clearly as to their species origin, lead to the conclusions that, under the experimental conditions explored, (1) type specificity prevailed over species specificity in guiding the association and grouping of embryonic cells of the given types of differentiation and (2) no transformation of cells of one type into another had taken place. It should be stressed at this point that these conclusions apply to cells which had evidently reached determination prior to their being dissociated, although they had not, at that time, become typically differentiated. It is thus conceivable that different results may be obtained with cells from earlier or later stages of development as well as with other types of cells, or different experimental conditions.

The problem of type-specific development in these experiments, as in the earlier ones, has two different aspects. One refers to the formation of the primary aggregates of cells, and the other to the sorting out of the cells according to kind, concurrently with or following aggregation and their subsequent differentiation. The former aspect, concerned mainly with the mechanisms of aggregation, has been only parenthetically mentioned here, and its discussion will therefore be postponed. In view of the pertinence of these problems to the observations reported, the following brief comment should be included. The formation of all types of aggregates and their histogenesis in vitro may be markedly affected by a variety of factors. Environmental changes, such as of the physical and chemical properties of the medium or the substrate, markedly influence cellular aggregation by their differential effects on the diverse types of cells. Changes in the proportionate concentrations of different cell types intermixed in the same culture become reflected in the histological development of the ensuing aggregates.[2] As mentioned before, the rates of migration of different types of cells, as well as of cells of different generic origin, vary considerably under identical conditions. For instance, mouse mesonephric cells migrate at a slower rate than chick mesonephric cells; in cultures containing both types of cells, this difference leads eventually to the formation of aggregates in which chick mesonephric cells predominate. Whether the different rates of migration are due to intrinsic cellular factors, to a differential response by the cells to culture conditions, or to specific activating stimuli is presently not clear.

Following formation of the primary cell aggregates, or perhaps concurrently with it, histologically identifiable tissues begin to develop, and eventually the cluster of cells becomes an organized tissue fabric. The available evidence suggests strongly that the processes of tissue formation are preceded or accompanied by a reshuffling of the aggregated cells; when more than one type of cell is incorporated in the cluster, they become sorted out to form type-specific cell groupings. The precise manner in which this occurs is still obscure, but time-lapse motion pictures, presently being undertaken in this laboratory, are expected to furnish pertinent information.

The structural differences between iso- and heterotypic cell combinations provide a striking indication of the specificities involved in cellular interactions whch lead to groupng. In the tissues reconstituted from isotypic chick and mouse cells, the cells remained intermingled

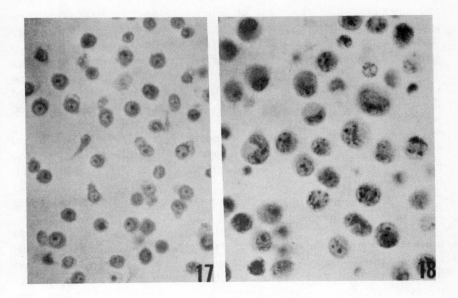

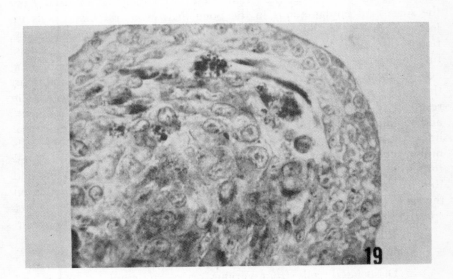

Fig. 17. Suspension of chick liver cells. ×530.
Fig. 18. Suspension of S91 melanoma cells. ×530.
Fig. 19. Section through a composite aggregate of hepatic chick and S91 cells, cultured for 4 days and showing a "capsule" of liver tissue surrounding the cluster of melanoma cells. ×530.

and interspersed in the form of cellular mosaics, without becoming segregated according to species origin. On the other hand, in aggregates of heterotypic cells the different types of cells became arranged in separate groups, so that the aggregates assumed the appearance of tissue mosaics. Thus, under the present experimental conditions, the type identities, rather than the generic identities, of the cells determined the manner of grouping. Typical grouping selectivity was also manifested by the dissociated embryonic cells when confronted with cells of the S91 tumor. However, following histogenesis of the embryonic tissue, S91 cells began, in some cases, secondarily to infiltrate between the normal cells. The nature of such manifestations, as well as the generality of such interactions, will become clearer when more is known of other combinations of dissociated normal and tumor cells and their patterns of aggregation.

The interpretation of cellular grouping in chimeric aggregates in terms of preferential, type-specific interactions between cells conforms well with observations on the tissue-specific localization of cells injected into the chick embryo[12] and into irradiated mice.[27-31] That the properties involved are effective across generic differences, not only under conditions of culture but in the organism as well, may be inferred from the successful implantations in the bone marrow of rat blood cells injected intravenously into irradiated mice.[28] In this connection, the question of the stability of chimeric cell aggregates is of interest. The successful persistence in vitro of cartilage chimeras beyond the embryonic age of their constituent cells suggested that, under such conditions, the cells, although generically alien, remained histocompatible. The response of heterologous combinations to suitable immune environments and to implantation into embryos and adults should provide additional information on the stability or the differential susceptibility of the cells under such conditions. Studies in this direction might also furnish information on the nature of histogenetic interactions between cells and the "recognition" (Weiss) effects involved, i.e., whether they function on the same basis as antibody-antigen systems[11,32,33] or whether they reflect specific properties, typical of this particular aspect of cellular behavior.

SUMMARY

1. Dissociated cells from various organ rudiments of chick and mouse embryos when intermixed in suspension cultures, readily aggregated and combined to form composite, chimeric tissues. Under suitable conditions of culture, such reconstituted tissues differentiated histotypically. This communication reports on combinations of chondrogenic,

nephrogenic, and hepatogenic cells of chick and mouse embryos and S91 mouse melanoma cells.

2. In aggregates of intermixed chick and mouse cells of same type (i.e., chick and mouse chondrogenic cells) the cells reconstructed a uniform fabric which differentiated histotypically into a chimeric tissue consisting of interspersed chick and mouse cells.

3. In aggregates of intermixed chick and mouse cells of different types (i.e., chick nephrogenic and mouse chondrogenic cells) the cells became associated according to type and formed separate groupings which developed in accordance with the original histogenetic properties of the cells.

4. Due to the clear morphological differences between chick and mouse cells, it was possible precisely to identify and localize them in the chimeric aggregates. The evidence thus obtained suggested conclusively that (a) in the course of tissue reconstruction the dissociated embryonic cells became grouped preferentially, according to their original type identities, regardless of their generic origin, and (b) under the present experimental conditions no transformation of one cell type to another was observed.

ACKNOWLEDGEMENTS

The author wishes to thank Dr. Paul Weiss, head of the Laboratory of Developmental Biology, for his interest and indispensable advice throughout this study. The aid of Dr. Dorothea Bennett in some phases of this work is gratefully acknowledged.

REFERENCES

[1]Moscona, A., *Exptl. Cell Research*, **3**, 535, 1952.

[2]Moscona, A., *Proc. Soc. Exptl. Biol. Med.*, **92**, 410, 1956.

[3]Moscona, A. and H. Moscona, *J. Anat.*, **86**, 287, 1952.

[4]Weiss, P. and R. James, *Exptl. Cell Research*, Suppl. 3, p. 381, 1955.

[5]Cavanaugh, M. W., *J. Exptl. Zool.*, **128**, 573, 1955.

[6]Cavanaugh, M. W., *Exptl. Cell Research*, **9**, 42, 1955.

[7]Grobstein, C., *J. Exptl. Zool.*, **130**, 319, 1955.

[8]Trinkaus, J. P. and P. W. Groves, these *Proceedings*, **41**, 784, 1955.

*Research aided by grants (Paul Weiss, principal investigator) from the American Cancer Society (through the Committee on Growth, National Research Council) and the Public Health Service, National Institutes of Health.

†The following terms will be used: (1) *isotypic* and (2) *heterotypic* to designate suspensions consisting of (1) predominantly one type of cell and (2) two or more cell types; (3) *homologous* and (4) *heterologous* for cells from embryos of the same specie (3) or (4) a mixture of cells from two species (i.e., chick and mouse cells).

[9]Weiss, P., *Yale J. Biol. Med.*, **19**, 235, 1947.

[10]Holtfreter, J., *Arch. f. exptl. Zellforsch.*, **23**, 620, 1939.

[11]Weiss, P., *Quart. Rev. Biol.*, **25**, 177, 1950.

[12]Weiss, P. and G. Andres, *J. Exptl. Zool.*, **121**, 449, 1952.

[13]Holtfreter, J., *J. Morphol.*, **80**, 25, 1947.

[14]Townes, P. L. and J. Holtfreter, *J. Exptl. Zool.*, **128**, 53, 1955.

[15]Chiakulas, J. J., *J. Exptl. Zool.*, **121**, 383, 1952.

[16]Baltzer, F., *Rev. suisse Zool.*, **48**, 413, 1941.

[17]Andres, G., *Genetica*, **24**, 1, 1949.

[18]Willmer, M. A., in *Essays on Growth and Form* (Oxford: Oxford Univ. Press, 1945).

[19]Twitty, V. C. and M. C. Niu, *J. Exptl. Zool.*, **108**, 405, 1948.

[20]Abercrombie, M. and J. E. M. Heaysman, *Exptl. Cell Research*, **5**, 111, 1953.

[21]Fell, H. B. and H. Gruneberg, *Proc. Roy. Soc. London, B*, 127, 257, 1939.

[22]Fell, H. B., *Science Progr.*, No. 162, p. 212, 1953.

[23]Grobstein, C. and J. S. Youngner, *Science*, **110**, 501, 1949.

[24]Wolff, E., *Bull. Soc. Zool. France*, **79**, 357, 1954.

[25]Wolff, E. and D. Bresch, *Compt. rend. Acad. sci.* (Paris), **240**, 1014, 1955.

[26]Reported at the International Congress of Developmental Biology at Brown University, Providence, Rhode Island, July, 1956.

[27]Lindsley, D. L., T. T. Odell, Jr., and F. G. Tausche, *Proc. Soc. Exptl. Biol. Med.*, **90**, 512, 1955.

[28]Ford, C. E., J. Hamerton, D. W. H. Barnes, and J. F. Loutit, *Nature*, **177**, 452, 1956.

[29]Miller, C. L., *Nature*, **178**, 142, 1956.

[30]Mitchison, N. A., *Brit. J. Exptl. Pathol.*, **37**, 239, 1956.

[31]Russel, E. S., L. J. Smith, and F. A. Lawson, *Science*, **124**, 1076, 1956.

[32]Billingham, R. E., L. Brent, and P. B. Medawar, *Nature*, **172**, 603, 1953.

[33]Tyler, A., in *Analysis of Development* (Philadelphia: W. B. Saunders Co., 1955).

15

autoradiography of
the interzone between tissues
in inductive interaction*

CLIFFORD GROBSTEIN
Department of Biological Sciences, Stanford University

Accumulating evidence indicates that materials active in certain inductive interactions can be demonstrated under appropriate conditions at some distance from their tissue source (Niu and Twitty, '53; Grobstein, '53; McKeehan, '58). The nature of such inductive materials is not yet fully defined, but the evidence suggests that they are large molecules (Grobstein, '56a). The possibility that they are normal components of the intercellular substance or matrix has been suggested (Grobstein, '55a).

It follows that information is needed on the production, mobility and metabolism of macromolecular materials in the vicinity of inductively active tissues. The present dearth of information stems at least in part from the difficulty of staining, or otherwise visualizing, materials of the embryonic intercellular matrix. It seemed possible that useful information might be obtained by radio-isotopic labeling coupled with autoradiography, a technique already employed to follow exchange of substances between tissues in inductive interaction (Waddington and Sirlin, '55). In the experiments to be reported autoradiography is applied to the trans-filter induction system previously described (Grobstein, '56b).

The system examined is metanephrogenic mesenchyme and embryonic dorsal spinal cord of the 11-day mouse embryo combined

Reprinted from The Journal of Experimental Zoology
Vol. 142, Nos. 1-3, October-December, 1959

in vitro. It was demonstrated earlier that, under the conditions employed, the metanephrogenic mesenchyme never forms epithelial tubules when cultured alone, but forms tubules regularly when in close association with dorsal spinal cord (Grobstein, '55b). The reaction proceeds across membrane filters up to 60-80 μ in thickness without cytoplasmic contact (Grobstein, '57; Grobstein and Dalton, '57). There is evidence that dorsal spinal cord deposits in the filter a protein-containing material which corresponds closely in extent with the area of tubule formation in the overlying metanephrogenic mesenchyme (Grobstein, '56b). The protein-containing material, by the procedures tested, stains irregularly and with difficulty. The experiments reported here demonstrate that a labeled material of similar distribution is produced by dorsal spinal cord pre-incubated in a mixture of tritiated amino acids.

MATERIAL AND METHODS

The procedures used were identical with those described earlier (Grobstein, '56b), with minor exceptions noted below. Dorsal spinal cord and metanephrogenic mesenchyme from 11-day mouse embryos were placed immediately opposite each other on a membrane filter[1], by a technique designed to assure close adherence of the tissue to the filter. The tissues were held in place by a chicken plasma clot. The assembly of filter, tissues, clot, and supporting ring and rods, was placed in a glass tissue dish in contact with a subjacent drop of nutrient fluid and incubated at 37.5°C in a CO_2-gassed and humidified incubator.

Dorsal spinal cord was labeled by pre-incubation at 37.5°C in a solution of tritiated amino acids[2] in Tyrodes solution for times specified below. The labeled tissues were washed through two 10-minute changes

---

[1]Obtained from Millipore Filter Corp., Bedford, Mass. All filters were of 25 ± 5 microns thickness from the same samples earlier used for electron microscopy (Grobstein and Dalton, '57). The least porous filter used is designated TV, the intermediate porosity TH and the most porous TA.

[2]I am indebted to Dr. Charles Yanofsky for the tritiated amino acids which were prepared for another investigation. Seventeen amino acids were combined in the following proportions: alanine (75.2), arginine·HCl (77.2), aspartic acid (78.0), cysteine (10.2), glutamic acid (103.6), glycine (31.2), histidine · HCl · H_2O (15.4), isoleucine (54.8), leucine (93.6), lysine · HCl (103.6), methionine (33.4), phenylalanine (58.0), proline (45.8), serine (36.2), threonine (36.6), tyrosine (37.4), valine (90.4). The dry mixture was tritiated by a commercial laboratory. It was dissolved in a distilled water at a concentration of 1 mg total amino acids per ml. The resulting stock solution had an activity of 0.142 mC/ml. When chromatographed by Dr. Irving Crawford activity was found to be strongest in arginine and lysine, fairly strong in leucine and phenylalanine, and quite weak in the remainder. This stock solution was stored frozen, and thawed to prepare each labeling medium by dilution 1: 100 in Tyrodes solution.

of Tyrodes before being placed on the filter. Dorsal spinal cord subjected to this procedure was found in preliminary experiments to be capable of transfilter induction of tubules in metanephrogenic mesenchyme.

Following varying periods of culture the assemblies were removed from the culture dish and immersed immediately in 10 percent formalin in absolute alcohol, the fixative earlier found to preserve protein-containing material in the filter. After one hour the filter, and affixed tissues and clot, were washed in absolute alcohol, removed from the plastic ring, cleared in toluene and embedded in paraffin. Serial sections transverse to the filter were cut at 5 μ, and mounted three sections per slide. Eastman Kodak AR-10 stripping film was placed over the sections, which were exposed in the refrigerator before photographic development for three intervals, usually 14, 28 and 56 days. Comparison of radioactivity was made only between slides processed together. Grain counts were made of representative cultures, viewed with a 100X oil immersion lens, using a reticule to define a constant area of twenty 6 μ $\times$ 6 μ sequares (total area: 720 μ^2). The recorded counts represent the average for a particular region counted for each of three sections of the culture. The regions counted are shown in Figure 1. Region A represents filter free of cytoplasmic penetration by spinal cord, region B metanephrogenic mesenchyme immediately adjacent to the filter, and region C filter at a distance from the tissue assumed to be free of all but background radiation.

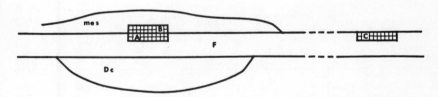

Fig. 1. Diagram of culture cross-section showing counting areas. A, filter interzone counting area; B, mesenchyme counting area; C, filter background counting area; Dc, spinal cord; mes, metanephrogenic mesenchyme.

RESULTS

Preliminary experiments showed that uptake and labeling of dorsal spinal cord exposed to tritiated amino acids, as indicated in autoradiograms, was significant by one hour of incubation, increased considerably by two hours, and was not much further increased by 4 hours of incubation. Labeling was stronger when the tritiated amino acids were

dissolved in Tyrodes solution than when they were dissolved in a
1 : 1 mixture of horse serum and Tyrodes. Labeling over the filter was
discernible only when the spinal cord was very heavily labeled, i.e., only
a small fraction of the fixed label was present in the filter. The grain
count was increased over both labeled and unlabeled tissues when
fixation involved Zenker acetic, presumably due to chemo-activation
of the photographic emulsion.

Six experiments were conducted, of which the results of counts on
14 cultures in two experiments will be described. In one experiment,
12 pieces of spinal cord were pre-incubated in tritiated amino acids
in horse serum and Tyrodes for 4 hours, washed in two 10-minute
changes of horse serum and Tyrodes, and placed on 12 TH filters.
Freshly dissected, unlabeled metanephrogenic mesenchyme was added
to the opposite side of 6 of these filters. Two pieces of unlabeled dorsal
spinal cord were placed on two additional filters as controls. The nutrient medium was horse serum, Tyrodes and 9-day chick embryo juice
(2:2:1). Following 7 hours of incubation two cultures each of labeled
spinal cord with and without mesenchyme were fixed in alcohol-formalin.
At 24 hours two more of each of these, plus the two controls, were
fixed. The remainder of the cultures were fixed at 48 hours. The autoradiograms were developed after 16, 57 and 87 days of exposure. Grain
counts were made on the 87 day exposures.

TABLE 1

Grain counts over regions indicated in Figure 1

Incubation	A	B	C	$\frac{\text{A-C}}{\text{C}}$	$\frac{\text{B-C}}{\text{C}}$	$\frac{\text{A-C}}{\text{B-C}}$
7 hrs.	43	89	10	3.3	7.9	2.4
	70	138	15	3.7	8.2	2.2
24 hrs.	32	107	16	1	5.7	5.7
	41	117	12	2.4	8.8	4.6
48 hrs.	52	138	24	1.1	4.8	4.1
	68	148	15	3.7	8.9	2.4

There was no noticeable difference between the amount of label in
the filter in the presence or absence of metanephrogenic mesenchyme,
and the control cultures showed no sign of radioactivity. Activity was
extremely high in the spinal cord and detectably higher than background
in the filter in the sector adjacent to the cord. The grain counts for the

6 cultures with mesenchyme are given in Table 1. Although the counts are low, it is clear that label is present in both the filter and mesenchyme. Over the filter, the increment over the background count ranges from 1.0 to 3.7 times the background count, over the mesenchyme on the opposite side of the filter from 4.8 to 8.9 times background. In the small sample represented there was no significant difference in the grain counts after 7, 24, and 48 hours of culturing, i.e., so far as could be told maximum labeling had occurred by 7 hours.

The experiment was repeated employing an altered labeling procedure, a different nutrient medium,[3] shorter culture periods and varying filter porosities. Dorsal spinal cord was pre-incubated for two hours in tritiated amino acids in Tyrodes without horse serum, and washed for one hour in Tyrodes. Four pieces were placed on TH filters, two on TA filters, and two on TV filters. Two control unlabeled pieces were placed on TH filters. Metanephrogenic mesenchyme was added in all instances directly opposite the spinal cord. After one hour of incubation one labeled and one unlabeled culture on TH filters were fixed in

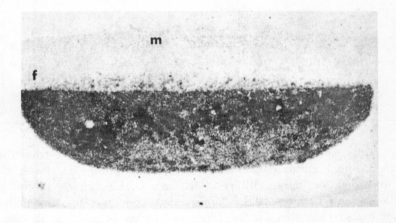

Fig. 2. X-section of culture of dorsal spinal cord and metanephrogenic mesenchyme with TA filter between. Spinal cord labeled in tritiated amino acids in Tyrodes for two hours, culture fixed at 24 hours, autoradiogram exposed for 28 days. Cf. Figure 1. Heavy concentration of grains over spinal cord, whose outline is relatively sharp. At filter interface (f) note evidence of cytoplasmic penetration approximately one-half filter thickness. Beyond this zone grains are less abundant until mesenchyme (m) is reached, where grains are somewhat more abundant. ×220.

---

[3]Eagle's basal medium supplemented with 10% horse serum and 3% 9-day chick embryo juice. I am indebted to Dr. Aron Moscona for his suggestion of this medium.

alcohol-formalin; at three and 6 hours one additional labeled culture on TH filters was similarly fixed; and at 24 hours all the remaining cultures were fixed. Autoradiograms were exposed for 14 and 28 days; counts were made on the longer exposure.

The control cultures showed no radioactivity. Results on the labeled cultures are given in Table 2. The counts are considerably higher than in the earlier experiment, but the data are otherwise concordant. The increment of filter counts over background in the 24 hour cultures ranges from 7.2 to 16.1 times background, while the same ratio for the mesenchyme just beyond the filter ranges from 9.8 to 24. These data include the three filter porosities. In the small sample there is no reliable correlation of counts with porosity.

TABLE 2

Grain counts over regions indicated in Figure 1

Incubation and Filter	A	B	C	$\frac{A-C}{C}$	$\frac{B-C}{C}$	$\frac{A-C}{B-C}$
1 hr.—TH	50	41	18	1.8	1.3	0.72
3 hr.—TH	155	156	13	10.9	10.9	1.0
6 hr.—TH	211	314	17	11.4	17.5	1.5
24 hr.—TH	213	282	26	7.2	9.8	1.4
TV	297	304	27	10.0	10.0	1.0
TV	188	275	11	16.1	24.0	1.5
TA	209	282	17	11.3	16.6	1.4
TA	222	279	21	9.6	12.3	1.3

Counts on the 6-hour culture are not notably different from those on the 24-hour cultures. Counts on the 3-hour culture are lower than any recorded for longer culture intervals, and differ from all but one of the 24-hour cultures in that the average count for the mesenchyme is not higher than that for the filter, but rather is equal to it. Counts for the one-hour culture are still lower, the increment over background being only 1.8 and 1.3 times background for filter and mesenchyme respectively. It is noteworthy that this is the only instance in which the count in the filter is higher than the count in the mesenchyme.

Although there is no significant difference among the filters of the three porosities when counts are made on the standard area (A) opposite to the spinal cord, there is a noteworthy difference in grain distribution across the filter cross-section (Figs. 2-5). Over the most porous filter (TA) grains are much more abundant in approximately

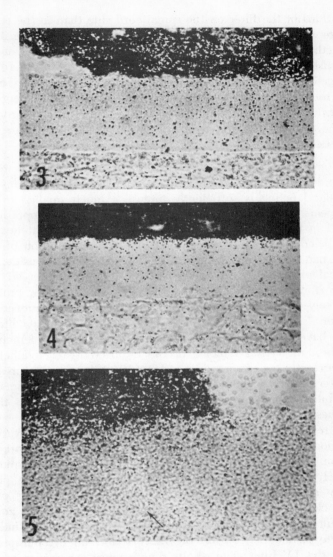

Figs. 3, 4, 5. Grain distribution over filters of three porosities between labeled dorsal spinal cord (above) and unlabeled metanephrongenic mesenchyme (below). Experimental details as in Figure 2. ×900.

Fig. 3. TV filter. Note uniform distribution of grains over filter.
Fig. 4. TH filter. Note denser grain distribution close to spinal cord.
Fig. 5. TA filter. Note heavy grain concentration over approximately half of filter thickness on spinal cord side. Opposite filter surface not clearly defined, position indicated by arrow.

the first third of the filter on the spinal cord side than in the remaining two thirds (Fig. 5). Grains also are more abundant over the TH filter close to the spinal cord (Fig. 4), though less noticeably and for a shorter distance than over the TA filter. Over the least porous filter (TV—Fig. 3), however, there is no signficant concentration of grains close to the spinal cord; rather the distribution is homogeneous across the filter.

DISCUSSION

Tritium-labeled amino acids clearly are abundantly taken up by dorsal spinal cord, and presumably synthesized into proteins. When intracellular labeling is sufficiently intense a much smaller amount of label appears in the filter and in mesenchyme on the opposite side. The label in the filter is confined to the region immediately adjacent to the labeled tissue, thus conforming with the distribution of trypsin-sensitive material earlier reported (Grobstein, '56). Considering the histological procedures used it seems likely that the observed label in the filter is present in large molecular form, probably in proteins. It is tentatively assumed, therefore, that the radio-isotopic procedure has labeled or "stained" the trypsin-sensitive spot. Technical difficulties, however, have so far prevented a direct and conclusive demonstration of this through trypsin removal of the radioactivity. The label within the mesenchyme on the opposite side of the filter may represent the same materials as are present in the filter, but the data do not exclude the possibility that small molecular label is transferred across the filter and synthesized into protein within the mesenchyme itself.

The results confirm earlier electron microscopic observations on the question of cytoplasmic penetration of the filter. The more intense labeling of the TA filter in a relatively broad zone on the spinal cord side clearly corresponds to the distribution of cytoplasmic processes previously reported. Similarly, the narrow zone of labeling over the TH filter close to the spinal cord, and the absence of such a zone over the TV filter, is in accord with the electron microscopic findings of sparse cytoplasmic penetration of the TH and no cytoplasmic penetration of the TV filter. The results thus support the earlier conclusion that kidney tubule induction proceeds without cytoplasmic contact.

The data are too limited to draw conclusions on the kinetics of transfer of the label to the filter, or from it to the tissue on the opposite side. But it is important to note that labeling of the filter appears to approach a maximum by 6 hours of incubation, and significant labeling of the reaction mesenchyme has occurred by this time. This early movement of materials into the filter is in conformity with unpublished observations on the rate of appearance of the visible, trypsin-sensitive spot. It must be considered also, however, in relation to the fact that tubule rudiments do not make their appearance until 24-30 hours of incubation, and fail to develop if the spinal cord is removed prior to that time. Hence, it certainly is not to be concluded that the labeled materials are immediately involved in the inductive process. The technique gives promise, however, of providing information on the synthesis, secretion and mobility of macromolecular materials of the embryonic intercellular matrix, information which may prove relevant to the question of inductive mechanisms.

SUMMARY

Dorsal spinal cord of the 11-day mouse embryo, heavily radioactive following incubation in tritiated amino acids, deposits significant amounts of labeled material in a membrane filter between it and metanephrogenic mesenchyme. Most of the label appears in both the filter and mesenchyme during the first 6 hours of incubation. The label is provisionally assumed to represent protein, and to be included in the trypsin-sensitive spot previously observed optically.

LITERATURE CITED

Grobstein, C., 1953, Morphogenetic interaction between embryonic mouse tissues separated by a membrane filter. Nature, **172**, 869.
——————, 1955a, Tissue interaction in the morphogenesis of mouse embryonic rudiments in vitro. In "Aspects of Synthesis and Order in Growth," D. Rudnick, Ed., Princeton University Press, 233-256.
——————, 1955b, Inductive interaction in the development of the mouse metanephros. J. Exp. Zool., **130**, 319-340.
——————, 1956a, Inductive tissue interaction in development. Adv. Canc. Res., **4**, 187-236.
——————, 1956b, Trans-filter induction of tubules in mouse metanephrogenic mesenchyme. Exp. Cell Res., **10**, 424-440.
——————, 1957, Some transmission characteristics of the tubule-inducing influence on mouse metanephrogenic mesenchyme. Exp. Cell Res., **13**, 575-587.
Grobstein, C., and A. J. Dalton, 1957, Kidney tubule induction in mouse metanephrogenic mesenchyme without cytoplasmic contact. J. Exp. Zool., **135**, 57-74.
McKeehan, M. S., 1958, Induction of portions of the chick lens without contact with the optic cup. Anat. Rec., **132**, 297-306.
Niu, M. C., and V. C. Twitty, 1953, The differentiation of gastrula ectoderm in medium conditioned by axial mesoderm. Proc. Nat. Acad. Sci., **39**, 985-989.
Waddington, C. H., and J. L. Sirlin, 1955, Studies in amphibian embryogenesis using labeled grafts. Proc. Roy. Phys. Soc. 24, Part **2**, 28-31.

*With the technical assistance of Patricia Barry and James Williams. Supported by grants from the National Science Foundation and the Fleischmann Foundation.

16

the development and sex differentiation of the gonad in the wood frog (rana sylvatica) following extirpation or orthotopic implantation of the intermediate segment and adjacent mesoderm*

R. R. HUMPHREY
*Department of Anatomy, School of Medicine,
University of Buffalo*

INTRODUCTION

Morphological studies dealing with the origin and so-called migration of the primordial germ cells in the Amphibia show a marked difference in the history of these elements in the two principal orders, the Caudata (urodeles) and the Salientia (anurans). In the urodeles (Fig. 1) these cells are first distinguishable in the mesoderm, at the junction of its axial and lateral divisions (Hall, '04; Dustin, '07; Allen, '11; Schapitz, '12; Beccari, '22; Humphrey, '25; et al.). They are here closely associated with those mesodermal cells which later give rise to the stroma, the rete cords, and the covering epithelium of the gonad. In the anurans the germ cells, when first recognizable, are included in the roof of the archenteron (Fig. 2). They become separated from the entoderm of the gut during the formation and elongation of the mesentery, and thus, relatively late in development, come into association with those mesodermal cells which participate in the formation of the gonad (Allen, '07; King, '08; Swingle, '21; Humphrey, '25; et al.).

Although the superficial position of the primordial germ cells in urodeles (Fig. 1) facilitates their removal in early embryonic stages (Humphrey, '27), their mesodermal situation renders it impossible to

Reprinted from The Journal of Experimental Zoology
Vol. 65, No. 2, May, 1933

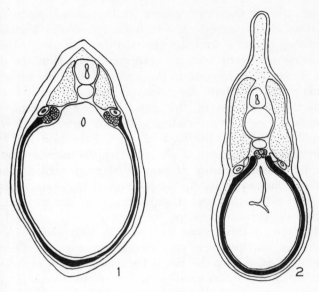

Figs. 1 and 2. Diagrammatic cross-sections of urodele and anuran embryos, to show the difference in the early position of the primordial germ cells. In both embryos the ectoderm, entoderm, neural tube, and notochord are unshaded; the axial mesoderm and mesenchyme are stippled; the lateral mesoderm (its somatic and splanchnic layers not separated by a coelom) are a solid black; and the germ cells are cross-hatched. Figure 1, Triturus torosus embryo of 3.9 mm (18 somites); the germ cells lie in the mesoderm, intermediate between its axial and lateral divisions. Figure 2, Rana pipiens embryo of 7.5 mm (after B. M. Allen, '07); the germ cells lie in the entoderm, dorsal to the archenteron.

accomplish such extirpation without at the same time removing those related mesodermal elements which enter into the make-up of the gonad. This, as previously pointed out by the writer ('27), makes difficult any analysis of the role placed by the primordial germ cells in the development and differentiation of the gonad when experimental methods involving extirpation or transplantation are used. It is impossible to determine with certainty whether the absence of a gonad following extirpation of the gonadic primordium is due to the loss of the germ cells, if they later migrate to the operated side, are either brought Similarly, one cannot rule out the possibility that the development of a gonad after transplantation of the gonadic primordium may depend upon the presence in the graft of these mesodermal elements rather than upon the germ cells themselves.

The entodermal situation of the germ cells of anurans in early embryonic life, on the other hand, offers a more favorable opportunity to test their role in the development of the gonad, since it permits the extirpation of the mesoderm which later becomes associated with them when they 'migrate' into the genital ridges, or allows the replacement of this mesoderm by that of another embryo. Thus the primordial germ cells, if they later migrate to the operated side, are either brought into relation with mesoderm far removed from that which commonly enters into the formation of the gonad (the nephrogenic or intermediate segment) or into association with this mesoderm furnished by another embryo. Since by the laws of chance the host and donor are of different sex in 50 percent of all cases, opportunity is thus afforded to test the relative importance of primordial germ cells and mesoderm in sex differentiation. It is the purpose of this paper to report the results of such extirpation and transplantation of the mesoderm in the wood frog (Rana sylvatica), a species particularly favorable for experiments of this type. In this anuran the relatively large size of the embryos makes operative manipulation easy; moreover, the sexes differentiate directly, without exhibiting the larval hermaphroditism characteristic of many other frogs, and differentiation occurs relatively early, the gonads of the two sexes showing characteristic differences after the third week of life (compare Witschi, '29).

MATERIAL AND TECHNIQUE

The developmental stages of anuran embryos most favorable for extirpation of the intermediate mesoderm (or its orthotopic transplantation) are those shortly following the appearance of the tail bud. In older stages the motility of the embryos makes operation difficult or impossible without the use of an anesthetic.

Extirpation of the intermediate mesoderm of the gonad-forming region is accomplished as follows: a longitudinal incision through ectoderm and mesoderm, cutting the lateral borders of the somites, is extended from the pronephric swelling to the base of the tail bud (Figs. 3 and 4); from the ends of this incision cuts are extended ventrally for a considerable distance, after which the flap of ectoderm and mesoderm thus outlined is detached from the underlying entoderm and removed by a final longitudinal cut parallel with the first incision. Care is taken that no mesoderm remains attached to the entoderm in the area thus exposed. The extent of the mesoderm removed is, of course, much greater than the extent of the region in which the genital ridges later appear—a provision necessary to insure the removal of all mesodermal material which ordinarily enters into the development of the gonad.

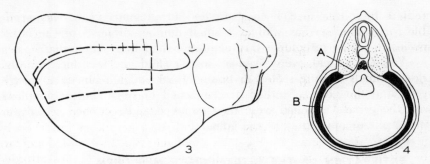

Figs. 3 and 4. Diagrams of Rana sylvatica embryos of the age used for operation (early tail-bud stage). Figure 3, lateral aspect; the broken lines indicate the extent of the area of ectoderm and mesoderm removed (or replaced by an orthotopic transplant). Figure 4, diagrammatic transection, to illustrate the relations of the primordial germ cells to the mesoderm extirpated (or implanted) at operation. The germ cells are at this stage indistinguishable from other cells of the entoderm; their probable position dorsal to the archenteron is indicated (cross-hatching). The axial mesoderm is stippled, the intermediate segment and lateral mesoderm a solid black. The lines A and B represent the longitudinal cuts by which the mesoderm and overlying ectoderm (unshaded) are removed. Compare relations to lateral mesoderm here with those shown in the older embryo of Figure 2.

In embryos which are to serve as hosts for orthotopic transplants, the site for the graft is prepared by removal of the intermediate mesoderm as described above. The embryo is then set aside for a short time to permit contraction of the wound, after which the graft (obtained by the same method as that employed in removal of the intermediate mesoderm of the host) is inserted. The transplant is carefully freed of any adherent entoderm before it is placed in the site prepared for it. When properly fitted and held in place by glass rods, such a transplant heals in very rapidly, and after a few hours, as a rule, the host shows no trace of the operation.. The embryo serving as a donor may usually be reared; such embryos furnish data on the results of extirpation of the intermediate mesoderm as well as a check on the sex of the animal furnishing any given transplant.

The material on which this report is principally based consists of a series of twenty-nine hosts grafted in April, 1932. These hosts were killed at from 6 to 7 weeks of age, being sacrificed, as a rule, at the onset of metamorphosis; the donors were killed at corresponding stages of development. Seven other hosts were killed at 3 to 5 days after grafting, in order to determine the effect of this operation upon the 'migration' of the primordial germ cells; the corresponding donors were killed at the same time as the hosts. In addition to this material, a large number of Rana sylvatica and Rana pipiens embryos from which the intermediate mesoderm had been extirpated in previous years was available for comparison, as well as a small number of hosts of the latter species in which orthotopic transplantation had been attempted.

Younger animals were fixed in Bouin's fluid and sectioned serially. Older animals were dissected in Bouin's fluid under a binocular microscope and the gonads studied and sketched in situ. The mesonephroi with the gonads attached were then removed and sectioned serially to permit microscopic study of the gonads.

EXTIRPATION OF THE INTERMEDIATE MESODERM

The conditions found in anuran embryos following this operation are somewhat variable, the differences apparently depending upon the age of the embryo, the extent of the area removed, and the rapidity and completeness of the subsequent healing. The several structures principally affected may be considered in turn.

The pronephric duct, subsequent to its partial removal at operation, may continue its backward growth until it joins the cloaca, or may end blindly, usually without marked dilatation or cyst formation. If the duct establishes an opening to the cloaca the pronephros commonly remains normal in appearance; it may undergo atrophy if the duct lacks such an opening.

The mesonephros, as a general rule, is completely absent following extirpation of the intermediate mesoderm. This result is apparently not dependent upon the absence of the pronephric or wolffian duct, since the latter frequently extends to the cloaca in animals in which the mesonephros is entirely lacking. In an occasional animal a small mass of mesonephric tubules, atrophic or otherwise, may be found. These masses may be located at almost any part of the site normally occupied by the mesonephros—a fact suggesting their development from small groups of mesodermal cells which remained adherent to the entoderm and escaped removal at operation. The development of the extreme caudal portion of the mesonephros, as commonly occurs in Amblystoma following a similar operation for removal of the intermediate mesoderm, is but rarely observed.

The presence or absence of mesonephric tubules on the operated side in animals of 3 weeks or over can usually be determined at dissection under the binocular microscope. Observations made at autopsy have been corroborated by study of serial sections of a large number of cases, particularly of those animals in which a gonad had developed on the operated side. From a comparison of these with younger animals it seems probable that in most cases mesonephric tubules never develop on the operated side, since their occurrence is no more common in the younger than in the older specimens. The complete absence of such tubules is of considerable theoretical importance in connection with the development of a gonad on the operated side.

The migration of the primordial germ cells following unilateral extirpation of the intermediate mesoderm varies greatly in different embryos. In eighteen animals killed within 2 weeks after operation primordial germ cells were found to be present on the operated side in seven cases and lacking in eleven. The younger embryos commonly show all the germ cells in a medial position at the root of the mesentery, while older specimens either indicate clearly the migration of some of the germ cells to the operated (right) side (Fig. 5) or show that they have all taken position on the opposite side of the mesentery (Fig. 6).

In older animals a gonad is found on the operated side in almost 50 percent of all cases. In a few instances this gonad is without germ cells, but in the majority of cases these cells are present and differ in no respect from those found in the gonad of the unoperated side. The derivation of these cells from the yolk-laden primordial germ cells seen on the operated side in younger embryos may be assumed, since no evidence of a mesodermal origin of secondary germ cells in Rana sylvatica has yet been presented (Witschi, '29a). Whether those gonads which lack germ cells have become sterile secondarily or have developed from the beginning without germ cells cannot be stated. They may occasionally be associated with a fat body of considerable size, suggesting their derivation from the progonad, the cephalic sterile portion of the genital ridge which ordinarily gives rise to the fat body.

Study of developmental stages of those gonads found after extirpation of the lateral mesoderm shows them to be structurally comparable to the corresponding stages of the gonads of normal animals. Rete cords make their way into the primary gonad cavity from the hilus in the usual manner (Fig. 9; compare Witschi, '29a). In the female these expand at their inner ends to form the characteristic ovarial sacs (Fig. 10). In the male the germ cells become associated with the rete cords, which in older animals can still be recognized as compact masses of small cells in the medulla and hilus of the testis (Fig. 17). These rete cords may appear as well developed as in gonads which have the usual anatomical relations to a mesonephros (compare Figs. 16 and 17). Their number, in those gonads in which it was ascertained, corresponded roughly to that in an equivalent extent of the animal's other gonad.

Anatomically the gonads which develop on the operated side are more variable than the normal. They may be very short, or, on the other hand, may extend much farther caudally than does the normal gonad. In one animal the gonad was joined at its caudal end to that of the opposite side, the two thus forming a Y-shaped structure. Frequently the gonad of the operated side is more slender than the normal and of more irregular outline, sometimes being of nodular or beaded form.

TRANSPLANTATION OF THE INTERMEDIATE MESODERM

Anatomically, the animals receiving orthotopic transplants of the intermediate mesoderm approximate the normal more closely than do those in which the extirpated mesoderm is not replaced. Such departures from the normal as are observed are generally those resulting from a partial loss of the graft or from the influence of one gonad upon the other.

The replacement of the intermediate mesoderm of one embryo by that of another is commonly followed by the normal development of both the pronephric duct and the mesonephros, these structures being found essentially typical in 24 out of 29 hosts autopsied at 6 to 7 weeks after operation. Of the remaining animals, two possess an atropic mesonephros on the operated side, the duct apparently having no outlet to the cloaca, while the other three have mesonephroi atypical in that only their caudal portions are present or functional. In no instance were mesonephric tubules completely absent, as is commonly found after simple extirpation of the intermediate mesoderm (p. 242).

Study of the seven hosts killed at 3 to 5 days after grafting indicates that the 'migration' of the primordial germ cells from the entoderm to the genital ridges tends to proceed much as in unoperated animals. In the youngest these germ cells may be found either separating from the entoderm or massed at the root of the mesentery (as in Fig. 7); in the older embryos they are located in the genital ridges, with considerable numbers always to be found on the operated side (Fig. 8). 'Migration' of the germ cells is followed by the development of a gonad, this organ being found on the operated (right) side in all but 1 of the 29 hosts autopsied at 6 to 7 weeks after operation.

In view of the absence of the mesonephros following extirpation of the intermediate mesoderm, it must be concluded that the mesonephros found after orthotopic transplantation is derived from the intermediate mesoderm introduced in the graft. From the close association of the mesonephros and gonad it may be concluded further that the mesodermal components of the latter are likewise derived from the transplant. On the other hand, the care used to free the transplant of any adherent entodermal cells, together with the observed 'migration' of primordial germ cells from the entoderm of the host into the genital ridges, warrant the conclusion that the primordial germ cells of the gonad on the operated side are derived entirely from the host. It would thus appear that this gonad arises from material supplied by two different embryos. With this double origin in mind, we may now consider its sex differentiation, with a view to determining the influence of each of its two components on this process.

Based on the study of both hosts and donors, the twenty-nine hosts autopsied at 6 to 7 weeks appear to have been grafted as follows:

	Cases
Host a female, donor a female,	10
Host a female, donor a male,	8
Host a male, donor a female,	5
Host a male, donor a male,	6

These combinations may be summarized briefly as 10 ♀ ♀ : 8 ♀ ♂ : 5 ♂ ♀ : 6 ♂ ♂, or as 13 heterosexual to 16 unisexual—a result which approximates the expected proportion fairly well, considering the small number of cases involved.

In all those cases in which donor and host differ in sex, the gonad of the grafted (right) side is found to agree in type with that of the donor, aside from such modification as may have been suffered by ovaries subjected to the influence of a host testis. In not a single case has the entodermal component supplied by the host (primordial germ cells) determined the sex type of a gonad whose mesodermal component was furnished by a donor of the opposite sex. This finding emphasizes the importance of structures other than the germ cells in controlling the processes of sex differentiation.

In the hosts of the present series in which the two gonads differ in sex type, the ovary may either show little departure from the normal structure, or be more or less advanced in modification or reversal. These ovaries have been classed in three groups for purposes of description.

The four ovaries which show least departure from the normal are typified by the ovary of Figure 11. A central cavity is present and numerous oocytes have begun enlargement. Degeneration of these enlarged oocytes (auxocytes), however, appears to be more frequent than in ovaries not subjected to testicular influence.

In the second group are four ovaries which are smaller in size than those of the first group, and show few or no enlarged oocytes. Some show degeneration of oocytes, but in others this is seldom observed.

These ovaries are typified by that shown in Figure 12, and are to be considered as retarded and modified rather than as definitely undergoing reversal.

In the third group are three gonads which are clearly ovaries in some stage of reversal. Two of these are the ovaries of hosts which carry a graft testis, while the third is an ovary developed on the grafted side in a male host. In all three the central ovarian cavity is absent in a consideratble extent of the gonad, being replaced by solid masses of rete cords with or without spermatogonia; these give the organ an appearance comparable to that of a testis. The structure of one of these modified ovaries (that of host 347) is well illustrated by figures 13 to 15. At its cephalic end this gonad has the form of an ovary (Fig. 13). Oocytes are few in number, however, and are sometimes to be seen in degeneration. Farther caudally, the central cavity is lacking, its place being occupied by masses of rete cords (Fig. 14). In this region young oocytes are found around the outside of the gonad, being most numerous at its distal margin, while undifferentiated gonia are found in smaller numbers at the hilus or in the medulla, generally associated with the rete cords of those regions. Toward its caudal end this gonad become much like a normal testis in structure (Fig. 15; compare with Fig. 16). No cavity or oocytes are present, spermatogonia are numerous, and the rete cords are prominent. The graft testis in this host is of large size and normal structure (Fig. 16).

In order to obtain a more accurate notion of the relative volumes of these ovaries, and to compare them with ovaries not under testicular influence, the serial sections of each gonad were projected at a magnification of 200 $\times$ and traced on paper of uniform thickness, and the tracings for each gonad were then cut out and weighed; the weight of the tracings of any gonad, expressed in centigrams, was then taken as giving its volume in arbitrary units. The ovaries not exposed to testicular influence were thus found to range in volume from 411 units to 2650 units, with an average of 1346 units for the fourteen studied. The ovaries exposed to testicular influence range in volume from 80 units to 1010 units. Those least modified (group 1) all have a volume of 675 units or over. Those showing more modification or retardation (group 2) are below 560 units, while the three showing the greatest degree of reversal have volumes of 193, 268, and 377 units—values much below those of the normal ovary, but well within the range of volumes determined for the normal testis.

Although there was little or no histological evidence that any ovary had exerted an inhibitory effect upon the growth of the testis developing in the same host, the volumes of the latter organs were also ascertained by the method described above, for comparison with the volumes of the organs in those hosts in which both gonads were testes. Testes developed in the presence of an ovary were found to range in volume from 136 to 362 units, with an average of 244 units for the ten examined. Those developing in the absence of an ovary (gonads of male hosts with testis grafts) were found to range from 129 to 487 units, with an average of 250 units for the ten examined. It would appear from these data that the ovary usually has little or no influence upon the growth of the testis developing contemporaneously with it in any host.

DISCUSSION

The results of extirpation and transplantation of the intermediate segment and adjacent mesoderm of anurans, as reported in the foregoing pages, raise a number of interesting questions. These may now be stated and briefly discussed.

First of all, what conditions are prerequisite to the development of a gonad following extirpation of the intermediate mesoderm? Does development of the gonad after this operation depend solely upon the migration of primordial germ cells to the operated side, or does it require in addition the presence of remnants of the mesonephric blastema not removed at operation? In attempting an answer to this question we may recall that the proportion of young embryos exhibiting a 'migration' of germ cells to the operated side corresponds roughly to the proportion of older animals showing a gonad on that side at autopsy. If mesonephric blastema, derived either from parts of the mesoderm not removed at operation, or from cells migrating across from the unoperated side, were to participate in the development of such gonads, the latter should be found more constantly associated with other derivatives of the mesonephric blastema (i.e., masses of mesonephric tubules). But since in older animals a nodule or mass of mesonephric tubules is found on the operated side only rarely, we may well doubt the participation of mesonephric blastema in the development of all gonads found on this side. In the majority of cases the primordial germ cells which 'migrate' to the operated side probably come into relationship with mesoderm quite different in developmental potentialities from that with which they ordinarily become associated— either mesoderm from the more dorsal and medial portion of the somite or mesoderm which has been shifted from a latero-ventral position during the healing process subsequent to operation. In either case this mesoderm is entirely lacking in nephrogenic potentialities. Since the structure of the gonad, nevertheless, approximates the normal in so many instances, we are forced to the conclusion that mesoderm far removed from the nephrogenic zone may form stroma, epithelial covering, and even rete cords for the developing gonad. Although the rete cords in particular are commonly regarded as derivatives of the mesonephric blastema (compare Witschi, '29a), they are nevertheless frequently developed on the operated side in the entire absence of distinguishable mesonephric tubules.

In view of the apparent importance of the primordial germ cells in the formation of the gonad[1], its absence on the operated side in over half of all cases may be ascribed to the failure of germ cells to be shifted to that side during the formation and elongation of the mesentery. The writer has previously ('25) expressed the opinion that the so-called 'migration' of the anuran germ cells is largely a shifting due to the growth activity of related structures. When these growth processes are greatly interfered with, abnormalities in the 'migration' of the germ cells may be expected. So, for example, when healing after extirpation of the intermediate mesoderm is somewhat delayed, the growth medialward of the mesoderm of the opposite (unoperated) side shifts the attachment of the mesentery beyond the median plane, and leaves the germ cells in a single genital ridge on the unoperated side. If, on the other hand, the healing process has been fairly well completed before the 'migration' of germ cells from the entoderm begins, the mesodermal growth on the two sides of the developing mesentery is probably more evenly balanced, and the median germ-cell mass tends to be divided and the cells shifted into the two genital ridges in the normal fashion. The earlier the removal of the mesoderm, therefore, and the more perfect the subsequent healing, the better are the chances for germ cells to be shifted to the operated side and a gonad to develop there. It seems quite evident that the 'migration' of germ cells to the operated side is entirely independent of the presence there of mesonephric blastema or wolffian duct.

The second question of interest concerns the role of the primordial germ cells in sex differentiation. The care taken to remove all adherent entodermal cells from transplants of the intermediate mesoderm before

---

[1]Although gonads apparently without primordial germ cells have been claimed by Kuschakewitsch ('10) to develop in embryos of Rana esculenta reared from overripe eggs, such gonads probably contain primordial germ cells of a somewhat modified form (Witschi, '14). It sems possible, however, that the intermediate mesoderm in the Amphibia may give rise to gonad structures in the absence of the primordial germ cells, since sterile gonads (or gonads with very few germ cells) may develop after partial extirpation of this mesoderm both in urodeles and anurans.

their implantation, and the regularity with which primordial germ cells are observed to separate from the entoderm and move into the genital ridge of the operated side in younger hosts, offer sufficient guarantee that the germ cells in any gonad developed on that side are derived from the host entoderm and not introduced with the engrafted mesoderm. Since in all cases in which donor and host are of different sex, the gonad on the grafted side has differentiated according to the sex of the donor, the role of the primordial germ cells in sex differentiation must be regarded as a passive one. The course which differentiation shall take is determined by the engrafted mesoderm which comes into association with the germ cells. This mesoderm doubtless furnishes both the rete cords and the covering epithelium for the developing gonad. According to Witschi ('29 b, p. 277), "the rete cords in the center of the sex gland contain the male-differentiating system," while "the deeper layers of the germinal epithelium include the female-differentiating system." If the former is activated, the germ cells migrate into the medulla and become spermatogonia, and a testis differentiates; if the female-differentiating system of the germinal epithelium becomes active, the germ cells develop into oocytes, the rete cords give rise to the ovarial sacs, and the gonad becomes an ovary. Since rete cords and germinal epithelium are both derived from the engrafted mesoderm, the presence of genetic or hereditary factors must determine which system is to become active and control the sex differentiation of the gonad. It is of considerable interest that these hereditary factors remain operative after transplantation of the mesoderm into a host of the opposite sex and its intimate association with the primordial germ cells derived from the entoderm of that host. Although modification of the ovary which develops in a male host does not occur, this must, of course, be charged to the influence of the host testis, and not to the action of the germ cells of the host which enter into association with the engrafted mesoderm, since a similar modification of a host ovary occurs when the graft gives rise to a testis. Mesoderm from a male donor in all cases resulted in the formation of a normal testis when implanted in a female host.

Although the present report furnishes the first experimental evidence of its kind for the passive role played by the germ cells in sex differentiation, a similar conclusion as to this role has been reached by Witschi ('32) on the basis of extensive morphological and experimental studies on anuran gonads. That the differentiation of the germ cells in the urodele is likewise dependent upon their environment is indicated by ovaries of Amblystoma in which sex reversal is in progress, since in these gonads the cells which are found at the hilus associated with the rete cords become spermatogonia and proliferate to form testicular lobules, while in testes undergoing reversal, on the other hand, the germ cells in the covering epithelium proliferate and differentiate as oocytes (Humphrey, '29, '30; Burns, '30, '31). Thus the environment rather than any factors intrinsic in the germ cells themselves would appear to control their differentiation and the consequent sex differentiation of the gonad.

Several questions arise in connection with the modification or reversal of the ovary under the influence of a testis in the same host. The variability in the effect of the testis is particularly striking: the ovary under its influence may at metamorphosis be found to be essentially normal or may have undergone almost complete reversal. To what factors are these differences to be ascribed? Can they be due entirely to variations in the distances separating the two gonads? According to Witschi ("31, '32), the interactions of the gonads in frog tadpoles joined in parabiosis are mediated by morphogenetic substances differing from typical hormones in that they are not released into the blood stream, but spread out slowly through the tissues. These substances according to Witschi, "spread with falling gradients of efficiency from the gonads of either animal into the body of its cotwin." On this basis Witschi explains the greater modification of the 'inner gonads' in heterosexual pairs, the 'inner gonad,' of course, being closer to the organs of the cotwin than the 'outer gonad.' It would seem improbable, however, that differences in the distances separating the testis from the ovary could alone explain the variations in the condition of the latter encountered in my experimental animals, since in these the gonad on the operated side is commonly in the normal position and hence is at approximately the same distance from the gonad of the opposite side in all the animals considered. Such slight differences in this distance as do exist would scarcely serve to explain the marked differences between the various ovaries under testicular influence. Are these differences, then, to be correlated with observable differences in the size or structure of the testes of the animals in question? For the present this question, too, must be answered in the negative. The testis in an animal carrying an essentially normal ovary may be as large as that associated with an ovary which is advanced in reversal, and appear fully as normal in structure. A decreased physiological activity might be assumed from its failure to cause a pronounced modification of the ovary under its influence. But may not this failure be due to the advanced stage in the differentiation of the ovary at the time the morphogenetic substances ('medullarin' or testicular hormone) produced by the testis attained the requisite threshold value? If, for example, the ovary became well differentiated as such throughout its entire extent before the testicular influence attained an effective level, its structure at metamorphosis would more closely approximate the normal than it would had the testis attained a dominance when the ovary was still essentially in the indifferent stage. In the former case reversal of the ovary would involve the inhibition of its cortical growth and the degeneration and removal of the cortex already developed; in the latter case the potential ovary would have its cortical growth inhibited from the onset of differentiation, thus permitting its medullary component to become dominant and causing the gonad to differentiate more or less directly as a testis.

It seems highly probable that the relative developmental rate of the two gonads in any host will vary within limits wide enough to account for the observed differences in their interactions reported in this paper. One or the other gonad may suffer retardation through delay in the germ-cell 'migration,' reduction in the number of germ cells, or delay in the formation of its rete cords or blood vessels. If in any host the gonad suffering such retardation chances to be the testis, the ovary present attains a more advanced stage of differentiation before being subjected to its inhibitory action; if, on the other hand, the ovary is retarded or delayed in its development, it comes under the influence of the testis while still in a relatively undifferentiated condition.

The occurrence in any modified ovary of ovarian, 'hermaphroditic,' and testicular regions arranged in cephalocaudal sequence (p. 253) is in all probability likewise to be ascribed to the early period in differentiation at which it came under testicular influence. An explanation on this basis must, of course, take into account the cephalocaudal mode of differentiation of the ovary. It is a well-known fact that the primordial germ cells of anurans become separated from the entoderm in cephalocaudal sequence, and that those most cephalic in position reach the genital ridges at a time when those located farther caudally are still massed at the root of the mesentery (Witschi, '29 a). It follows that the resulting gonads will differentiate in cephalocaudal fashion; in a developing ovary, for example, the rete cords will appear earlier at the cephalic end, and will develop cavities (ovarial sacs) before these make their appearance in the more caudal rete cords. Such cephalocaudal sequence in the formation of the ovarial sacs has been recently figured by Witschi ('32, Fig. 17) for the ovary of the toad. Due to this cephalocaudal plan of development, an ovary which is brought under the influence of a testis very early in its sex differentiation may still be essentially indifferent in the more caudal parts of its extent. In consequence, its cephalic portion, after further development, may still show the ovarian character which had begun to appear before the onset of testicular inhibition; regions caudal to this will exhibit a hermaphroditic structure due to a partial inhibition of the cortex and hypertrophy of the medulla; while farther caudally the complete inhibition of cortical development and the migration of the germ cells into the medulla will give the organ a testicular structure. Thus a seriation of ovarian, hermaphroditic, and testicular structures may occur in any ovary, not alone as the result of differences in the concentration of the male inductor (medullarin, testicular hormone), but as the result of differences in the stage of differentiation of the part on which this substance acts.

Although in many cases in my experimental animals the ovary under testicular influence showed relatively little modification, it is highly probable, nevertheless, that in these cases it would eventually have undergone reversal to a testis. The animals were killed, as a rule, at the onset of metamorphosis. At that time none of the testes in combination with ovaries gave indication of being adversely affected thereby, while degeneration of oöcytes was frequent even in the largest ovaries. It seems probable that the continued action of the testis on these ovaries would have induced further degeneration of their cortex and this eventually would have permitted the medullary hypertrophy requisite for reversal.

SUMMARY AND CONCLUSIONS

1. The gonads of anurans are derived from two embryonic germ layers, entoderm and mesoderm. The primordial germ cells are separated from entoderm of the roof of the archenteron during the formation of the mesentery and are shifted dorsally and laterally to reach the genital ridges of the two sides. In this situation they come into relation with that mesoderm which gives rise to the stroma, rete cords, and covering epithelium of the gonad.

2. Separation of the two components which normally enter into the make-up of the anuran gonad may be accomplished experimentally by extirpation of the intermediate mesoderm together with the closely adjacent parts of the axial and lateral mesoderm. Unilateral extirpation of this mesoderm, if carried out in early tail-bud stages of development before 'migration' of the germ cells has begun, does not prevent the

movement of these cells to the operated side in a considerable percentage of cases. In older animals a gonad is found on the operated side in a proportionate number of cases.

3. Since the mesonephros in many animals is completely lacking on the operated side, it is concluded that the mesodermal components of the gonad found on that side must arise from other sources than nephrogenic blastema derived from the intermediate mesoderm. It is concluded that mesoderm which ordinarily never enters into the make-up of the gonad may differentiate into rete cords, covering epithelium, and stroma for that organ, if it comes into association with a mass of primordial germ cells.

4. When the extirpated intermediate segment and adjacent mesoderm of anurans are replaced by the corresponding material from another embryo, a mesonephros and gonad develop normally on the operated side in a very high percentage of cases. Since the primordial germ cells of grafted animals killed from 3 to 5 days after operation are found to be undergoing separation from the entoderm in the normal fashion, and since no entoderm is implanted with the graft, it is concluded that the germ cells in any gonad on the operated side are furnished by the host, while its mesodermal components are derived from the graft.

5. The sex differentiation of the gonad on the operated side depends upon the sex of the donor furnishing the engrafted mesoderm. When donor and host are unlike in sex, this gonad always differentiates according to the sex of the donor. It is therefore concluded that the primordial germ cells contributed to the gonad by the host are unable to alter or counteract the genetic or hereditary factors carried in the implanted mesoderm, and that these cells play only a passive role in the differentiation of sex.

6. When the two gonads of any host differ in sex type, the testis is commonly found to be normal in structure, while the ovary shows some degree of retardation, degeneration, or sex reversal. Variations in the extent to which different ovaries may be affected are interpreted as resulting from differences in the time in their differentiation at which the influence of the testis becomes effective.

7. The cephalocaudal seriation of ovarian, hermaphroditic, and testicular structures found in the more highly modified ovaries is interpreted as resulting from the normal cephalocaudal sequence of differ-

*This study has been aided by a grant from the Committee for Research in Problems of Sex of The National Research Council.

entiation in the ovary, and the fact that the influence of the testis became effective at an early period when the caudal end of the gonad was still essentially indifferent in structure although its cephalic end had begun its differentiation as an ovary.

LITERATURE CITED

Allen, B. M., 1907, An important period in the history of the sex cells of Rana pipiens. Anat. Anz., Bd., **31**, S. 339-347.

——————, 1911, The origin of the sex cells in Necturus. Science, N. S., vol. **33**, pp. 268-269.

Beccari, N., 1922, Studi sulla prima origine delle cellule genitali nei Vertebrati. II. Richerche nella Salamandrina perspicillata. Arch. Ital. di Anat. e di Embriol., vol. **18**, supp., pp. 29-95.

Burns, R. K., Jr., 1930, The process of sex transformation in parabiotic Amblystoma. I. Transformation from female to male. J. Exp. Zoöl., vol. **55**, pp. 123-169.

——————, 1931, The process of sex transformation in parabiotic Amblystoma. II. Transformation from male to female. J. Exp. Zoöl., vol. **60**, pp. 339-387.

Dustin, A. P., 1907, Recherches sur l'origine des gonocytes chez les Amphibiens. Arch. de Biol., T. **23**, pp. 411-522.

Hall, R. W., 1904, The development of the mesonephros and müllerian ducts in Amphibia. Bull. Museum Comp. Zoöl., Harvard, vol. **45**, pp. 31-128.

Humphrey, R. R., 1925, The primordial germ cells of Hemidactylium and other Amphibia. J. Morph. and Physiol., vol. **41**, pp. 1-43.

——————, 1927, Extirpation of the primordial germ cells of Amblystoma: its effect upon the development of the gonad. J. Exp. Zoöl., vol. **49**, pp. 363-397.

——————, 1929, Studies on sex reversal in Amblystoma. I. Bisexuality and sex reversal in larval males uninfluenced by ovarian hormones. Anat. Rec., vol. **42**, pp. 119-155.

——————, 1931, Studies on sex reversal in Amblystoma. III. Transformation of the ovary of A. tigrinum into a functional testis through the influence of a testis resident in the same animal. J. Exp. Zoöl., vol. **58**, pp. 333-365.

King, Helen D., 1908, The oogenesis of Bufo lentiginosus. J. Morph., vol. **19**, pp.439-468.

Kuschakewitsch, S., 1910, Die Entwicklungsgeschichte der Keimdrüsen von Rana esculenta. Festscrift f. R. Hertwig, Jena, Bd., **2**, S. 61-224.

Schapitz, R., 1912, Die Urgeschlechtszellen von Amblystoma. Ein Beitrag zur Kenntnis der Keimbahn der urodelen Amphibien. Arch. mikr. Anat., Bd., **79**, Abt. II, S. 41-78.

Swingle, W. W., 1921, The germ cells of anurans. I. The male sexual cycle of Rana catesbeiana larvae. J. Exp. Zoöl., vol. **32**, pp. 235-331.

Witschi, E., 1914, Experimentelle Untersuchungen über die Entwicklungsgeschichte der Keimdrüsen von Rana temporaria. Arch. mikr. Anat., Bd., **85**, Abt. II, S. 9-113.

———————————, 1929a, Studies on sex differentiation and sex determination in amphibians. I. Development and sexual differentiation of the gonads of Rana sylvatica. J. Exp. Zoöl., vol. **52**, pp. 235-265.

———————————, 1929b, Studies on sex differentiation and sex determination in amphibians. II. Sex reversal in female tadpoles of Rana sylvatica following the application of high temperature. J. Exp. Zoöl., vol. **52**, pp. 267-292.

———————————, 1931, Studies on sex differentiation and sex determination in amphibians. V. Range of the cortex-medulla antagonism in parabiotic twins of Ranidae and Hylidae. J. Exp. Zoöl., vol. **58**, pp. 113-146.

———————————, 1932, Sex deviations, inversions, and parabiosis. Chapter V. in Sex and Internal Secretions, Williams & Wilkins, Baltimore, Md.

PLATE 1. *Explanation of Figures.*

5   Transection of Rana sylvatica embryo 359 D, killed 3 days after right unilateral extirpation of the intermediate segment and adjacent mesoderm. Photograph, × 100. The operated side is at the right. Some of the primordial germ
cells are migrating to this side (see arrow) or to the left, although the majority
are still in a median position at the point of attachment of the mesentery. No
Wolffian duct is seen on the operated side.

6   Transection of Rana sylvatica embryo 351 D, killed 5 days after right
unilateral extirpation of the intermediate segment and adjacent mesoderm. Photograph, × 100. The primordial germ cells in this animal are all in the genital
ridge of the left side (see arrow). Neither wolffian duct nor genital ridge is seen
on the operated side (reader's left). M, mesentery.

7   Transection of Rana sylvatica embryo 360 H, killed 3 days after orthotopic
implantation of the intermediate segment and adjacent mesoderm on the right
side. Photograph, × 100. The primordial germ cells (see arrow) have just separated
from the entoderm and occupy a median position, ventral to the aorta. The wolffian
duct on the operated side (reader's left) is still without a well-defined lumen.

8   Transection of Rana sylvatica embryo 364 H, 4 days after orthotopic
implantation of the intermediate segment and adjacent mesoderm on the right side.
Photograph, × 100. At this level of the body the primordial germ cells are
now located in the genital ridges, with that of the operated side (see arrow) containing approximately the same number as the other; farther caudally, many of the
germ cells are still in a median position. The wolffian duct now shows a distinct lumen.

9   Transection of gonads of Rana pipiens larva 130 D, killed about 2 months
after right unilateral extirpation of the intermediate segment and adjacent
mesoderm. Photograph, × 250. The gonad of the operated side (at right) shows
a solid rete cord in the primary gonad cavity. Rete cords in this gonad appear
to have developed without association with mesonephric tubules.

10   Transection of gonads of Rana pipiens larva 135 D, killed about 2 months
after right unilateral extirpation of the intermediate segment and adjacent mesoderm. Photograph, × 250. The gonad of the operated side (reader's left) shows
the usual ovarial sac or central cavity. No mesonephros is present on this side.

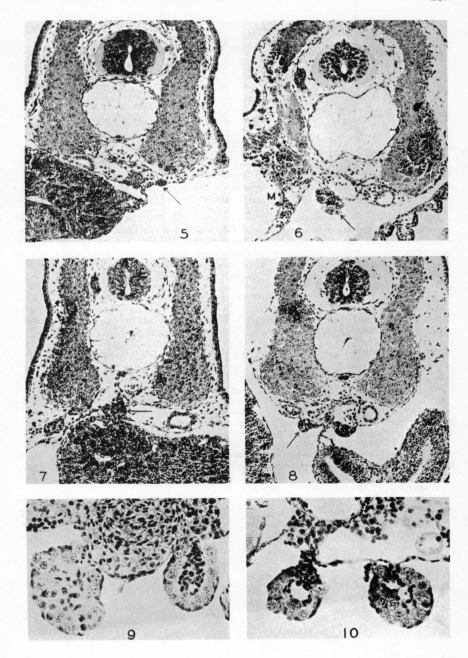

PLATE 2. *Explanation of Figures.*

11   Transection of the gonads in a Rana sylvatica female killed during meta-morphosis, 38 days after orthotopic implantation of the intermediate segment and adjacent mesoderm from a male donor. The testis developed on the grafted side is at the reader's left; both graft and host gonads are essentially normal. Host no. 367; photograph, × 100.

12   Transection of the gonads in a Rana sylvatica female killed during meta-morphosis, 39 days after orthotopic implantation of the intermediate segment and adjacent mesoderm from a male donor. The testis developed on the grafted side (reader's left) is of normal structure; the ovary of the host is greatly retarded, and contains very few enlarging oocytes. Host no. 368; photograph, × 100.

13 to 15   Transections of the ovary of a Rana sylvatica female killed during metamorphosis, 41 days after orthotopic implantation of the intermediate segment and adjacent mesoderm from a male donor. This ovary has undergone partial reversal under the influence of the testis derived from the graft (Fig. 16). At its cephalic end it has the form of an ovary (Fig. 13); farther caudally, it exhibits a bisexual or hermaphroditic structure (Fig. 14), the central cavity or ovarial sac being replaced by solid rete cords and spermatogonia, and the cortex consisting only of young oocytes; still farther caudally, it has the structure of a normal testis (Fig. 15), no cortex with oocytes being present. Host no. 347; photograph, × 250.

16   Transection of the normal testis developed on the grafted side in host no. 347 (see above) in which the ovary had undergone partial reversal (see Figures 13 to 15). Photograph, × 250.

17   Transection of the testis developed on the right side in donor no. 339 following removal of the intermediate segment and associated mesoderm. This testis is of normal structure, although entirely without association with meso-nephric tubules. Photograph, × 250.

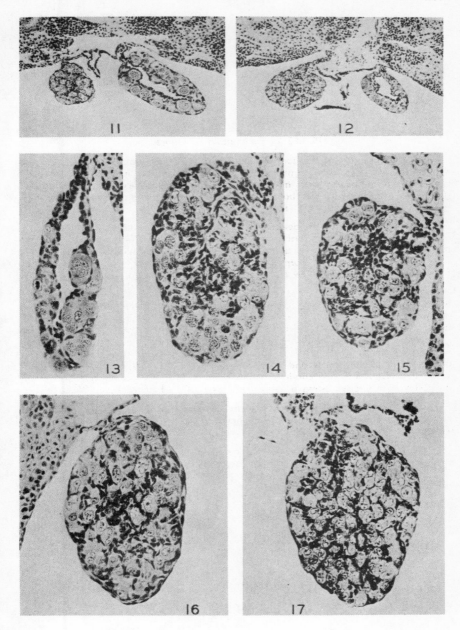